TRENDS IN WATER POLLUTION RESEARCH

TRENDS IN WATER POLLUTION RESEARCH

JAMES V. LIVINGSTON
(EDITOR)

Nova Science Publishers, Inc.
New York

NOTICE TO THE READER

The Publisher has taken reasonable care in the preparation of this book, but makes no expressed or implied warranty of any kind and assumes no responsibility for any errors or omissions. No liability is assumed for incidental or consequential damages in connection with or arising out of information contained in this book. The Publisher shall not be liable for any special, consequential, or exemplary damages resulting, in whole or in part, from the readers' use of, or reliance upon, this material.

This publication is designed to provide accurate and authoritative information with regard to the subject matter covered herein. It is sold with the clear understanding that the Publisher is not engaged in rendering legal or any other professional services. If legal or any other expert assistance is required, the services of a competent person should be sought. FROM A DECLARATION OF PARTICIPANTS JOINTLY ADOPTED BY A COMMITTEE OF THE AMERICAN BAR ASSOCIATION AND A COMMITTEE OF PUBLISHERS.

Library of Congress Cataloging-in-Publication Data
Available upon request

ISBN 1-59454-328-3

Published by Nova Science Publishers, Inc. ✦ New York

Contents

Preface

In Chapter **I,** *Drinking Water Disinfection: Microbial Risk and Disinfection By-Products*, Luigi Rizzo, Vincenzo Belgiorno, Rodolfo MA Napoli, and Sureyya Meriç,

Obtaining safe drinking water involves the control of the water quality at the source, effective water treatment for pathogens removal and organic precursors removal for avoiding the disinfection by-products (DBPs) formation due to disinfection, subsequently to diminish the risk of bacterial regrowth including pathogens in the distribution network. This chapter evolves above subjects by reviewing the recent studies and summarizing Italian experience. In this context the following subjects are included: i) occurrence of pathogens, re-emerging pathogens, detection and monitoring of the pathogens in drinking water systems, the use of heterotrophic plate count bacteria in controlling the drinking water quality; ii) bacterial regrowth, effective factors, biofilm formation in distribution system, iii) disinfection, chlorine and alternative disinfectants; iv) DBPs formation and health hazards; v) DBPs precursors removal, enhanced coagulation experience; vi) predicting models for DBPs formation.

Xiang-zhong Li, Fang-bai Li,and Yi-bing Xie in *Photocatalytic Oxidation Using Lanthanide Ion-Doped Titanium Dioxide Catalysts for Water and Wastewater Treatment* study the photocatalytic oxidation using lanthanide ion-doped TiO_2 catalysts may provide a more efficient approach for mineralization of organic pollutants in the environment.

In the next chapter, *The Modification of Clay as a Coagulant and the Use of Modified Clay for Car-Washing Wastewater Treatment*, J.-Q. Jiang, C. G. Kim, C.-H. Choi and Z. Zeng, discuss the modification and use of clays as a new type of coagulant for the treatment of car washing effluent. Marisa Canterino, Marcella de Champdoré, Roberto Andreozzi and Raffaele Marotta investigate the reaction kinetics for the ozonation and H_2O_2/UV photolysis of two selected pharmaceuticals, propranolol (beta-blocker) and ofloxacin (antibiotic) in *Removal of Ofloxacin and Propranolol from Water by Means of Ozonation and H_2O_2/UV System*.

Ming-Chun Lu and Hsu-Hui Huang, in *Catalytic Decomposition of Hydrogen Peroxide and Monosubstituted-Chlorophenol in the Presence of Modified Activated Carbons* examine the heterogeneous catalytic decomposition of H_2O_2 and monosubstituted - chlorophenols (MCP) in the presence of activated carbons modified with chemical pretreatments. The sixth chapter *Natural Adsorbent Materials for Effluent Treatment*, Marco Aurélio, Zezzi Arruda,

César Ricardo, Teixeira Tarley and Geraldo Domingues Matos report some examples in the literature relating to alternative materials for effluent treatment as well as pointing out some parameters that should be taken into account when effluent treatments are carried out, such as characterization (physical and chemical), adsorption isotherms, costs involved, and others.

Idil Arslan – Alaton investigate the effects of ozonation and Fenton's treatment on the biodegradability of pharmaceutical wastewater originating from the *Sultamycillin Tosylate Diydrate* penicillin formulation in *Biodegradability Improvement of Penicillin Formulation Effluent by Ozonation And The Fenton Reagents.* In *Three-Dimensional Modeling of Hydrodynamic and Transboundary Pollutant Transport in Pearl River Estuary of South China,* K. W. Chau discusses the effect of pollution in the Pearl River Delta Region (PRDR). During the past two decades, substantial economic development took place in the Pearl River Delta Region (PRDR), which is the largest river system in South China with Hong Kong and Macau at eastern and western sides of its entrance, respectively. This prosperity, however, is accompanied with the exertion of serious potential pollution impacts to areas in the vicinity and complication of the task of environmental protection in Hong Kong and Macau. In this chapter, a coupled three-dimensional numerical model on hydrodynamic and pollutant transport, with orthogonal curvilinear coordinate in the horizontal direction and sigma coordinate in the vertical direction, is developed and implemented to simulate the unsteady transport of a representative water quality constituent, chemical oxygen demand, in PRDR. In this model, which is based on the Princeton Ocean Model (POM), a second moment turbulence closure sub-model is embedded, and the stratification caused by salinity and temperature is considered.

Chapter IX, *Relevance of the Multixenobiotic Defence Mechanism (MXDM) for the Biological Monitoring of Freshwaters - Example of its Use in Zebra Mussels,* Sandrine Pain, Sylvie Biagianti-Risbourg and Marc Parant gives an example of the use of the MXDM response assessed in a bivalve species, the zebra mussel *Dreissena polymorpha.* Experiments were performed in a river that receives the effluent of a chlorine bleached pulp and paper mill. The effluent was shown to worsen the water quality downstream by increasing the organic content and by generating organohalogenated compounds. In the last chapter, *Photodegradation of Organic Pollutant,* R. K. Sharma and S. Mary Celin investigate photodegradation, a potential technique, which results in complete destruction of organic contaminants, unlike other treatment options such as activated carbon adsorption, air stripping which merely transfer the target contaminant from one phase to another. The end products of this promising technology are CO_2, water and other simple non-toxic molecules. Hydroxyl radicals are the main oxidizing species involved in destruction of the organic pollutant on photodegradation and are produced by the different photodegradative processes.

J. V. Livingston
Sept. 2005

In: Trends in Water Pollution Research
Editor: J. V. Livingston, pp. 1-30

ISBN 1-59454-328-3
©2005 Nova Science Publishers, Inc.

Chapter I

Drinking Water Disinfection: Microbial Risk and Disinfection by-Products

Luigi Rizzo[1]*, Vincenzo Belgiorno*,
Rodolfo MA Napoli**,and Sureyya Meriç*+

*University of Salerno, Department of Civil Engineering, 84084 Fisciano (SA), Italy
** University of Naples Parthenope, Faculty of Engineering, Naples, Italy.
+ present address

Introduction

Obtaining safe drinking water involves the control of the water quality at the source, effective water treatment for pathogens removal and organic precursors removal for avoiding the disinfection by-products (DBPs) formation due to disinfection, subsequently to diminish the risk of bacterial regrowth including pathogens in the distribution network. This chapter evolves above subjects by reviewing the recent studies and summarizing Italian experience. In this context the following subjects are included: i) occurrence of pathogens, re-emerging pathogens, detection and monitoring of the pathogens in drinking water systems, the use of heterotrophic plate count bacteria in controlling the drinking water quality; ii) bacterial regrowth, effective factors, biofilm formation in distribution system, iii) disinfection, chlorine and alternative disinfectants; iv) DBPs formation and health hazards; v) DBPs precursors removal, enhanced coagulation experience; vi) predicting models for DBPs formation.

[1] (E-mail: l.rizzo@unisa.it; v.belgiorno@unisa.it; r.napoli@unisa.it, smeric@tin.it)

Waterborne Diseases Outbreak: Classification, Sources, and Properties of Human Pathogens

Between 1972 and 1999, 35 new agents of disease were discovered and many more have re-emerged after long periods of inactivity, or are expanding into areas where they have not previously been reported. Amongst this group are pathogens that may be transmitted by water (WHO, 2003). Since 1970, several species of micro-organism from human animal faeces and from environmental sources, including water, have been confirmed as pathogens. Examples include *Crytosporidium*, *Legionella*, *Escherichia coli* O157 (*E. Coli*O157), rotavirus, hepatitis E virus and norovirus. Between 1998 and 2001 cholera (*Vibrio cholerae* O1 and O139) was the most frequent, with acute diarrhoea as the fourth on the basis of 578 infectious diseases outbreaks happened in 132 countries in the world (Ashbolt, 2004a). While the pathogenic outbreaks mostly occurred in developing countries (Ashbolt, 2004a) many *Crytosporidiosis* outbreaks occurred in the European countries, i.e. in England and Wales 13 outbreaks occurred between 1986 and 1996 (Kramer et al., 2001). In 2000 the biggest outbreak (bloody diarrhoea) due to *E. coli* O157:H7 and to a lesser extent, *Campbylobacter jejuni* occurred in Walkerton, Canada (Ali, 2004). The cause of the illness was determined to be the contamination of a drinking well by cattle manure. *Helicobacter pylori* (*H. Pylori*) ,which has been correlated with gastric cancer, is an example of a recently emerged pathogen that may be transmitted through water (Rupnow et al., 2000). In tropical regions, *Mycobcterium* (MAC) *ulcerans* is found in aquatic environments and MAC and M. intracellular bacteria appear to grow in piped (and chlorinated) water biofilms and they are a major concern to immuno-supressed individuals (Falkinham et al., 2001).

For a more realistic assessment of the overall pathogen risk, it is necessary to understand the critical variables controlling pathogen fate and distribution in each part of the water supply system including lakes and reservoirs (Brookes et al., 2004). For example, Lisle et al. (1988) showed that *Escherichia coli* can persist for days to weeks in aquatic system simulating natural conditions, adapting to and surviving environmental stresses.

Edzwald and Kelley (1998) suggested a classification on the basis of *Cryptosporidium* oocysts for surface water, protected reservoirs (0.52 oocysts/l), pristine lakes (0.3-9.3 oocysts/100 l), polluted rivers (43-60 oocysts/100 l) and polluted lakes (58 oocysts/100 l). The factors controlling pathogen transport and distribution in lakes and reservoirs are dispersion, dilution horizontal and vertical transport. The settling velocity, aggregation and resuspension of the particles, recreational activities also play important role in pathogen transport. The turbidity, humid season with elevated water levels in river is the surrogate for *Crytosporidium* and *Giardia* pathogens (Brookes et al., 2004). The fate of *Crytosporidium* due to UV light inactivation in reservoir can occur at opposite ends of the scale, depending on the location of the oocysts in the water column and the extinction coefficient for UV light. For this reason, the extinction coefficient for UV light appears to be a vitality important parameter for determining the risk of *Crytosporidium* contamination (Brookes et al., 2004).

The persistence of the pathogens in the reservoirs is related to inactivation mainly by solar radiation (visible and UV light), temperature, and salinity, pressure, predation by organisms higher in the food chain. For example, the persistence (12 to several weeks) of *C. parvum* was due to biological antagonism (Chauret et al., 1998) while light intensity was the major loss mechanism for *E. coli* (30 days of persistence) (Wcislo and Chrost, 2000). The relative susceptibility to sun light of a range of microbes was found in the order as enterococci>faecal coliforms >*E. coli*> somatic coliphages>F.RNA phages (Sinton et al., 2002). The most lethal wavelengths are within the ultraviolet range because the inactivation of *Crytosporidium* occurred at the wavelengths between 250 and 270 nm (Linden et al., 2001). Sinton et al. (2002) reported that the inactivation of faecal indicators was more acute at shorter wavelengths, however, the greatest inactivation occurred at full sunlight.

The piped water systems, their inadequate design and operation, water treatment and disinfection, wastewater management are referred for *the sources of the pathogens* (WHO, 2003).Waterborne disease outbreaks occurred in the USA between 1978 and 1998 are shown in Table 1. More than 49% of the 294 waterborne disease outbreaks reported in community water system (CWSs) were associated with treatment inadequacies, whereas 30% were associated with distribution system deficiency (Table 2). A water source was identified for 78% of the distribution-associated outbreaks in CWSs, and outbreaks were categorized by type of system and water source. Distribution system outbreaks occurred in both ground water and surface water systems. A 52% of the distribution system outbreaks in CWSs were reported in groundwater systems (Craun and Calderon, 2001).

Table 1 Causes of waterborne disease outbreaks in Public water systems between 1971-1998 (Craun and Calderon, 2001)

System type	Contaminated water source, no treatment	Treatment inadequacies	Distribution system deficiencies	Miscellaneous or unknown causes	All causes
CWS	39	146	89	20	294
NCWS	145	127	24	29	325
PWS	184	273	113	49	619

CWS-community water system, NCWS-noncommunity water system, PWS-public water system

No single water quality indicator can reliably assess the bacterial, protozoan and viral contamination of aquatic environments in all circumstances. The strategy for risk assessment of any given pathogen in water supply reservoirs is to sample and analyse for the target organism in a systematic way (Borrkes et al., 2004). The Polymerase Chain Reaction (PCR) for the analysis of pathogens in water has been fundamental to understand the distribution of some of the most important water-related viral pathogens: i.e. noroviruses, rotaviruses and hepatitis E virus (Di Giovanni et al., 1999). One of the major disadvantages to cell culture PCR is the possibility of detecting oocysts or sporooites on the surface of the cell monolayer that have failed to cause infection (Rose et al., 2002). Schwartz et al. (1998) detected facultative pathogenic bacteria (non-pneumophila *Legionella)* in biofilms using PCR, southern blot hybridization and *in situ* hybridization.

Table 2 Etology of outbreaks caused by distribution system contamination between 1971 and 1998 (Craun and Calderon, 2001)

Etiology	CWS		NCWS	
	Outbreaks	%	Outbreaks	%
Chemical	35	39.3	3	12.5
Unidentified pathogen	29	32.6	11	45.8
Giardia	8	9.0	4	16.7
Salmonella	4	4.5	1	4.2
Norwalk-like virus	3	3.4	1	4.2
Shigella	3	3.4	1	4.2
Campylobacter	3	3.4	1	4.2
Hepatitis A	1	1.1	1	4.2
Salmonella typhimurium	1	1.1		
Cyclospora	1	1.1		
Escherichia coli O157:H7	1	1.1		
Vibrio cholerae			1	4.1
Total	89	100	24	100

CWS-community water system, NCWS-noncommunity water system

Flow cytometry, more recent technique, is a powerful technique using laser light to quantify particles or to recognize structural features of cells. The analytic capability of the technique can be further enhanced by fluorescent monoclonal antibodies that are specific for a particular pathogen. This technique allows us to detect and quantify water-related pathogens in real time (WHO, 2003).

Information Collection Rule (ICR) by USEPA provided many information about pathogen monitoring, particularly on *Giardia* cysts and *Cryptosporidium* oocysts. However, ICR can be considered at best a screening test when cysts or oocysts are found because the method has the problems including poor reproducibility, poor sensitivity, high detection limit (>100 organisms/ml), inability to differentiate *Giardia* or *Cryptosporidium* using immunofluorescence assay (IFA)- based technology, high false-positive rate, and high false-positive rate (Allen et al., 2000). In 1998, the USEPA (1999) established the methods 1622 and 1623. Although these methods provided significant improvements in pathogen monitoring, they still have major drawbacks. First, provide no information on species (other species can react with the monoclonal antibodies and could be erroneously reported as pathogens). They also provide no information on viability or infectivity, particularly infectivity to humans. Finally, the methods provide no information other than fluorescence patterns and size to identify the object as a cyst or an oocyst (Allen et al., 2000).

Heterotrophic Plate Count (HPC) Measurement

A group of microbiology and public health experts including regulatory and medical expertise was convened in 2002 to consider the utility of HPC measurements in addressing drinking water quality and safety (Bartram et al., 2004). The measurements of HPC, which denotes all bacteria in any water, food, soil, air etc. requiring organic nutrients, are used to indicate the effectiveness of water treatment processes, thus as an indirect indication of pathogen removal; as a measure of numbers of regrowth organisms that may not have sanitary significance; as a measure of possible interference with coliform measurements on lactose-based culture methods. Bacteria typically described as "opportunistic pathogens" that may be recovered amongst HPC microbiota include strains of *P. aeruginosa*, *Acinetobacter* spp., *Aeromonas* spp., *Klebsiella pneumoniae*, etc. In the absence of faecal contamination there was no evidence of association of any of these with gastro-intestinal infection through the water-borne route among the general population (Hellard et al., 2001). Wadhwa et al. (2002) stated that naturally occurring bacteria (HPC or autochthonous flora) do not have virulence factors, making their numbers in drinking water irrelevant to health risk except in the most severely immunocompromised subpopulations. Duncan (1988) reported that *Klebsiella* in water supplies should not be considered a hazard to human health. Because of its ubiquitous nature, it is not practical to eliminate *Pseudomonas aeruginosa* from our food and water, but attempts to do so would produce disinfection by-products (Hardalo and Edberg, 1997). Similar to Kelbsiella and *Pseudomonas aeruginosa*, there is insufficient evidence that *Aeromonas hydrophila* can be considered as opportunistic pathogen when present in drinking water (Allen et al., 2004). Pavlov et al. (2004) demonstrated the potential pathogenic features of HPC bacteria isolated from treated and untreated water. The isolated bacteria were subjected to a battery of screening tests, namely: haemolysis, enymatic analyses, antibiotic susceptibility, cyctotoxicity, adherence and invasiveness. 55% of isolates were α or β-haemolysis on human and horse-blood agar media. Stelma et al. (2004) showed the rare occurrence of heterotrophic bacteria with pathogenic potential in potable water. They detected a large number of heterotrophic bacteria and newly discovered *Legionella*-like organisms that parasitize amoebae.

HPC monitoring can be used in drinking water supplies along with other information for validation and verification of treatment process performance and other applications including:

- monitoring of performance of filtration or disinfection processes,
- in piped distribution systems, HPC measurements are assumed to respond primarily to (and therefore provide a general indication of) distribution system conditions. These arise from stagnation, loss of residual disinfectant, high levels of Assimilable Organic Carbon (AOC) in the water, higher water temperature, and availability of particular nutrients.

In systems treated by chloramination or that contain ammonia in source waters, measurement of a variety of parameters including HPC, but especially nitrate (which are regulated for health protection), can sometimes indicate the possible onset of nitrification (Bartram et al., 2004). Uhl and Schaule (2004) reported that standard plate counts of HPC bacteria using the spread plate technique on nutrient rich agar according to German Drinking Water Regulations (HPC-GDWR) had proven to be very good indicator of hygienically safe drinking water and to demonstrate the effectiveness of water treatment. However, the method proved insensitive for early regrowth detection at around 30 μg/l of AOC concentrations.

While there is a lack of health-related justification for setting an upper HPC limit in drinking water, a wide range from 20 to 1000 cfu/ml has been established in different countries (Allen et al., 2004) while the HPC bacteria were detected between 100 and 10000 cfu/ml in South African drinking water (Pavlov et al., 2004). According to the U.S. Safe Drinking Water Act Regulations (1989) drinking water systems may measure HPC instead of disinfectant residual and sites with HPC< 500 cfu/ml are considered equivalent to sites with detectable residuals for determining compliance. Typically, public sewer systems with conventional treatment are able to limit HPC bacterial limit populations to below 100 cfu/ml in the distribution system, although many systems experience increased HPC populations (500-1000 cfu/ml) during summer (Allen et al., 2004). A maximum HPC population of 500 cfu/ml in drinking water is often cited as a health-related standard (Allen et al., 2004). Moreover, HPC populations greater than 500-1000 cfu/ml in drinking water can interfere with the detection of coliform/*E.coli* analysis by lactose-based methods, which include the membrane filtration method (Allen et al., 2004).

The Final Coliform Rule (USEPA, 1991) established that the preferable (but not mandatory) HPC measurement is by pour plate (PP), spread plate (SP) or membrane filter (NF) using R2A medium. However, the choice of the incubation temperature and duration is left to the system while the US SDWARs refers the 35 ^{0}C and 48 h for temperature and incubation (Reasoner, 2004) reported that at overall temperatures and media studies in the previous works the SP counts were usually higher than both the PP and the MF results which were roughly equivalent. R2A medium was much more sensitive than the 35 ^{0}C, 48 h, PP method but the R2A counts were considered to be too variable (1-5 $\log_{10}$) to be a good parameter for use in quality control.

The conclusion on HPC by Allen et al. (2004) was that HPC determinations can be useful tool to the monitor efficacy of drinking water treatment processes and undesirable changes in bacterial water quality during storage and distribution, but not because of health-risk reasons.

Bacterial Regrowth and Biofilm Formation in Distribution System

Almost all of the 498 hospitalisations between 1971 and 1998 that resulted from distribution system outbreaks were reported in community water system in the USA. : most of these illnesses were caused by *Giardia* and bacterial pathogens (Craun and Calderon, 2001). In most distribution system outbreaks of known or suspected infectious etiology, total or faecal coliforms were detected in water samples as seen in Table 3 (Craun and Calderon, 2001).

The occurrence of bacteria in drinking water distribution network was attributed to: (i) infiltrations in pipe system and (ii) disinfection treatment inefficiency (LeChevallier et al., 1988). The inefficiency of disinfection can cause the breakthrough phenomenon, that is the increase in bacterial number in the distribution system resulting from viable bacteria passing through the disinfection process (Van der Wende and Characklis, 1990). The concern connected to this phenomenon is due to the matter that injured bacteria can restore theirs vital functions as soon as environmental conditions in drinking water system are suitable. The factors affecting regrowth of the bacteria in distribution system were explained due to disinfectant residual, temperature and nutrient level in distribution system (LeChevallier et al., 1996; Power et al., 1997; Volk and LeChevallier, 1999; Bresner et al., 2002).

Table 3 Total and/or faecal coliforms detected between 1971 and 1998 in distribution system contamination (Craun and Calderon, 2001)

System type	Infectious etiology	Number of Outbreaks		
		Water quality data reported	Coliforms detected	Coliforms not detected
CWS	54	39	28	11
NCWS	21	17	14	3
PWS	75	56	42	14

CWS-community water system, NCWS-noncommunity water system, PWS-public water system

Kirmeyer et al. (1999) proposed a prioritization of entry routes of the pathogens into the distribution system as shown in Table 4 (Bresner et al. 2002). Karim et al. (2003) evaluated the infiltration possibility of bacteria in distribution network analyzing water samples collecting from soil near to pipes, and they found that total and fecal coliform bacteria were detected in the half of the samples.

Table 4 Prioritization of pathogen entry routes into distribution systems *

Entry routes priority	Ranking
Water treatment breakthrough; transitory contamination; cross-connection; water main repair or breakage	High
Uncovered storage facilities	Medium
New main installation; covered storage facilities; deliberate contamination	Low

Modified from Bresner et al. (2002)

The previous studies have shown that maintenance of a chlorine residual dose (also up to 2.5 mg/l) does not necessarily prevent occurrence of bacteria (McFeters et al., 1986; LeChevallier et al., 1987; LeChevallier et al., 1999; Lund and Ormerod, 1995) showed that no biofilm was formed from the chlorinated water containing a residual of 0.04-0.05 mg/l free chlorine. The greatest biofilm formation was found from the ozonated water, closely followed by the control (microstrained) water. The U.V. irradiated water showed considerably less production of biofilm. The rate of biofilm formation was closely related to the seasonal fluctuations in water temperature. The water having total organic carbon concentrations in the range 1.5-3.9 mg/l, a free chlorine residual of 0.2 mg/l was needed to reduce biofilm concentration (Hallam et al., 2001). Camper (2004) also obtained similar results.

Schwartz et al. (1998) demonstrated that the type of pathogen depended on the material used in the distribution system. They reported that there was no significant changes in bacterial subclass composition of the biofilms taken from the water works and house branch connections. Volk and LeChevallier (1999) reported that the decrease in nutrient concentrations following implementation of biological filtration to decrease biodegradable organic matter (BOM) levels resulted in lower biofilm densities. They addressed three issues for limiting biofilm problems: nutrient levels, corrosion, and disinfection. Lu et al. (1999) showed that at steady state biofilm chlorine demand increased linearly with BDOC of water and according to the ratio surface/volume. Assimilable organic carbon (AOC) was the significant factor for regrowth in the distribution system. AOC level was more than 100 µg/l which higher than 50-100 µg/l stability concentration (Liu et al., 2002). The biofilm development in Sydney water was limited by organic carbon and that biofilm development promoted chloramine decay (Chandy and Angles, 2001). The ability of biofilms to respond to increases in disinfectant concentrations was dependent on the biomass of the biofilms. Meanwhile, more than residual chlorine concentration temperature affected the nitrifying bacterial activity in drinking water network (Pintar et al., 2003). Some biofilms have been shown to contain one or more species of emerging pathogen, including *Mycobacterium avium* complex (MAC) (WHO, 2003).

Groundwaters were found less susceptible to favor bacterial regrowth in distribution system of Brussels while the regrowth could be decreased notably when BDOC levels were below 0.25 mg C/l in treated surface water (Niquette et al., 2001). Boulam et al. (2002) found that coliform bacteria lost their culturability in diluted river (0.5-1.5 mg/l of DOC) and in diluted algal bloom (1.3-2.5 mg/l of DOC) water samples. At lower initial DOC values the culturability was lost more rapidly.

Hallam et al. (2001) reported that pipe material influenced biofilm activity far less than chlorine. LeChevallier et al. (1996) found a positive relationship between coliform occurrence and iron pipe subjected to corrosion. Zacheus et al. (2000) demonstrated that the accumulation of biofilm on different surface materials was quite similar among polyvinyl chloride (PVC), polyethylene(PE) and stainless steel pipes. However, the cell volume was slightly higher on PE than on PVC surface. On the other hand, soft deposits were recorded as the key site of microbial growth, mainly eterotrophic bacteria, actinomycetes and fungi, in drinking water distribution networks (Zacheus et al., 2001). They reported that the bacterial biomass production was higher in the new than old deposits.

Typically, the compliance control to check microbiological water quality in distribution system is carried out by detection of coliforms (Bresner et al., 2002). Singh and McFeters (1990) expressed the recovery capacity of the bacteria determined using m-Endo medium after 48 h incubation. They reported that there is a temporary reduction or loss of virulence in pathogenic bacteria after injury and under suitable conditions virulence is fully restored following recovery from injury.

Zhang and DiGiano (2002) developed regrowth equation of HPC bacteria in distribution system as below:

$$HPC = k \, C^a \, T^b \, AOC^c \, pH^d$$

where C is the disinfectant concentration (either chlorine or chloramine), T is temperature, k is model constant, and a, b, c, d are exponents of the independent variables. These correlation analysis showed that disinfectant residual is the most important factor determining HPC level.

A recent study conducted on the groundwater samples taken from a town of Salerno province, Southern Italy (Figure 1) evaluated the effects of (i) to monitor chlorine occurrence in the distribution system; ii) to evaluate the regrowth of coliform bacteria injured by free chlorine residual concentrations using more selective (m-Endo) and less selective (m-T7) media; (iii) the addition of carbon source on regrowth of coliform bacteria (Rizzo et al., 2004). The groundwater is currently disinfected by 0.3-0.4 mg/l of sodium hypochlorite directly applied into pipes with impulse pump before distribution into network. The existing network is 30 years old and it is composed of mixed materials such as cast-iron, galvanized iron, PVC, HDPE, eternit. The residual free chlorine concentration, temperature and coliform occurrence were monitored in the city network system by taking uniformly spatial distributed samples from 25 points as shown in Figure 2. The free residual chlorine concentrations were detected ranging form 0.01-0.25 mg Cl_2/l. Coliform occurrence was significant in summer season due to temperature although free residual concentrations were at the same level or even more than winter season.

They applied low chlorine concentrations (0.014, 0.021, 0.035 and 0.07 mg Cl_2/l) on raw well water samples to evaluate the coliform regrowth. The chlorinated samples were incubated at 20°C for 1, 4, 24 and 48 h, respectively. As shown in Figure 3, illustrating bacteria detected with m-Endo and m-T7 media, the natural growth of coliform bacteria in two samples taken from well showed various behaviours depending on incubation periods. After 1 h incubation period the number of coliform bacteria detected with m-T7 medium decreased to 64.4% and 97.2% (for 0.014 and 0.035 mg Cl_2/l dose respectively) respect to unchlorinated water. Subsequently, the number of bacteria increased approximately 3 log units between 1 and 48 h of incubation. The coliform bacteria injured by 0.021 mg/l of chlorine could regrowth after 24 h of incubation without additional carbon source (1:40 of C:N). When the ratio between C and N was increased to 11:40, bacterial regrowth could be detected after 4 h of incubation using m-T7 medium. However, m-Endo medium allowed to detect coliform bacteria regrowth after 24 h of incubation.

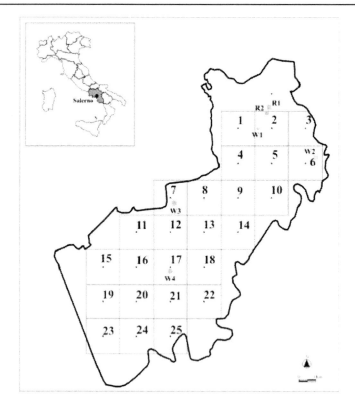

Figure 1 The location of study area and sampling points

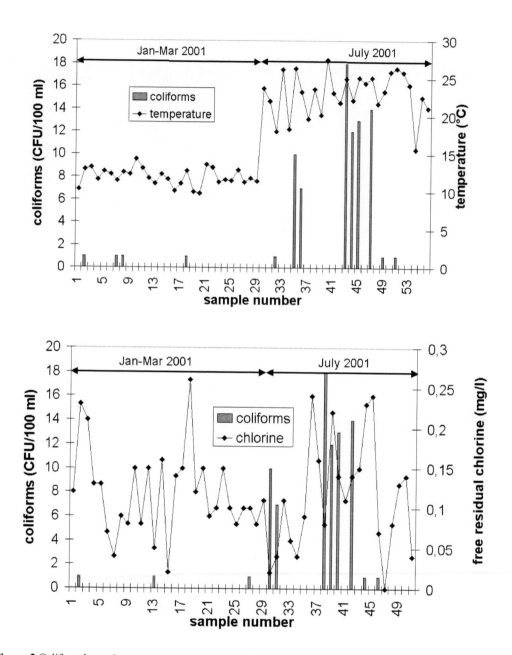

Figure 2 Coliform bacteria occurrence vs temperature, free residual chlorine in the drinking water distribution network.

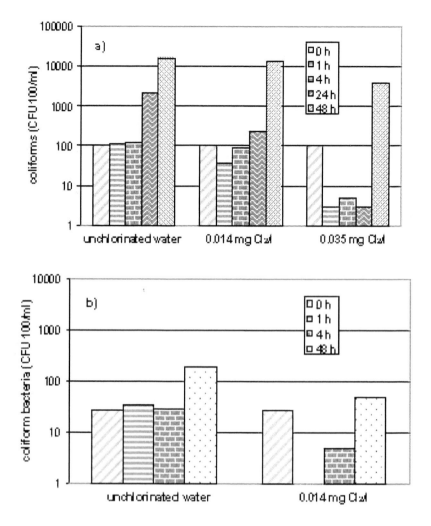

Figure 3. Regrowth of coliform bacteria detected with m-T7 (non-selective) medium (a) and m-Endo (selective) medium (b): comparison between unchlorinated and chlorinated water samples.

Pathogen Removal: Disinfectants

The chlorination has been successfully used for the control of waterborne infectious disease up today (White, 1999). However, although, it is effective against most vegetative bacteria and viruses when used at the normal concentration for treatment, it will not inactivate *Crytosporidium* oocysts. Singh and McFeters (1990) showed that several bacterial species (*Y. enterocolitica, S. typhimurium,* and *Shigella* sp.) were more resistant to the action of chlorine than the coliform bacteria. However, chlorine gas and sodium hypochlorite are considered the best option to groundwater disinfection because of both low capital and maintenance cost and usual NOM content causing less concern of disinfection by-products (DBPs) formation (Rook, 1974; USEPA, 1998).

Filtration of water is along known and very effective process for eliminating pathogens from drinking water. The disinfection should be used to minimize the residual risk due to the presence of pathogens in the water but can not be used for bringing faecally contaminated water onto a hygienically sound condition (Schoenen, 2002). In order to able to deliver drinking water with a sufficient microbial quality, The German Federal Environment Authority has given recommendation for avoidance of drinking water contamination by parasites that the water has to be checked for the classical faecal indicator organisms after the treatment before disinfection. The water has to be normally free *E. coli* and coliform organisms before disinfection (Anonym, 2001; Schoenen, 2002).

The effect of filter process on pathogens removals from water has been studied followed by the effective UV disinfection (Soini et al., 2002). Varjus et al. (2004) studied different filter materials (polypropylene (PP), stainless steel (SS), nylon and glass fibre (GF)) to remove the pathogens measured by heterotrophic viable plate counts from drinking water. PP filter most efficiently removed microbes, but had a high pressure loss and a short life time of 60 days. Moreover, it was the most efficient one to accumulate microbes from the water hydraulic system by the most applicable filter material.

The strong trend toward replacing free chlorine with chloramine (i.e. combined chlorine) to avoid from DBPs may also have an impact on bacterial regrowth. Chloramine is known to produce a more stable residual than free chlorine and thus provide lasting protection against regrowth. In addition it may penetrate more deeply than chlorine within the biofilm thus providing of greater inactivation (LeChevallier et al., 1990; Norton and LeChevallier, 1997).

Both medium and low pressure ultraviolet irradiation have been extremely effective for the inactivation of *Cryptosporidium* oocysts in drinking water (Craik et al., 2001). The recent studies focused on the inactivation of *Cryptosporidium* using ozone showed that ozone proved to be much more effective disinfectant than chlorine and chloramine (Korich et al., 1990; Rennecker et al., 1999). However, it has a drawback point of the bromate formation when the bromide concentration in water is greater than 50 µg/l (Rose et al., 2002). To avoid from the bromate formation pH is lowered below than 6.5-7 which precludes the use ozone in water utilities in some cases. Ct equation was developed using Chick-Watson modelling approach for the inactivation of *Cryptosporidium* with ozone (Clark et al., 2002) and chlorine dioxide (Clark et al., 2003). Clark et al. (2002; 2003) reported that temperature had a dramatic effect on the inactivation of *Cryptosporidium* oocysts with both ozone and chlorine dioxide. They expresses that the water utilities having to treat cold source waters may have difficulty in achieving reasonable levels of inactivation without also incurring high costs.

DBPs Formation

The interactions of chlorine and/or bromine with some organics (e.g., humic and fulvic acids) naturally occurring in raw water are known to result in chlorinated or brominated disinfection by-products (DBPs) (Rook, 1974; Peters et al., 1980). DBPs levels can vary greatly within a single water supply, depending on both water quality (e.g., total organic carbon (TOC) which expresses the NOM (natural organic matter), mainly are humic and fulvic acids in natural waters, bromide, pH, temperature, ammonia, carbonate alkalinity, and treatment conditions (e.g., disinfectant dose, contact time, removal of NOM before the point of disinfectant application, prior addition of disinfectant) (USEPA, 1998).

DBPs include trihalomethanes which are the first category to be detected in drinking water, followed by haloacetic acids (HAAs) and haloacetonitriles (HANs), haloketones, and chloropicrin at lower concentrations (Rook, 1974; Nikolaou et al., 1999) for the use of chlorine. Reckhow et al. (1990) showed a linear relationship between chlorine consumption and the activated aromatic content of the various humic and fulvic acids extracted from natural waters. Garcia-Villanova et al. (1997a, b) showed the relation among chlorine dose, temperature and THM formation in finished water and distribution network. The yield of trihalomethanes was reported to increase (Krasner et al., 1989) while that of HAAs and total organic halogen (TOX) were decreased with increasing pH. Table 5 shows the disinfectants and disinfection by-products occurrence (Ashbolt, 2004b).

Table 5 Disinfectants and disinfection by-products

Disinfectant	Significant organohalogen		Significant inorganic DBPs	Significant non-halogenated DBPs
Chlorine	THM, HAA, HAN, CH, CP, CPh, N-chloramines, halofuranones, bromohydrins		Colorate (mostly from hypochlorite use)	Aldyehydes, cyanoalkanoic acids, alkanoic acids, benzene, carboxylic acids
Chlorine dioxide			Chlorite, chlorate	Unstudied
Chloramine	HAN, cyanogens chloride, organic chloramines, CH, chloramino acids, haloketones	Nitrate, nitrite, chlorate, hydrazine	Aldehydes, ketones, nitrosamines	
Ozone	Broform, MBA, DBA, dibromoacetone, cyanogens bromide		Colorate, iodate, bromate, hydrogen peroxide, HOBr, epoxides, ozonates	Aldehydes, ketoacids, ketones, carboxylic acids

THM: trihalomethanes, HAA: haloacetic acids, HAN: haloacetonitriles, HK: haloketones, MBA-CP: chlorophenols, CH: chloral hydrade

Health Hazards

Human exposure to THMs in chlorinated water has been implicated epidemiologically in cancers of the lower intestinal tract and bladder (Morris et al., 1992; Bull et al., 1995; USEPA, 2000). In Taiwan adverse birth outcomes occurred due to chlorinated drinking water (Yang, 2004). In animal studies, both chloroform and bromodichloromethane (BDCM) induced cytotoxicity and cancer in the kidney and liver (Larson et al., 1994), and BDCM was defined as the more potent renal toxicant and carcinogen (Lilly et al., 1994). However, mutagenicity tests showed a contrasting result that BDCM and chloroform were mutagenic only at high, non-realistic concentrations (Pegram et al., 1997). In recent years, toxicity and carcinogenity studies were carried out in standard animal models; transgenic mouse models and fish models; in *vitro* mechanistic and toxicokinetic studies; reproductive, immunotoxicity, and developmental effects have been designed to establish a toxicity database reflecting a wide range of DBPs resulting from different disinfection practices (Boorman et al., 1999). These data were used to estimate potential health effects of DBPs in drinking water using computer-based QSTR (Quantitative Structure Toxicity Relationship) models (Moudgal et al., 2000). The USEPA (2002) has also defined the hazard classes for THMs, HAAs and inorganic DBPs; however, further investigations are required about DBP toxicity as a mixture problem (Teuschler and Simmons, 2003), particularly for the new detected DBPs such as chlorinated furanones (CHFs) (Komulainen, 2004).

Standards

As shown in Table 6, the standards for the main DBPs in drinking water vary in wide range depending on the water characteristics or origin (surface or ground water). For example, Italy having more than 80% of drinking water consumption from groundwater with high quality a relatively lower value was set on the basis of total THMs (TTHMs), while Germany and Denmark set the lowest values (10-15 µg/l). It is remarkable that EC has not set any standard for HAAs, clorite (ClO_2^-) and bromate (BrO_3^-) yet.

DBPs Speciation

Previous data obtained from different disinfection utilities using chlorination in Belgium, France, Germany, Spain, The Netherlands, and Italy showed that THMs were the most abundant compounds, whereas HAAs were present in much lower concentrations (Palacios et al., 2000). Nikolaou et al (2002; 2004) reported that the concentrations of THMs ranged from 5 to >100 µg/l in three distribution systems (Greece) supplied from different water resources (e.g., lakes, boreholes and wells). The wide ranges were attributed to the high TOC levels of raw water and the highest levels of THMs were detected in summer and fall seasons compared to spring and winter (Golfinopoulos and Nikolaou, 2001). Instead, no significant concentrations of THMs were detected in a distribution network (southern Italy) supplied by groundwater with very low TOC content (Bekbolet et al., 2004). Several DBPs other than THMs have also been detected in the drinking water including HAAs, HANs, haloketones, chloral hydrate and chloropicrin (Villanueva et al., 2003). Yu and Cheng (1999) reported 100-1130 µg/l of THMs in Hong Kong tap water while 1.5-44 µg/l of THMs were measured in finished water with 1.7-2 mg/l of DOC concentrations (El-Shafy and Grunwald, 2000). THMs were detected the most abundant species in Australian chlorinated drinking water supplied from surface water with the elevated levels (100-190 µg/l) (Simpson and Hayes, 1998) while a low level of TTHMs (6 µg/l) was detected in chloraminated drinking water according to Li et al. (1996) who reported 10 and 18 µg/l of TTHMs formation without irradiation and with irradiation, respectively, when 15 mg/l of ClO_2 was used. In Lake raw water the level of HAA was detected almost zero and after ozonation HAA did not increase however, the first and second chlorination (2.1-3.7 mg/l of Cl_2) increased significantly HAA level in parallel to THMs in finished water.

Table 6 Drinking water standard for main DBPs in various countries (modified from Yoon et al., 2003; Sadiq and Rodriguez, 2004).

Country	TTHMs (µg/l)	$CHCl_3$ (µg/l)	HAAs (µg/l)	ClO_2^- (µg/l)	BrO_3^- (µg/l)
Australia	250	--	[f]	--	--
Canada	100[a]	--	--	--	10
China	--	60	--	--	--
Denmark	10-15[b]	--	--	--	--
France	--	30	--	--	--
Germany	10		--	--	--
Japan	100[c]	60	--	--	--
Korea	100	--	--	--	--
Taiwan	100	--	--	--	--
UK	100[d]	--	--	--	--
Italy	30	--	--	200	10
USA	80	0.0[e]	60	1000	10
WHO	--	200	[g]	200	--
EC	100	--	--	--	--

[a] 350 as guidance value;
[b] as low as possible;
[c] $CHCl_2Br$ 60 µg/l, $CHClBr_2$ 100 µg/l, $CHBr_3$ 100 (µg/l);
[d] average;
[e] maximum contaminant level goal;
[f] chloroacetic acid 150 µg/l, dichloroacetic acid 100 µg/l, trichloroacetic acid 100 µg/l;
[g] dichloroacetic acid 50 µg/l, trichloroacetic acid 100 µg/l;

The speciation of THMs can vary depending on the nature of the source of water. In two Australian chlorinated surface water the order of the species were detected different; i.e. chloroform was the dominant while in the other source dibromochloromethane was the major specie (Simpson and Hayes, 1998) whereas chloroform was the dominant specie in Canadian (Rodriguez and Serodes, 2001). The study conducted on an Italian surface and ground water with the characteristics given in Table 7, showed the similar results (Bekbolet et al., 2004) as illustrated in Figure 4.

The average TTHMFP of surface raw water was measured as 234 µg/l. As well as the high level of TTHMFP in raw water, distributions of the species in total amount is important because the brominated species are still under suspicions of the carcinogenicity studies (Lilly et al., 1994; USEPA, 2002). TTHMFP level of GW1 resource and the water from wells was measured much lower (25-109 µg/l) than SW because the groundwater with too low TOC content contributed to hold low THMs formation risk. However, the groundwater yielded the highest concentrations of brominated species, particularly $CHBr_3$ and little chloroform formation (GW1, WW2, WW3). These results are in accord with Ichihashi et al. (1999) who showed that in the presence of excess NaOCl, addition of NaOBr enhanced the formation of brominated THMs (Br-THMs) but reduced the formation of $CHCl_3$ although bromide concentration was below detection limit.

Table 7 Water characteristic of some drinking water sources in Salerno province.

Resource	Type	T (°C)	pH	Br- (mg/l)	UV$_{254}$ (1/cm)	TTHMFP (μg/l)
SW	Surface water	18.6	7.66	-	0.070	234.0
GW1	Groundwater	13.7	7.14	0.19	0.002	66.5
GW2	Groundwater	14.2	-	0.06	0.079	109.1
WW1	Well water	16.7	7.13	0.16	0.011	66.6
WW2	Well water	11.6	6.3	0.12	0.001	62.8
WW3	Well water	15.2	7.17	0.06	0.010	24.7
WW4	Well water	15.2	7.01	0.07	0.004	58.4

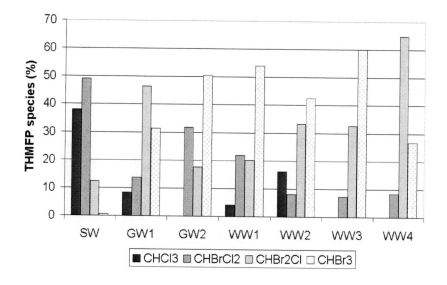

Figure 4 TTHMFP species detected in raw water in Salerno province

DBPs Precursors Removal

The control of DBPs by reducing organic precursors, commonly expressed as NOM removal, using enhanced/optimized coagulation has a prime relevance (Bell-Ajy et al., 2000; Volk et al., 2000). TOC (or DOC) concentration, the DOC characteristics, coagulant type, coagulant dosage, and pH are important parameters for NOM removal by coagulation (Edzwald and Tobiason, 1999). The USEPA (1999) has established TOC removal ranges, regarding both alkalinity and TOC of raw water, for reducing THMs formation by enhanced coagulation, involving a strict pH control and elevated coagulant doses. According to the USEPA (1999) procedure, the necessity of TOC removal increases by raw water TOC content and was related to low alkalinity. For hard waters with high alkalinity and pH levels, it is often a matter of discussion from economic and practical perspectives whether to use inorganic acids or coagulant overdosing in order to depress coagulation pH to optimum levels with respect to NOM removal (Exall and Vanloon, 2000).

The risks related to DBPs forces the community to seek alternative water sources or treatment methods of drinking water. Among the alternative systems, chlorine dioxide (ClO_2) is commonly used in preoxidation and disinfection steps of surface water treatment due to low formation of THMs. However, disinfection with ClO_2 results in chlorite formation, a DBP not yet classifiable as to health effects and, namely, human carcinogenicity (USEPA, 2002). A recent study showed that a level of 200 µg/l of chlorite was found to be ecologically risky on *D. magna* (Fisher et al., 2003).

Ozone offers municipal water purveyors the benefits of being the strongest commercially available oxidizing agent. Ozone is superior to chlorine, chlorine dioxide, or chloramines for the inactivation of water-borne pathogens such as *Giardia* and *Cryptosporidium* which have been recognized as a serious cause of water-borne diseases in humans (von Gunten, 2003a). Thus, it has become common using ozone in water treatment plants in the USA and Europe (Le Paulou and Langlais, 1999; Rice, 1999). Ozone has also some disadvantages which are; *(i)* increased biodegradable organic carbon (BDOC); *(ii)* in the presence of bromide in raw water, formation of brominated disinfection by-products (BrDBPs) such as bromate, depending on influent bromide concentration, pH, total organic carbon (TOC) concentration and the treatment conditions (O_3 dose, dissolved O_3 and contact time) (von Gunten, 2003b); *(iii)* not stabile for the protection of the treated water in distribution system; *(iv)* ozonation is more expensive and has more technological requirements than chlorination. Three iodinated trihalomethanes, ITHMs, ($CHCl_2I$, $CHBrClI$, and $CHBr_2I$) were detected in Barcelona water treatment plant where sand filters and ozonation are applied at average levels lower than 1 µg/l while no ITHMs were measured in distribution system (Cancho et al., 2000).

Photocatalysis is a promising advanced oxidation technology and among many kinds of semiconductors, TiO_2 is the most widely employed photocatalyst due to its low cost, physico/chemical stability and its ability to mineralise chlorinated by-products precursors such as humic acids (HA) to CO_2, as well as to remove pathogenic organisms in water (Bekbölet and Ozkosemen, 1996; Bekbölet et al., 1998; 2002; Rincon and Pulgarin, 2004). The operational parameters are the concentration of humic acid, temperature, oxygen, light intensity and pH (Palmer et al., 2002). However the TiO_2/UV process has also some major disadvantages in that the separation of colloidal TiO_2 particles from the reacting aqueous suspension has proven to be difficult. In recent years, many attempts have been made to immobilize TiO_2 on solid, glass, or metal surfaces such that the separation step could be avoided (Lee et al., 2002). Besides, some reports provided evidence for toxicity of photocatalysed water samples in Daphnia magna and Vibrio fisheri (Parkinson et. al., 2001). Photocatalysis with solar energy is an innovative use of energy to drive photochemical treatment; this processes consists in utilising the near-UV part of the solar spectrum (<380 nm) to photoexcite a semiconductor catalyst in the presence of oxygen (Malato et al., 2002).

Electrochemical removal (Electrolysis) of bromide by oxidizing it to bromine and subsequently its volatilization has been succeeded (Kimbrough and Suffet, 2002). Selcuk et al. (2004) removed humic acids and bromate formation using photoelectrocatalysis process.

Enhanced Coagulation Experiences

Jar-test conducted on raw water samples taken from a constructed basin, of which characteristics are presented in Table 8, showed that the removal of organic THMs precursors increased by increasing the doses of coagulants.

Table 8. Raw water samples characteristics
(evaluated from 11 samples)

Parameter	Average	Stand. Dev.	Max.	Min.
T (°C)	9.89	3.96	22.4	8.3
pH	7.55	0.25	8.2	7.3
TOC (mg /l)	2.82	0.18	3.32	2.61
DOC (mg/l)	2.74	0.18	3.22	2.56
UV_{254} (1/cm)	0.1	0.02	0.13	0.06

In these experiments up to 73-90 mg/l of alum $(Al_2(SO_4)_3.18H_2O)$, ferric chloride $(FeCl_3 \cdot 6H_2O)$ and poly-aluminium chloride (PACl) were added without pH correction. In figure 5 the comparison between maximum TOC removal and TOC removal according to pH 7, target value set by USEPA (1999) for raw water with an alkalinity > 120 and < 240 mg $CaCO_3$/l, is showed for alum and ferric chloride. The TOC removal efficiency according to pH target criterion was always grater than 15% (minimum value required by EPA for raw water with TOC < 4.0 mg/l and alkalinity > 120 mg $CaCO_3$/l); the maximum removal was in the range of 33-46%.

PACl was the more effective coagulant; Figure 6 shows the UV_{254} removal efficiencies for the three coagulants used. PACl proved the highest removal up to 36-48 mg Al_2O_3/l dose range, than the removal diminished according to low final pH values (<6.5).

Modelling of DBPs Formation in Finished Water and Distribution System

The type and dosage of the disinfectant determines the types and amounts of DBPs formed during disinfection. Other water quality constituents, such as organic carbon (measured by TOC, DOC or UV absorbance), ammonia which reduces the effective disinfectant dosage and, consequently, reduce the formation of DBPs, pH, temperature, inorganic carbon concentration, bromide concentration are also affecting parameter as shown in Table 9 which summaries the empirical models proposed for DBPs (TTHMs and HAA) formation during chlorination and ozonation. The length of reaction time, t, is also another important factor for DBPs formation. Most DBPs formation occurs at a fast initial rate followed by a slower rate of formation that often continues for days in the presence of residual disinfectants. Formation of brominated DBPs is a relatively fast reaction compared to the formation of chlorinated by-products (Amy et al., 1987; Chowdhury and Amy, 1999).

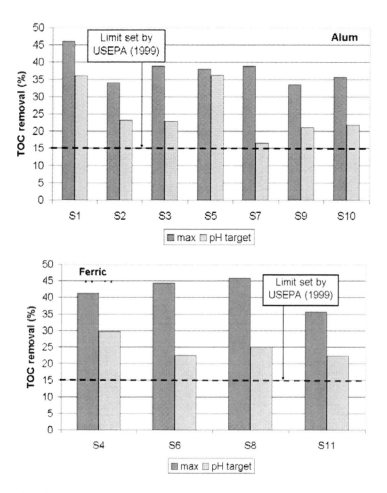

Figure 5. Comparison between maximum TOC removal and TOC removal according to target pH (USEPA, 1999) for both alum and ferric chloride respectively and different water samples (S1,.., S11).

The equations for chlorination were based on raw water chlorination and not chlorination of treated waters (e.g. coagulated-settled waters or granular activated carbon (GAC)-treated waters), thus are most appropriate for prechlorination. The other principal limitation of these models is the restrictive boundary conditions because they can predict the actual level of DBPs outside the treatment plant. Efforts are currently underway to developed predictive equations based on reaction kinetics of DBPs formation that will be appropriate to coagulated-settled waters and may remove some of the restrictions regarding boundary conditions. As mentioned by Chowdhury and Amy (1999) and recently revised by Sadiq and Rodriguez (2004), models to predict the concentration of ozonation by-products, other than bromate, e.g. aldehydes, biodegradable organic carbon or assimilable organic carbon, bromoform, are scarce yet. However, the progress in development of new models by

Table 9 Empirical model for DBP formation in chlorinated and ozonated drinking water

Reference	Model equation	Remarks
Tuthill and Polakoff (1979)*	$CHCl_3$ (mg/l) = -11.24 + 22.23 (Cl_2 dose, mg/l)	Low bromide
Trussel and Umphres (1978)*	$[d(TTHM)/dt] = k_n \cdot (Cl_2) \cdot (C)^m$	m = the order of the reaction with respect to the concentration of organic carbon precursor, kn = reaction rate constant
Kavanaugh et al. (1980)*	$[d(TTHM)/dt] = k_n \cdot (TOC) \cdot (Cl_2)$ dose $-(3(TTHM)^m/f)$	f = THM yield parameter
Amy et al. (1987)*	TTHM (μmoles/l) = 0.0039. $(UVABS(1/cm)_{254} \cdot TOC(mg/l))^{0.44} \cdot (Cl\ dose(mg/l))^{0.409}$ $\cdot (RXNTM(h))^{0.265} \cdot (TEMP)^{1.06} \cdot (pH-2.6)^{0.715} \cdot (BR(mg/l)+1)^{0.0358}$	RXNTM: reaction time; TEMP: Temperature(°C); BR: bromide concen.
Amy et al. (1991)*	THM specie = a $[UV. TOC]^b \cdot [Cl_2\ dose]^c \cdot [t]^d \cdot [Temp]^e \cdot [pH-2.6]^f \cdot [Br+I]^g$ $TTHM = [CHCl_3] + [CHCl_2Br] + [CHClBr_2] + [CHBr_3]$	A , b, c, d, e, f, g : constants (TOC: 3.0-13.8 mg/l; t: 0.1-168 h; T: 10-30°C; pH:4.6-9.8; UV: 0.063-0.489 1/cm; Br: 0.010-0.245 mg/l; Cl₂: 1.5-41.4 mg/l)
AWWARF(1991)*	$MCCA = 1.64(TOC)^{0.753} \cdot (Br+0.01)^{-0.085} \cdot (pH)^{-1.124} \cdot (Cl_2\ dose)^{0.509} \cdot (t)^{0.300}$ $DCAA=0.605(TOC)^{0.291} \cdot (UV)^{0.726} \cdot (Br+0.01)^{-0.568} \cdot (Cl_2\ dose)^{0.480} \cdot (t)^{0.239}\ (Temp)^{0.665}$ $TCAA=87.182(TOC)^{0.355} \cdot (UV)^{0.901} \cdot (Br+0.01)^{-0.679}\ (pH)^{-1.732} \cdot (Cl_2\ dose)^{0.881} \cdot (t)^{0.264}$ $MBAA=0.176(TOC)^{1.664} \cdot (UV)^{0.624} \cdot (Br)^{0.795} \cdot (pH)^{-0.927} \cdot (t)^{0.145}\ (Temp)^{0.450}$ $DBAA=84.94(TOC)^{-0.620} \cdot (UV)^{0.651} \cdot (Br)^{1.073} \cdot (Cl_2\ dose)^{-0.200} \cdot (t)^{0.120}\ (Temp)^{0.657}$	Haloacetic acid formation as a result of chlorination (TOC: 2.8-11 mg/l, t: 0.1-105 h; T: 13-20°C; pH:5.6-9.0; UV: 0.05-0.38 1/cm; Br: 0.005-0.430 mg/l, Cl₂: 3.0-25 mg/l) MCAA=Monochloroacetic acid, μg/l DCAA=Dichloroacetic acid, μg/l TCAA=trichloroacetic acid, μg/l MBAA=monobromoacetic acid, μg/l DBAA=dibromoacetic acid, μg/l
Amy et al. (1998)*	$[BrO_3^-]=2.32*10^{-6}[DOC]^{-1.47} \cdot [O_3\ dose]^{1.65} \cdot [Br^-]^{0.81} \cdot [NH_3-N]^{-0.121} \cdot [pH]^{5.35} \cdot [t]^{0.28}$	BrO₃: bromate concentration, mg/l; DOC: dissolved organic carbon concentration, mg/l; O3 dose: transferred ozone dose at the beginning of the formation reaction, mg/l; Nh3-N: ammonia nitrogen concentration, mg/l; Br: bromide concentration, mg/l
Song et al. (1996)*	$[BrO_3^-]=10^{-6.11}[DOC]^{1.18} \cdot [O_3\ dose]^{1.42} \cdot [Br^-]^{0.88} \cdot [NH_3-N]^{-0.18} \cdot [pH]^{5.11} \cdot [t]^{0.27} \cdot [IC]^{0.18}$	IC: inorganic carbon concentration, mgCaCO₃/l
Ozekin (1994)*	$[BrO_3^-]=1.63*10^{-6}[DOC]^{-1.26} \cdot [O_3\ dose]^{1.57} \cdot [Br^-]^{1.57} \cdot [pH]^{5.82} \cdot [t]^{0.28}$	Bromide: 0.07-0.44 mg/l; t: 1-120 min; pH: 6.5-8.5; O3: 1-10 mg/l; IC: 1-216 mgCaCO₃/l; T: 20-30°C; DOC: 1.1-8.4 mg/l

*(modified from Chowdhury and Amy, 1999)

Abdullah et al. (2003), Elshorbagy et al. (2000), Golfinopoulos, et al., (1998), Golfinopoulos and Arhonditsis (2002), Gallard and Gunten (2002), Milot et al. (2000), Nokes et al. (1999), Sohn et al. (2001) contributed to optimize the use of coagulant type and dose.

Beyond all the efforts have been done today, a more realistic approach to achieving public health protection is through source water protection, treatment optimization, and maintenance of water quality through storage and distribution (Von Gunten et al., 2001; Allen et al., 2002).

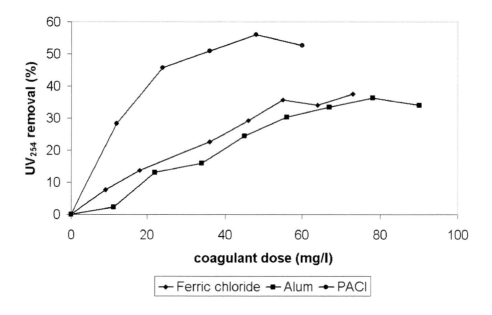

Figure 6 UV$_{254}$ adsorbance removal from three types of coagulants

References

Abdullah, MA., Yew, C.H., Ramli, M.S. (2003). Formation, modeling and validation of trihalomethanes (THM) in Malaysian drinking water: a case study in the districts of Tampin, Negeri Sembilan and Sabak Bernam, Selangor, Malaysia. *Wat Res,* 37, 4637-4644.

Allen, M.J., Clancy, J.L., Rice, E.W. (2000). The plain, hard truth about pathogen monitoring. *Jour. of Ame. Wat. Wor. Ass.,* 92(9), 64-76.

Allen, M.J., Edberg, S.C., Reasoner, D.J. (2004). Heterotrophic plate count bacteria-what is their significance in drinking water? *Int. Jour. of Food Microb.,* 92, 265-274.

Ali, S.H. (2004). A socio-ecological autopsy of the E. coli O157: H7 outbreak in Walkerton, Ontario, Canada. *Soc. Sci. and Med.,* 58, 2601-2612.

Amy, G.L., Chadic, PA., Chowdhury, Z.K. (1987). Developing model for predicting trihalomethane formation kinetics. *Jour. of Ame. Wat. Wor. Ass.,* 70(7), 89-97.

Anonym (2001). Recommendation for avoidance of drinking water contamination with parasites (Empfehlung zur Vermeidung von Kontaminationen des Trinkwassers mit Parasiten). *Bundesgesundheitsblatt Gesundheitforsch Gesundheitsschutz,* 44, 406-408.

APHA, AWWA, WEF (1998). Standard Methods for the Examination of Water and Wastewater, 20th Ed.; Ame. Pub. Hea. Ass./Ame. Wat. Wor. Ass./Wat. Env. Fed. Washington D.C., USA, 5-45.

Ashbolt, N.J. (2004a). Microbial contamination of drinking water and disease outcomes in developing regions. *Toxicology,* 198, 229-238.

Ashbolt, N.J. (2004b) Risk analysis of drinking water microbial contamination versus disinfection by-products (DBPs). *Toxicology,* 198, 255-262.

Bartram, J., Cotruco, J., Exner, M., Fricker, C., Glasmacher, A. (2004). Heterotrophic plate count measurement in drinking water safety management. *Int. Jour. of Food Microb.,* 92, 241-247.

Bell-Ajy, K., Abbaszadegan, M., Ibrahim, E., Verges, D., LeChevallier, M. (2000). Conventional and optimized coagulation for NOM removal. *Jour. of Ame. Wat. Wor. Ass.,* 92(10), 44-58.

Bekbolet, M., Ozkosemen, G. (1996). A preliminary investigation on the photocatalytic degradation of a model humic acid. *Wat. Sci. Tech.* 33, 189-194.

Bekbölet, M., Boyacioglu, Z., Özkaraova, B. (1998). The influence of solution matrix on the photocatalytic removal of color from natural waters. *Wat. Sci. Tech.* 38(6), 155-162.

Bekbolet, M., Suphandag, A.S., Uyguner, C.S. (2002). An investigation of the photocatalytic efficiencies of TiO2 powders on the decolourisation of humic hacids. *Jour. Photoch. Photobio. A: Chem.* 148, 121-128.

Bekbolet, M., Rizzo, L., Belgiorno, V., Napoli, R.M.A., Meriç, S. (2004) Evaluation of TTHMs formation in drinking water: Istanbul (Turkey) and Salerno (Italy) cases", SIDISA'2004 *International Environmental Engineering Symposium,* Taormina (Sicily) 23-26 June 2004.

Boorman, G.A., Dellarco, V., Dunnick, J.K., Chapin, R.E., Hunter, S., Hauchman, F., Gardner, H., Cox, M., Sills, R. (1999). Drinking water disinfection byproducts: Review and Approach to Toxicity Evaluation. *Environ. Heal. Persp.* 107 (Suppl 1), 207-217.

Boualam, M., Mathieu, L., Fass, S., Cavard, J., Gatel, D. (2002). Relationship between coliform culturability and organic matter in low nutiritive waters. *Wat. Res.,* 36, 2618-2626.

Bresner, M., Gauthier, V., Servais, P., Camper, A. (2002). Explaining the occurrence of coliforms in distribution systems. *Jour. of Ame. Wat. Wor. Ass.,* 94(8), 95-109.

Brookes, J.D., Antenucci, J., Hipsey, M., Burch, M.D., Ashbolt, N.J., Ferguson, C. (2004). Fate and transport of pathogens in lakes and reservoirs. *Environ. Intern.,* 741-759.

Bull, R.J., Birnbaum, L.S., Cantor, K.P., Rose, J.B., Butterworth, B.E., Pegram, R., Tuomisto, J. (1995). Water chlorination: Essential process or cancer hazard? *Fund. Appl. Tox.* 28 (2), 155-166.

Camper, A.K. (2004). Involvement of humic substances in regrowth. *Int. Jour. of Food Microb.,* 92, 355-364.

Cancho, B., Ventura, Galceran, M., Diaz, A., Ricart, S. (2000). Determination, synthesis, and survey of iodinated trihalomethanes in water treatment process. *Wat. Res.*, 34(13), 3380-3390.

Chandy, J.P., Angles, M.L. (2001). Determination of nutrients limiting biofilm formation and the subsequent impact on disinfectant decay. *Wat. Res.*, 35(11), 2677-2682.

Chauret, C., Nolan, K., Chen, P., Sprinthorpe, S., Sattar, S. (1998). Aging of Crytosporidium parvum oocysts in river water and their susceptibility to disinfection by chlorine and monochlorine. *Can. Jou. Microb.*, 44(12), 1154-1160.

Chowdhury, Z.K., Amy, G.L. (1999). Modelling disinection by-product formation. In "Formation and control of disinfection by-products in drinking water". Singer, P.C., Editor. *Ame. Wat. Wor. Ass.*, Denver, CO.

Clark, R.M., Sivaganesan, M., Rice, E., Chen, J. (2002). Development of a Ct equation for the inactivation of Cryptosporidium oocysts with ozone. *Wat. Res.*, 36, 3141-3149.

Clark, R.M., Sivaganesan, M., Rice, E., Chen, J. (2003). Development of a Ct equation for the inactivation of Cryptosporidium oocysts with chlorine dioxide. *Wat. Res.*, 37, 2773-2783.

Craik, S.A., Weldon, D., Finch, G.R., Bolton, J.R., Belossevic, M. (2001). Inactivation of Cryptosporidium parvum oocysts using medium and low pressure ultraviolet radiation. *Wat. Sci. Tech.*, 35, 1387-1398.

Craun G.F. and Calderon R.L. (2001) Waterborne disease outbreaks caused by distribution system deficiencies. *Jour. of Ame. Wat. Wor. Ass.*, 93 (9), 64-75.

Di Diovanni, G.D., Hashemi, F.H., Shaw, N.J., Abrams, F.A., LeChevallier, M.W., Abbasadegan, M. (1999). Detection of infectious Cryptosporidium parvum oocysts in surface and filter backwash water samples by immunomagnetic separation and integrated cell culture-PCR. *Appl. Environ. Microbiol.*, 65, 3427-3432.

Dojlido, J., Zbiec, E., Swietlik, R. (1999) Formation of the haloacetic acids during ozonation and chlorination of water in Warsaw waterworks (Poland). *Wat. Res.*, 33(14), 3111-3118.

Duncan, I.B.R. (1988). Waterborne Klebsiella and human disease. *Toxic. Assess.*, 3(5), 581-598.

Edzwald, J.K. and kelley, M.B. (1998). Control of Cryptosporidium-from reservoirs to clarifiers to filters. *Wat. Sci. Tech.,* 37(2), 1-8

Edzwald, J.K. and Tobiason, J.E. (1999). Enchanced coagulation: US requirements and a broader view. *Wat. Sci. Tech.,* 40(9), 63-70.

Exall, K.N. and Vanloon, G.W. (2000) Using coagulants to remove organic matter. J AWWA, November, 93-102.

El-Shafy, M.A. and Grunwald, A. (2000). THM formation in water supply in south Bohemia, Czech Republic. *Wat. Res.*, 34(13), 3453-3459.

Elshorbagy, W.E., Abu-Qadais, H., Elsheamy, K. (2000). Simulation of THM species in water distribution systems. *Wat. Res.*, 34(13), 3431-3439.

Falkinham, J.O., Norton, C.D., LeChevallier, M.W. (2001). Factors influencing numbers of Mycobacterium avium, Myco bacterium intracellulare, and other mycobacteria in drinking water distribution systems. *Appl. Environ. Microbiol.*, 67(3), 1225-1231.

Fisher, D.J., Burton, D.T., Yonkas, L.T., Turley, S.D., Ziegler, G.P., Turley, B.S. (2003). Derivation of acute ecological risk criteria for chlorite in freshwater ecosystem. *Wat. Res.*, 37(18), 4359-4368.

Gallard, H. and Gunten, U. (2002). Chlorination of natural organic matter: kinetics of chlorination and THM formation. *Wat. Res.*, 36, 65-74.

Garcia-Villanova, R.J., Garcia, C., Gomez, J.A., Garcia, M.M., Ardanuy, R. (1997a). Formation, evolution and modeling of trihalomethanes in the drinking water of a town: I. At the municipal treatment utilities. *Wat. Res.*, 31(6), 1299-1308.

Garcia-Villanova, R.J., Garcia, C., Gomez, J.A., Garcia, M.M., Ardanuy, R. (1997b). Formation, evolution and modeling of trihalomethanes in the drinking water of a town: II. In the distribution system. *Wat. Res*, 31(6), 1405-1413.

Golfinopoulos, S.K., Xilourgidis, N.K., Kpstopoulou, M.N., Lekkas, T.D. (1998). Use of a multiple regression model for predicting trihalomethane formation. *Wat. Res.*, 32(9), 2821-2829.

Golfinopoulos, S.K. and Nikolaou, A.D. (2001). Disinfection by-products and volatile organic compounds in the water supply system in Athens, Greece. *Jou. Environ. Sci. Heal.*, A36(4), 483-499.

Golfinopoulos, S.K. and Arhonditsis, G.B. (2002). Quantitative assessment of trihalomethane formation using simulations of reaction kinetics. *Wat. Res.*, 36, 2856-2868.

Hallam, N.B., West, J.R., Forster, C.F., Simms, J. (2001). The potential for biofilm growth in water distribution systems. *Wat. Res.*, 35 (17), 4063-4071.

Hardalo, C., Edberg, S.C. (1997). Pseudomonas aeruginosa: assessment of risk from drinking water. *Crit. Rev. in Microbiol.*, 23(1), 47-75.

Hellard, M.E., Stewart, M.I., Forbes, A.B., Fairley, C.K. (2001). A randomized, blinded, controlled trial investigation of the gastrointestinal health effects of drinking water quality. *Environ. Heal. Persp.*, 109(8), 773-778.

Ichihashi, K., Teranish, K., Ichimura, A. (1999) Brominated trihalomethane formation in halogenation of humic acid in the coexistence of hypochlorite and hypobromite ions. *Wat. Res.*, 33(2), 477-483.

Karanfil, T., Schlautman, Erdogan, I. (2002). Survey of DOC and UV measurement practices with implications for SUVA determination. *Jour. of Ame. Wat. Wor. Ass.*, 94(12), 68-80.

Karim. M., Abbaszadegan, M., LeChevallier, M.W. (2003). Potential for pathogen intrusion during pressure transients. *Jour. of Am. Wat. Wor. Ass.*, 95 (5), 134-146.

Kimbrough, D.E. and Suffet, I.H. (2002). Electrochemical removal of bromide and reduction of THM formation potential in drinking water. *Wat. Res.*, 36, 4902-4906.

Komulainen, H. (2004). Experimental cancer studies of chlorinated by-products. *Toxicology*, 198, 239-248.

Korich, D.G., Mead, J.R., Madore, M.S., Sinclair, N.A., Sterling, C.R. (1990). Effects of ozone, chlorine dioxide, chlorine and monochloramine on Cryptosporidium parvum oocycts viability. *Appl. Environ. Microbiol.*, 56, 1423-1428.

Kramer, M.H., Quade, G., Hartemann, P., Exner, M. (2001). Waterborne diseases in Europe – 1986-1996. *Jour. of Am. Wat. Wor. Ass.*, 93, 48-53.

Krasner, S.W., McGuir, M.J., Jacangelo, J.C., Patania, N.L., Reagan, K.M., Aieta, E.M. (1989). The occurrence of disinfection by-products in US drinking water. *Jour. of Am. Wat. Wor. Ass.*, 81(8), 41-53.

Larson, J.L., Wolf, D.C., Butterworth, B.E. (1994). Induced cytolethality and regenerative cell proliferation in the livers and kidneys of male BandC3F1 mice given chloroform by gavage. *Fundam. Appl. Toxicol.* 23, 537-543.

Lee, J.C., Kim, M.S., Kim, B.W. (2002). Removal of paraquat dissolved in a photoreactor with TiO2 immobilized on the glass-tubes of UV lamps. Wat. Res., *36(7), 1776-1782.*

LeChevallier, M.W., Babcock, T. M., Lee, R.G. (1987). Examination and characterization of distribution systems biofilms. *Appl. and Environ. Microbiol.*, 53(12), 2714-2724.

LeChevallier, M.W., Cawthon, C.D., Lee, R.G., (1988). Factors promoting survival of bacteria in chlorinated water supplies. *Appl. and Environ. Microbiol.*, 54(3), 649-654.

LeChevallier, M.W., Lowry, C.D., Lee, R.G. (1990). Disinfection of biofilms in a model distribution system. *Jour. of Am. Wat. Wor. Ass.*, 82(7), 87-99.

LeChevallier, M.W., Welch, N.J., Smith, D.B., (1996). Full-scale studies of factors related to coliform regrowth in drinking water. *Appl. and Environ. Microbiol.*, 62(7), 2201-2211.

LeChevallier, M.W. (1999). Biofilms in drinking water distribution systems: significance and control. In "Identifying Future Drinking Water Contaminants". National Research Council. National Academic Press.

Le Paulou, J., Langlais, B. (1999). State of the art of ozonation in France. Ozone Sci. Eng., *21, 153–62.*

Li, J.W., Yu, Z., Cai, X., Gao, M., Chao, F. (1996). Trihalomethanes formation in water treated with chlorine dioxide. Wat. Res., *30(10), 2371-2376.*

Lilly, P.D., Moore, T.C., Pegram, R.A. (1994). Comparative renal and hepatic toxicity of bromodichloromethane(BDCM) and chloroform (CHCl3) following acute oral aqueous administration to rats. Toxicologist, *14, 280.*

Linden, K.G., Shin, G., Sobsey, M.D. (2001). Comparative effectiveness of UV wavelengths for the inactivation of Cryptosporidium parvum oocysts in water. *Wat. Sci. Tech.*, 43(12), 171-174.

Lisle, J.T., Broadaway, S.C., Prescott, A.M., Pyle, B.H., Fricker C., McFeters, G.A. (1998). Effects of starvation on physiological activity and chlorine disinfection resistance in Escherichia Coli O157:H7. *Appl. and Environ. Microbiol.*, 64 (12), 4658-4662.

Lu, W., Kiene, L., Levi, Y. (1999). Chlorine demand of biofilms in water distribution systems. *Wat. Res.*, 33(3), 827-835.

Liu, W., Wu, H., Wang, Z., Ong, S.L., Hu, J.Y., Ng, W.J. (2002). Investigation of assimilable organic carbon (AOC) and bacterial regrowth in drinking water distribution system. *Wat. Res.*, 36, 891-898.

Lund, V., Ormerod, K. (1995). The influence of disinfection processes on biofilm formation in water distribution systems. *Wat. Res.*, 29(4), 1013-1021.

Malato, S., Blanco, J., Vidal, A., Richter, C. (2002). Photocatalysis with solar energy at a pilot-plant scale: an overview. *Appl Cat B: Environ,* 37, 1-15.

McFeters, G.A., Kippin, J.S., LeChevallier, M.W. (1986). Injured coliforms in drinking water. *Appl. and Environ. Microbiol.*, 51(1), 1-5.

Milot, J., Rodriguez, M.J., Serodes, J.B. (2000). Modelling the susceptibility of drinking water utilities to form high concentrations of trihalomethanes. *Jour. of Environ. Manag.*, 60, 155-171.

Morris, R.D., Audet, A., Angelillo, I.F., Chalmers, T.C., Mosteller, F. (1992). Chlorination, chlorination by-products, and cancer: A metanalysis. *Am J Pub. Heal.*, **7**, 955-963.

Moudgal, C.J., Lipscomb, J.C., Bruce, R.M. (2000). Potential health effects of drinking water disinfection by-products using quantitative structure toxicity realtionship. *Toxicol.*, 147, 109-131.

Nikolaou, A.D., Kostopoulou, M.N., Lekkas, T.D. (1999). Organic by-products of drinking water chlorination. *Global Nest*, 1(3), 143-156.

Nikolaou, A.D., Golfinopoulos, S.K., Lekkas, T.D. (2002). Formation of organic by-products during chlorination of natural waters. *Jour. of Environ. Monit.*, 4(4), 910-916.

Nikolaou, A.D., Golfinopoulos, S.K., Lekkas, T.D., Kostopoulou, M.N. (2004). DBP levels in chlorinated dirnking water: Effect of humic substances. *Environ. Monit. and Asses.*, 93, 301-319.

Niquette, P., Servais, P., Savoir, R. (2001). Bacterial dynamics in the drinking water distribution system of Brussels. *Wat. Res.*, 35(3), 675-682.

Nokes, C.J., Fenton, E., Randall, C.J. (1999). Modelling the formation of brominated trihalomethanes in chlorinated drinking waters. *Wat. Res.*, 33(7), 3557-3568.

Norton, C.D. and LeChevallier, M.W. (1997). Chloroamination: its effect on distribution system water quality. *Jour. of Am. Wat. Wor. Ass.*, 89(7), 66-77.

Palacios, M., Pampillon, J.F., Rodriguez, M.E. (2000). Organohalogenated compounds levels in chlorinated drinking waters and current compliance with quality standards throughout the European Union. *Wat. Res.*, 34(3), 1002-1016.

Palmer, F.L., Eggins, B.R., Coleman, H.M. (2002). The effect of operational parameters on the photocatalytic degradation of humic acid. *Jour. Photoch. and Photobiol. A: Chemistry*, 148, 137-143.

Parkinson, A., Barry, M.J., Roddick, F.A., Hobday, M.D. (2001). Preliminary toxicity assessment of water after treatment with UV-irradiation and UVC/H_2O_2. *Wat. Res.* 35, 3656-3664.

Pavlov, D., de Wet, C.M.E., Grabow, W.O.K., Ehlers, M.M. (2004). Potentially pathogenic features of heterophic plate count bacteria isolated from treated and untreated drinking water. *Int. Jour. of Food Microb.*, 92, 275-287.

Pegram, R.A., Andersen, M.E., Warren, S.H., Ross, T.M., Claxton, L.D. (1997). Gluthaione S-Transferase-mediated mutagenity of trihalomethanes in *Salmonella typhimurium*: contrasting results with bromodichloromethane and chloroform. *Toxicol. Appl. Pharmacol.*, 144, 183-188.

Peters, C.J., Young, R.J., Perry, R. (1980). Factors influencing the formation of haloforms in the chlorination of humic materials. *Environ. Sci. Technol.* 14, 1391-1395.

Pintar, K.D.M., Slawson, R.M. (2003). Effect of temperature and disinfection strategies on ammonia-oxidizing bacteria in a bench-scale drinking water distribution system. *Wat. Res.*, 37, 1805-1817.

Power, K.N., Schneider, R.P., Marshall, K.C. (1997). The effect of growth conditions on survival and recovery of *Klebsiella Oxytoca* after exposure to chlorine. *Wat. Res.*, 31(1), 135-139.

Reasoner, D.J. (2004). Heterotrophic plate count methodology in the United States. *Int. Jour. of Food Microbiol.*, 92, 307-315.

Reckhow, D.A., Singer, P.C., Malcolm, R.L. (1990). Chlorination of humic materails: by-product formation and chemical interpretations. *Environ Sci Technol.*, 24(11), 1655-1664.

Rennecker, J.L., Marinas, B.J., Owens, J.H., Rice, E.W. (1999). Inactivation of Cryptosporidium parvum oocysts with ozone. *Wat. Res.*, 33, 2481-2488.

Rice, R.G. (1999). Ozone in the United States of America — State of the art. *Ozone Sci. Eng.* 21, 99–118.

Rincon, E-G., Pulgarin, C. (2004). Bacterial action illuminated TiO_2 on pure *Escherichia coli* and natural bacterial consortia: post-irradiation events in the dark and assessment of the effective disinfection time. *Appl. Catal. B: Environ.*, 49, 99-112.

Rizzo, L., Belgiorno, V., Napoli, R.M.A. (2004) Regrowth evaluation of coliform bacteria injured by low chlorine doses using selective and nonselective media. *Jour. of Environ. Sci. and Heal.* Part A, 39(8), 2081–2092.

Rodriquez, M. and Serodes, J.B. (2001). Spatial and temporal evolution of trihalomethanes in three water distribution systems. *Wat. Res.*, 35(6), 1572-1586.

Rook, J.J. (1974). Formation of haloforms during the chlorination of natural water. *Wat. Treat. Exam.* 23, 234-243.

Rose, J.B., Huffman, D.E., Gennaccaro, A. (2002). Risk and control of waterborne cryptosporidiosis. *FEMS Microb. Rev.*, 26, 113-123.

Rupnow, M..T., Shacter, R.D., Owens, D.K., Parsonnet, J. (2000). A dynamic transmission model for predicting trends in Helicobacter pylori and associated diseases in the United States. *Emerg. Inect. Dis.*, 6(3), 228-237.

Sadiq, R. and Rodriguez, M.J. (2004). Disinfection by-porducts (DBPs) in drinking water and predictive models for their occurence: a review. *Sci. of the Total Environ.*, 321, 21-46.

Schoenen, D. (2002). Role of disinfection in suppressing the spread of pathogens with drinking water: possibilities and limitations. *Wat. Res.*, 36, 3874-3888.

Schwartz, T., Hoffmann, S., Obst, U. (1998). Formation and bacterial composition of young, natural biofilms obtained from public bank-filtered drinking water systems. *Wat. Res.*, 32(9), 2787-2797.

Selcuk, H., Sene, J.J., Zanoni, M.V.B., Sarikaya, H.Z., Anderson, M.A. (2004). Behaviour of bromide in the photoelectrocatalytic process and bromine generation using nanoporous titanium dioxide thin-film electrodes. *Chemosph.* 54, 969-974.

Simpson, L.L. and Hayes, K.P. (1998). Drinking water disinfection by-products: an Australian perspective. *Wat. Res.*, 32(5), 1522-1528.

Singer, P.C. (1999). Humic substances as precursors for potentially harmful disinfection by-products. *Wat. Sci. Tech.*, 40(9), 25-30.

Singh, A., McFeters, G.A. (1990). Injury of enteropathogenic bacteria in drinking water. In "*Drinking Water Microbiology*" (McFeters G.A. Ed.). Springer-Verlag, New York Inc.

Sinton, L.W., Hall, C.H., Lynch, P.A., Davies,-Colley, R.J. (2002). Sunlight inactivation of faecal indicator bacteria and bacteriophages from waste stabilization pond effluent in fresh and saline waters. *Appl. Environ. Microbiol.*, 68(3),1122-1131.

Sohn, J., Gatel, D., Amy, G. (2001). Monitoring and modelling of disinfection by-products (DBPs). *Environ. Monit. and Asses.*, 70, 211-222.

Soini, S.M., Koskinen, K.T., Vilenius, M.J., Puhakka, J.A. (2002). Potential of microbial growth control in water hydraulic systems by UV irradiation and filtration. *Jour. Chem. Tech. Biotech.*, 77(8), 903-909.

Stelma, G.N. Jr., Lye, D.J., Smith, B.G., Messer, J.W., Payment, P. (2004). Rare occurence of heterotrophic bacteria with pathogenic potential in potable water. *Int. Jour. of Food Microb.*, 92, 249-254.

Teuschler, L.K., Simmons, J.E. (2003). Approaching DBP toxicity as a mixtures problem. *Jour. of Am. Wat. Wor. Ass.,* 95(6), 131-138.

Uhl, W., Schaule, G. (2004). Establishment of HPC (R2A) for regrowth control in non-chlorinated distribution systems. *Int. Jour. of Food Microb.*, 92, 317-325.

USEPA (1989). *National Primary Drinking WaterRregulations: Filtration, Disinfection; Turbidity, Giardia lamblia, Viruses, Legionella, and Heterotrophic Bacteria;* Final Rule. Fed. Reg., V.54, No.124, 27486-27541, 40 CFR, parts 141 and 142. .

USEPA (1991). *National Primary Drinking Water Regulations; Total Coliforms; Partial Stay of Certain Provisions of Final Rule. Fed. Reg.,* V. 56, No.10, 1556-1557, 40 CFR, Parts 141 and 142.

USEPA (1998). *National Primary Drinking Water Regulations: Disinfectants and Disinfection By-Products*; Final Rule , Fed. Reg., 63/241/69478.

USEPA (1999). *Enhanced coagulation and enhanced precipitative softening guidance manual.* EPA 815-R-99-012.

USEPA (2000). *Conducting Risk Assessment of mixtures of disinfection by-products (DBPs) for drinking water treatment systems.* EPA/600/R-03/ORD/NCEA, Cincinnati.

USEPA (2002). *National Primary Drinking Water Regulations: Long Ter Enhanced Surface Water Treatment Rule; Final Rule Disinfectants and Disinfection By-Products.* F.R. Vol.67, no.9.

Van der Wende, E., Characklis, W.G. (1990). Biofilms in potable water distribution systems. In *"Drinking Water Microbiology"* (McFeters G.A. Ed.). Springer-Verlag, New York Inc.

Varjus, S.H., Riipinen, H., Soini, S.M., Koskinen, K.T., Vilenius, M.J., Puhakka, J.A. (2004). Microbial growth control in water hydraulic systems by conventional filtration. *Filtration and Separation*, April, 41-47.

Villanueva, C.M., Kogevinas, M., Grimalt, J.O. (2003). Haloacetic acids and trihalomethanes in finished dirinking waters from heterogeneous sources. *Wat. Res.* 37, 953-958.

Volk, C.J., LeChevallier, M.W. (1999). Impacts of the reduction of nutrient levels on bacterial water quality in distribution systems. *Appl. and Environ. Microbiol.*, 65(11), 4957-4966.

Volk, C., Bell, K., Ibrahim, E., Verges, D, Amy, G., LeChevallier, M. (2000). Impact of enhanced and optimized coagulation on removal of organic matter and its biodegradable fraction in drinking water. *Wat. Res.,* 34(12), 3247-3257.

Von Gunten, U., Griedger, A., Gallard, H., Salhi, E. (2001). By-products formation during drinking water disinfection: A tool to assess disinfection efficiency? *Wat. Res.*, 35(8), 2095-2099.

Von Gunten, U. (2003a) Ozonation of drinking water: Part I. Oxidation kinetics and product formation. *Wat Res*, 37, 1443-1467.

Von Gunten, U (2003b). Ozonation of drinking water: Part II. Disinfection and by-product formation in presence of bromide, iodide or chlorine. *Wat. Res.* 37(7), 1469–1487.

Wadhhwa, S.G., Khaled, G.H., Edberg, S.C. (2002). Comparative microbial character of consumed food and drinking water. *Crit. Rev. in Microb.*, 28, 249-279.

Wcislo, R. and Chrost, R.J. (2000). Survival of Escherichia coli in freshwater. *Pol. J. Environ Stud.*, 9(3), 215-222.

White, G.C. (1999). *Handbook of Chlorination and Alternative Disinfectants*, 4th Ed.; John Wiley and Sons: USA.

WHO (2003). *Emerging Issues in Water and Infectious Disease.* (Ed. Pond, K.) Geneve, Switerland.

Yang, C-Y. (2004). Drinking water chlorination and adverse birth outcomes in Taiwan. *Toxicology*, 198, 249-254.

Yoon, J., Choi, Y., Cho, S., lee, D. (2003). Low trihalomethane formation in Korean drinking water. *The Sci. of the Total Environ.*, 302, 157-166.

Yu, J.C., Cheng, L.N. (1999). Speciation and distribution of trihalomethanes in drinking water of Hong Kong. *Environ. Int.*, 25(5), 605-611.

Zacheus, O.M., Iivanainen, E.K., Nissinen, T.K., Lehtola, M.J., Martikainen, P.J. (2000). Bacterial biofilm formation on polyvinyl chloride, polyethylene and stainless steel exposed to ozonated water. *Wat. Res.*, 34(1), 63-70.

Zacheus, O.M., Lehtola, M.J., Korhonen, L.K., Martikainen, P.J. (2001). Soft deposits, the key site for microbial growth in drinking water distribution networks. *Wat. Res.*, 35(7), 1757-1765.

Zhang, W., Di Giano, F.A. (2002). Comparison of bacterial regrowth in distribution systems using free chlorine and chloramine: a statistical study of causative factors. *Wat. Res.*, 36, 1469-1482.

In: Trends in Water Pollution Research
Editor: J. V. Livingston, pp. 31-74

ISBN 1-59454-328-3
©2005 Nova Science Publishers, Inc.

Chapter II

Photocatalytic Oxidation Using Lanthanide Ion-Doped Titanium Dioxide Catalysts for Water and Wastewater Treatment

Xiang-zhong Li[1]*, Fang-bai Li,[1,2] and Yi-bing Xie[1,3]
[1]Department of Civil and Structural Engineering,
The Hong Kong Polytechnic University, Hong Kong, China
[2]Guangdong Key Laboratory of Agricultural Environment Pollution Integrated Control,
Guangdong Institute of Eco-Environment and Soil Science, Guangzhou, 510650, China
[3]Key Laboratory of Molecular and Biomolecular Electronics, Southeast University,
Nanjing 210096, China

Abstract

Two types of lanthanide ion-doped titanium dioxide (Ln^{n+}-TiO_2) catalysts, Ln^{n+}-TiO_2 powder and Ln^{n+}-TiO_2 sol, were prepared by doping the lanthanide ions with a special $4f$ electron configuration onto titanium dioxide (TiO_2). The Ln^{n+}-TiO_2 powder catalysts including La^{3+}-TiO_2, Ce^{3+}-TiO_2, and Nd^{3+}-TiO_2 were prepared by a sol-gel process, while the crystallized Ln^{n+}-TiO_2 sol catalysts including $Ce^{4+/3+}$-TiO_2, Nd^{3+}-TiO_2, and Eu^{3+}-TiO_2 were prepared by a chemical coprecipitation-peptization method. The prepared catalysts were fully characterized by X-ray diffraction (XRD), atom force microscope (AFM), Brunauer-Emmett-Teller method (BET), X-ray photoelectron spectroscopy (XPS), UV-Visible diffusive reflectance spectrometry (DRS), and photoluminescence (PL) analyses. The XRD results confirmed that all Ln^{n+}-TiO_2 catalysts were dominated with anatase and had a crystalline structure. The BET results showed that the powder catalysts had an

---

* To whom correspondence should be addressed. Fax: (852) 2334 6389; Email: cexzli@polyu.edu.hk

increased specific surface area owing to the lanthanide ion doping. The results of AFM and particle size distribution showed that the sol catalysts had the average particle sizes of 8, 10 and 12 nm owing to Nd^{3+}, $Ce^{4+/3+}$, and Eu^{3+} doping, respectively. The DRS results indicated that Ce^{3+}-TiO_2 catalyst had significant optical absorption in the visible region between 400 nm and 500 nm, while Nd^{3+}-TiO_2 had an insignificant shift of absorption band edge only. The results of PL analyses found that the separation efficiency of hole-electron pairs increased with the increase of lanthanide ion dosage at a low range and then decreased when the lanthanide ion dosage exceeded an optimal amount. In this study, an odorous chemical of 2-mercaptobenzothiazole (MBT) and an azo dye of reactive brilliant red X-3B were used as model pollutants to evaluate the photocatalytic activity of Ln^{n+}-TiO_2 catalysts in aqueous solution. The experimental results showed that all the Ln^{n+}-TiO_2 catalysts had higher photocatalytic efficiency than pure TiO_2 catalysts under either UV or visible light irradiation. The enhancement of photocatalytic activity was crucially attributable to the enhancement of the electron-hole pairs separation and partially attributable to the improvement of the substrate adsorption in aqueous solution. It is proposed that the formation of two sub-energy levels (defect level and Ln $4f$ level) in Ln^{3+}-TiO_2 might be a critical reason to eliminate the recombination of electron-hole pairs and also to shift light absorption toward the visible region. This study indicates that the photocatalytic oxidation using lanthanide ion-doped TiO_2 catalysts may provide a more efficient approach for mineralization of organic pollutants in environment.

Introduction

Titanium dioxide (TiO_2)-based photocatalytic oxidation techniques have been paid much attention to their application potential for complete mineralization of many toxic and non-biodegradable organic contaminants in environment. There have been a number of literatures focusing on water and wastewater treatment in order to promote this technique to be applied in practice [1-3]. Some studies indicated that the photocatalytic activity of TiO_2 catalyst depends strongly on three factors of adsorption behavior, optical absorption property, and the separation efficiency of electron-hole pairs [1-5]. The adsorption capacity can be generally improved by adjusting the surface-zero-charge point of catalyst particles or increasing the specific surface area and pore volume in catalyst structure [6-8]. It had been extensively reported that doping with a group of transitional metal ions [7-13] or depositing some noble metals such as Au [6, 12, 14-15] and Pt [16-17], or coupling metal oxides [18-20] with d electronic configuration into TiO_2 lattice could result in an extension of their wavelength response into the visible light region. Unfortunately, it should be noted that the fundamental photocatalytic activity of TiO_2 under UV light was actually reduced in many cases, while the emphasis was focused on a visible-light response [21].

Alternatively, TiO_2 photocatalytic activity could be significantly enhanced by doping with lanthanide ions/oxides with $4f$ electron configuration because lanthanide ions could form complexes with various Lewis bases including organic acids, amines, aldehydes, alcohols, and thiols in the interaction of the functional groups with their f-orbital [22-24]. Xu et al.[22] reported that the doping with La^{3+}, Ce^{3+}, Er^{3+}, Pr^{3+}, Gd^{3+}, Nd^{3+}, or Sm^{3+} was beneficial to NO_2^- adsorption. Ranjit and his co-workers [23, 24] reported the increase of saturated adsorption capacity and the adsorption equilibrium constant simultaneously for salicylic acid, t-cinnamic acid, and p-chlorophenoxy-acetic acid owing to the Eu^{3+}, Pr^{3+}, or Yb^{3+} doping. However, the effect of lanthanide oxides on the separation of electron-hole pairs and the photoresponse had not been extensively investigated in these literatures. For all the lanthanide ions, they have the special electronic structure of $4f^x 5d^y$ which would lead to different optical properties and dissimilar catalytic properties, and also have a redox couple of $Ln^{n+}/Ln^{(n+1)+}$ which would be able to form the labile oxygen vacancies (OV) with the relatively high mobility of bulk oxygen species [20].

Moreover, the precursor and preparation procedure are major factors to affect the physico-chemical properties of the synthesized catalysts [25]. In general, a high-temperature calcination process (usually above 723 K) is required to form a regular crystal structure and obviously causes a decline in TiO_2 surface area and a loss of surface hydroxyl groups. So, it is very interesting to synthesize crystalline TiO_2 catalyst using a low-temperature method, which may improve its particles distribution and allow a wide use of some thermal-resistant materials such as polymer, optical fiber, plastics, wood, or paper as supporting media.

This study performed a comprehensive investigation on the photocatalytic oxidation of organic pollutants in aqueous solution with different lanthanide ion-doped titanium dioxide (Ln^{n+}-TiO_2) catalysts in order to disclosing the mechanisms of photocatalytic activity enhancement resulting from the doping of lanthanide ions with a $4f$ electron configuration onto TiO_2 structure.

Experimental Section

Preparation of Ln^{n+}-TiO_2 Catalyst Samples

Three forms of Ln^{n+}-TiO_2 powder samples were prepared by doping lanthanum ion (La^{3+}), neodymium ion (Nd^{3+}), and cerium ion (Ce^{3+}) onto TiO_2, respectively in a sol-gel process. In which 17 mL of tetra-n-butyl titanium ($Ti(O-Bu)_4$) was dissolved in 80 mL of absolute ethanol and then this $Ti(O-Bu)_4$ solution was added dropwise under vigorous stirring into 100 mL of a mixture solution containing 84 mL of 95% ethanol, 1 mL of 0.1M Ln^{3+} solution ($La(NO_3)_3 \cdot 6H_2O$, $Nd(NO_3)_3 \cdot 6H_2O$, or $Ce(NO_3)_3 \cdot 6H_2O$), and 15 mL of acetic acid (>99.8%). The resulting transparent colloidal suspension was stirred for 2 h and aged for 2 d till the formation of gel. The gel was dried at 353 K under vacuum and then ground. The powder was calcined at 773 K for 2 h and the Ln^{n+}-TiO_2 catalysts were eventually obtained in a nominal atomic doping level of 0.2% abbreviated as 0.2% Ln^{n+}-TiO_2. Other lanthanide ion-doped TiO_2 samples prepared according to the above procedure with the dosage of 0.7%, 1.2%, 1.6%, and 2.0%, respectively. In the meantime, pure TiO_2 as a blank catalyst was also prepared in the same way without doping lanthanide ions.

Three forms of Ln^{n+}-TiO_2 sol samples were also prepared by a chemical method of coprecipitation-peptization with the following procedure: Lanthanide oxide (Nd_2O_3, Eu_2O_3, or CeO_2) was respectively dissolved into 100 mL of diluted hydrochloric acid solution with a proper amount up to 3.0% of Ti^{4+} by weight; 50 mL of titanium titrechloride ($TiCl_4$) was hydrolyzed and diluted with the above frozen acidic solutions at temperature below 273 K under vigorous stirring for 2 h; To ensure a complete hydrolysis, a diluted aqueous $NH_3 \cdot H_2O$ solution (10 wt.%) was added dropwise into the transparent $TiCl_4$ solution to ultimately obtain colloid precipitation at pH 10; The residual NH_4^+ and Cl^- ions in the precipitate need to be removed by washing with deionized distilled water till the pH of filtrate dropped to 7.5; The purified Ln^{n+}-TiO_2 colloid was continuously stirred at room temperature with addition of nitric acid as a peptization aid and also a phase-transfer accelerant till pH was further down to 1.5 to form the transparent Ln^{n+}-TiO_2 sol as primary rough sol; This sol was further peptized for 8 h at 298 K under a stirring condition, and then digested at 343 K for 12 h in an air-proof condition; Eventually the product Ln^{n+}-TiO_2 regular sol was formed with uniform, stable, and transparent properties. These nano-sized sol particles can maintain its homogenous distribution for a quite long time. In this study, the Ln^{3+}-TiO_2 powder was also prepared to compare with the sol catalysts, in which the Ln^{3+}-TiO_2 primary sol was gelled at aging temperature of 343 K in the vacuum condition and the dried at 373 K for 12 h as a xerogel powder. Then the xerogel powder was dried and calcined at 723 K for 2 h to obtain the Ln^{n+}-TiO_2 powder sample.

Characterization of Ln^{n+}-TiO_2 Catalysts

To determine the crystal phase composition of the prepared Ln^{n+}-TiO_2 catalysts, X-ray diffraction (XRD) measurement was carried out at room temperature using a Rigaku D/MAX-IIIA diffractometer with CuK_α radiation (λ = 0.15418 nm). The accelerating voltage of 35 kV and an emission current of 30 mA were applied. The specific surface area of all samples was measured by the Brunauer-Emmett-Teller (BET) method, in which the N_2 adsorption at 77 K was applied and a Carlo Erba sorptometer was used. The pore-size distribution of the different catalysts was determined by Barrett-Joyner-Halenda (BJH) method.

To study the valance band and chemical state of the catalysts, X-ray photoelectron spectra (XPS) was recorded with a PHI quantum ESCA microprobe system, using the MgK_α line of a 250-W Mg X-ray tube as a radiation source with the energy of 1253.6 eV, 16 mA × 12.5 kV and a working pressure of lower than 1×10^{-8} N m^{-2}. As an internal reference for the absolute binding energy, the C 1s peak at 284.80 eV of hydrocarbon contamination was used. The fitting data of XPS curves were analyzed with the software of Multipak 6.0A.

To study the recombination of electrons and holes, the photoluminescence (PL) emission spectra of the samples were measured with the following procedure: at room temperature or 77 K, a 325 nm He-Cd laser was used as an excitation light source; The light from the sample was focused into a spectrometer (Spex500) and detected by a photo-multiplier tube (PMT); The signal from the PMT was inputted into a photon counter (SR400) before recorded by a computer.

The particulate morphology of sol catalysts was observed on atom force microscope (AFM, Nanoscope III System, American Digital Corporation. The average particle size and particle size distribution (PSD) were determined by a light-scattering size analyzer (Zetasizer 3000HSA).

UV-VIS absorption spectrometry was applied to determine the azo dye (X-3B) concentration with a UV-VIS recording spectrophotometer (Shimadazu UV-2201). The photoelectrochemical property of Ln^{3+}-TiO_2/X-3B hydrosol system was investigated by means of photocurrent spectrum. The measurements were carried out by using a standard three-electrode quartz cell system consisting of a catalyst working electrode (WE), platinum plate counter-electrode (CE), and also a saturated calomel reference electrode (SCE). The optically transparent In_2O_3-SnO_2 oxide conductive glass sheet as the WE was placed in the quartz cell containing aqueous mixture of 1.0 g L^{-1} Ln^{3+}-TiO_2 sol and 100 mg L^{-1} X-3B with pH 3.5. In this condition, the catalyst sol and dye can be easily adsorbed on the surface of WE. While the WE was irradiated by a light from the front side, the photocurrent-time (I–t) measurement was recorded with an electrochemical station (CHI660 workstation).

Chemicals

An odorous chemical, 2-mercaptobenzothiazole (MBT) [26] with analytical grade, was provided by BDH and used as a model substrate in the photocatalytic degradation experiments. TiO_2 powder chemical (Degussa P25) with 80% anatase and 20% rutile was purchased from the Degussa AG Company, which had a BET area of ca. 50 m^2 g^{-1}. Titanium tetrachloride ($TiCl_4$) with chemical reagent grade was obtained from JandK Chemical Ltd. $La(NO_3)_3$ Neodymium oxide (Nd_2O_3), europium oxide (Eu_2O_3), and cerium oxide (CeO_2) with purity of > 99.9% were purchased from Aldrich. Reactive brilliant red azo dye (X-3B) with chemical reagent grade was obtained from Shanghai Dyestuff Chemical Plant and used without further purification. All other chemicals including ammonium hydroxide, nitric acid, hydrochloric acid, and others were used with analytical grade. Deionized distilled water was used throughout this study.

Experimental Procedures

Photocatalytic Degradation of MBT using Ln^{n+}-TiO_2 Powder Catalysts

A Pyrex cylindrical photoreactor was used in the experiments, in which an 8-W medium-pressure mercury lamp (Institute of Electrical Light Source, Beijing) with main emission at 365 nm was positioned at the center of the cylindrical vessel and surrounded by a circulating water jacket to control the temperature during the reaction as shown in the literature [27]. The MBT chemical was dissolved into distilled water to prepare MBT solution prior to experiments. To determine the adsorption behavior of Ln^{n+}-TiO_2 powder catalysts, a set of adsorption isotherm tests was first performed in the dark, in which 0.10 g of Ln^{3+}-TiO_2 powder was added into 10 mL of MBT aqueous solution with different initial concentration.

The suspension was put into a shaker operated at 4,000 rpm for 24 h at 298 ± 1 K. The MBT concentration in the suspension before and after the adsorption tests was analyzed to determine the adsorbed amount of MBT on the catalysts on a basis of mass balance. To evaluate the photocatalytic activity of the Ln^{n+}-TiO_2 powder catalysts, several sets of photoreaction tests were carried out, in which 0.25 g of photocatalyst powder was added into 250 mL of MBT aqueous solution. Prior to the photoreaction, the suspension was magnetically stirred in the dark for 30 min to approach an adsorption/desorption equilibrium status. The aqueous suspension containing MBT and catalyst was irradiated under the UV lamp with constant aeration. At the given time intervals, the analytical samples were taken from the suspension and immediately centrifuged at 4000 rpm for 20 min, then filtered through a 0.45 µm Millipore filter to remove particles. The filtrate was analyzed as required.

Photocatalytic Degradation of Azo Dye using Ln^{n+}-TiO_2 Sol Catalysts.

A cylindrical quartz photoreactor with an effective volume of 50 mL was used as illustrated in Fig. 1. A 150-W high-pressure mercury lamp with the average radiation intensity of 10.15 mW cm^{-2} and a main emission at 365 nm was employed as a UV light source. A 150-W halogen tungsten lamp with the average radiation intensity of 48.9 mW cm^{-2} and a main emission in the range of 400-800 nm was used with a UV and IR cut-off filter together as a visible light source. Degussa P25 TiO_2 powder was used as a standard catalyst to compare the photoactivity with the Ln^{n+}-TiO_2 sol catalysts. Reactive brilliant red X-3B dye with main absorption spectrum at 536 nm was selected as a model chemical to prepare aqueous X-3B solution. Prior to experiments, different amount of Ln^{3+}-TiO_2 sol in the range of 0-20 mg was added into 10 mL of X-3B solution with an initial concentration of 100 mg L^{-1}. This aqueous mixture was kept at 298 K and stirred for 120 min in the dark. Then the samples were centrifuged at a speed of 10,000 rpm for 15 min and then filtrated through a 0.22-µm Millipore filter. The X-3B concentration in the filtrate was determined by a UV-VIS spectrometer. Prior to photoreaction, X-3B and photocatalysts were magnetically stirred in a dark condition for 30 min to establish the adsorption-desorption equilibrium. Then, the aqueous reaction mixture with constant stirring was irradiated by visible light (or UV light) from top. During the photoreaction, samples were collected at an interval of 15 min and measured by the UV-VIS spectrometer after filtration.

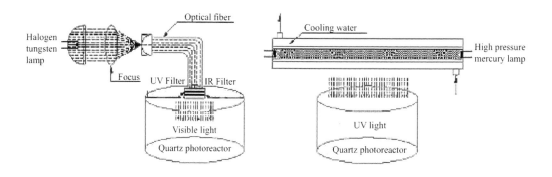

Fig. 1. Schematic diagrams of two photoreactor systems

Analytical Methods

HPLC Analysis

MBT concentration was determined by high performance liquid chromatography (HPLC), which consists of a gradient pump (Spectra System P4000), an autosampler (Spectra System Tem AS3000) with a 20 μL injection loop, a Thermo Ques Hypersil ODS column (C18, 5 μm, 250 × 4.6 mm ID) and a UV detector (Spectra SYSTEM UV6000LP). A mobile phase consisting of 70% methanol (HPLC grade) and 30% water (HPLC grade) acidified by adding 1% (v/v) acetic acid was operated at a flow rate of 0.5 mL min^{-1}. The UV detector was used to determine the MBT concentration at the wavelength of 323 nm.

UV-VIS spectrum analysis. X-3B azo dye concentration was determined by the UV-VIS spectrometer (Shimadazu UV-2201) at its maximum absorption of 536 nm.

Ion Chromatography Analysis

The mineralized products from the MBT degradation including sulfate ion, nitrate ion, and ammonium ion were determined by ion chromatography (Shimadzu HIC-6A) with a conductivity detector, in which a Shim-Pack IC-A1 anion column with a mobile phase containing 2.5 mM phthalic acid and 2.4 mM tris(hydroxymethyl)-aminomethane at a flow rate of 1.5 mL min^{-1} was used for determination of sulfate and nitrate ions, while a Shim-Pack IC-C1 cationic column with a mobile phase containing 5.0 mM nitrate acid at a flow rate of 1.0 mL min^{-1} was used for determination of ammonium ion.

DOC Analysis

Dissolved organic carbon (DOC) was determined by a TOC analyzer (Shimadzu 5000A) equipped with an autosampler (ASI-5000).

Results and Discussion

Characteristics of Ln^{n+}-TiO$_2$ Catalysts

XRD Analysis

The prepared Ln^{n+}-TiO$_2$ powder samples were first analyzed by XRD and the analytical results showed that all samples had a similar pattern of XRD, being dominated by anatase. The results of their crystal size and lattice were calculated and are listed in Table 1. These data indicated that the crystal size of Ln^{n+}-TiO$_2$ powders decreased owing to the Ln^{n+} doping. It may indicate that the lanthanide ion doping could hinder the increase of crystallite size. In fact, the ionic radii of La^{3+}, Nd^{3+}, and Ce^{3+} are 1.15, 0.99, and 1.03 Å, respectively, which are bigger than that of Ti^{4+} (0.68 Å). It seems not possible for these lanthanide ions to really enter the lattice of TiO$_2$ structure. In addition, these lanthanide ions could become lanthanide oxides during the calcination. However, there is a slight difference of the lattice parameters 'c' between TiO$_2$ and 1.2% Ln^{n+}-TiO$_2$ catalysts. Xu et al. [22] thought that lanthanide ion could not get into the lattice of TiO$_2$ to replace Ti^{4+} ion; on the contrary, on the interface of

Ln^{n+}-TiO_2, Ti^{4+} ion might substitute for lanthanide ions in the lattice of lanthanide oxides and a Ti-O-Ln bond could be formed. Shah et al. [13] proposed that Nd^{3+} resides in the octahedral interstitial site for Nd^{3+}-TiO_2 and the high oxygen affinities of interstitially locating neodymium ion effectively create a localized positive charge around Ti or form an oxygen vacancy. It would rather be believed that lanthanide ion inside in the octahedral interstitial site because of a low dosage in this study. However, if Ti^{4+} replaces Ln^{n+} inside the octahedral interstitial site, it will make an unbalanced charge. The formation of Ti-O-Ln bond and the charge imbalance might influence the surface chemical state of Ln^{n+}-TiO_2 greatly as discussed in the later part of this paper.

Table 1 Crystal Sizes and Crystal Lattice of Ln^{n+}-TiO_2 Powders

Dosage (%)		0	0.2	0.7	1.2	2.0
Crystal size (nm)	La^{3+}	32.9	25.8	22.9	17.7	17.6
	Nd^{3+}	32.9	25.8	19.2	19.8	17.8
	Ce^{3+}	32.9	20.2	10.1	9.16	10.1
Crystal lattice "c" (Å)	La^{3+}	9.502	9.472	9.472	9.484	9.492
	Nd^{3+}	9.502	9.498	9.483	9.498	9.493
	Ce^{3+}	9.502	9.456	9.480	9.480	9.480

The XRD patterns of pure TiO_2 and Ln^{n+}-TiO_2 sol catalysts as shown in Fig. 2 demonstrated that the TiO_2 rough sol particles mainly appeared scattering peaks, which means this rough TiO_2 sol still had predominant amorphous structure. Although the nearly linear or some branched oligomers (-Ti-O-Ti-O-) had been almost formed through the hydrolysis, precipitation, and neutralization pretreatment from the precursor of $TiCl_4$, $Ti(OH)_4$ and $TiO(OH)_2$ still did not achieve a complete condensation-polymerization process to form inorganic network structure. Therefore, it still could not form regular long-range order of composite atoms arrangement (TiO_6 face-sharing structure) within the bulk phase of TiO_2 rough sol. After peptization-ageing treatment for a long time, pure TiO_2 sol had gradually transformed into regular anatase crystal structure according to the appearance of characteristic diffraction peaks at 2θ = 25.4°, 38.0°, 47.8°, 54.6°, 63.2°, 68.8°, 75.3°, and 82.8° in the XRD pattern. In the meantime, the Ln^{n+}-TiO_2 sol samples also showed few scattering peaks in the XRD patterns as same as the pure TiO_2 sol, which could be considered due to the coexistence of somewhat semicrystalline structure in the bulk phase of Ln^{n+}-TiO_2 sol. All the Ln^{n+}-TiO_2 sol particles showed very broad diffraction peaks because they had very small grain size. The Nd^{3+}-TiO_2, Eu^{3+}-TiO_2, and Ce^{4+}-TiO_2 sol samples didn't show any other new crystal phase apart from anatase phase. The main reason was attributed to the difference of ionic radius between lanthanide ion and titanium ion (Ti^{4+} = 0.68 Å, Nd^{3+} = 0.995 Å, Eu^{3+} = 0.947 Å, Ce^{4+} = 1.01 Å). Moreover, it is noticeable that transformation from amorphous to anatase structure, commonly at high temperature above 723 K, can be achieved by digesting and peptizing-digesting treatment under this experimental conditions (T = 343 K, pH 1.5) for 12 h in this study. These results confirmed that the protonation of amorphous

TiO_2 in strong acidic inorganic medium with hot water treatment could induce a TiO_2 crystallization process under moderate temperature [28].

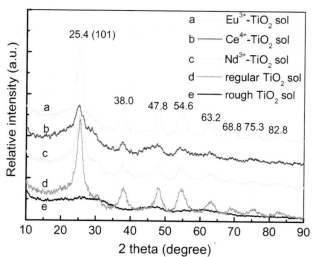

Fig. 2. XRD patterns of different sol catalysts

AFM Analysis

The morphology of TiO_2 sol catalysts and P25 TiO_2 powder catalyst were observed by AFM on a quartz glass sheet by means of spin-coating and the results are shown in Fig. 3. AFM image showed that the TiO_2 sol particles had a spherical shape and uniformly spread out on the support where particles agglomeration did not appear. The average size of the TiO_2 sol particles was determined to be about 25 nm, while that of the P25 TiO_2 powder particles was about 45 nm. However, the P25 TiO_2 powder particles in colloidal suspension obviously formed the agglomerates with a larger size of hundreds nanometer. These results indicated that the TiO_2 sol particles in hydrosol were more stable than the TiO_2 powder particles in suspension.

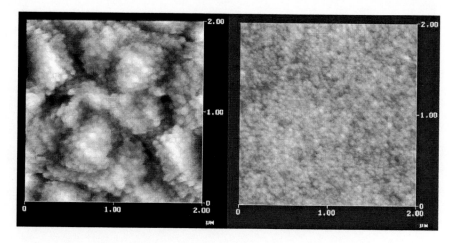

Fig. 3. AFM micrograph of P25 TiO_2 powder and TiO_2 sol

The morphology of Ln^{n+}-TiO_2 sol particles and calcined Ln^{n+}-TiO_2 powder particles were also observed by AFM and the results are shown in Fig. 4. The images of Ln^{n+}-TiO_2 sol particles showed that individual particles with a similar spherical shape were homogenously dispersed on the quartz support. The average sizes of Nd^{3+}-TiO_2, Eu^{3+}-TiO_2, and Ce^{4+}-TiO_2 sol particles were determined to be about 10, 8, and 12 nm, respectively. No obvious particles agglomeration was found. To be compared with the TiO_2 sol sample, the Ln^{n+}-TiO_2 sol particles were smaller in size. It means that lanthanide ion modification could preferably retard the aggregation and growth of Ln^{n+}-TiO_2 sol particles, which resulted in a decrease in grain size and an increase in specific surface areas. In addition, the positively-charged surface of Ln^{n+}-TiO_2 sol particles was also beneficial to the colloidal stabilization. After in-situ heating treatment on the quartz support at high temperature of 723 K for 2 h), the dispersion nanoparticles aggregated and grew up to about 34 nm for Nd^{3+}-TiO_2, 45 nm for Eu^{3+}-TiO_2, and 55 nm for Ce^{4+}-TiO_2, respectively.

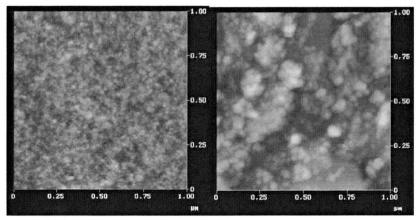

Fig. 4A.

Fig.4A.AFM micrograph of Nd^{3+}-TiO_2 sol and calcined Nd^{3+}-TiO_2 powder

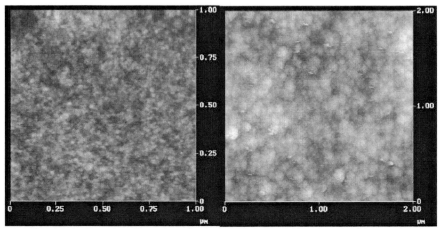

Fig. 4B.

Fig.   **4B**.
AFM
micrograph of Eu^{3+}-TiO_2 sol and calcined Eu^{3+}-TiO_2 powder

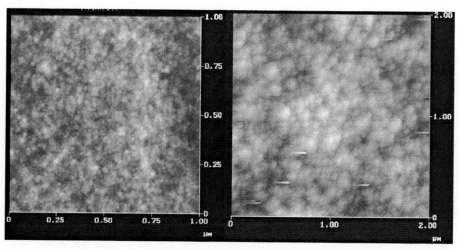

Fig. 4C

Fig. 4C. AFM micrograph of Ce^{4+}-TiO_2 sol and calcined Ce^{4+}-TiO_2 powder

BET Analysis

The specific surface area, t-plot total surface area, t-plot surface area, monolayer volume, micropore surface area, and total pore volume of TiO_2 and Ln^{n+}-TiO_2 powders were measured by the BET method and the results are listed in Table 2. The BET results showed that surface area except for micropore surface area increased significantly, owing to the Ln^{n+} doping. In particular, the 0.7% Ln^{n+}-TiO_2 samples had the largest micropore surface area, the micropore volume, and also the total pore volume.

Table 2 BET Data of TiO_2 and Ln^{n+}-TiO_2 Powders

Photocatalysts	Pure TiO$_2$	La^{3+}-TiO$_2$			Nd^{3+}-TiO$_2$		
		0.7%	1.2%	2.0%	0.7%	1.2%	2.0%
Specific surface area $(m^2\,g^{-1})$	50.20	73.87	83.81	76.42	71.25	78.54	90.81
t-plot total surface area $(m^2\,g^{-1})$	55.94	81.60	83.81	86.33	79.09	88.68	90.81
t-plot surface area $(m^2\,g^{-1})$	51.94	75.00	78.78	82.80	72.38	82.92	85.78
Monolayer volume $(cm^3\,g^{-1}$, STP)	11.53	16.97	19.25	17.55	16.36	18.04	20.86
Micropore surface area $(m^2\,g^{-1})$	4.00	6.60	5.03	3.53	6.71	5.76	5.03
Micropore volume $(10^{-3}\,cm^3\,g^{-1})$	1.13	2.06	1.15	0.51	2.17	1.53	1.26
The total pore volume $(cm^3\,g^{-1})$ $(P_s/P_0 = 0.9814$, adsorption)	0.152	0.270	0.228	0.205	0.252	0.248	0.234

To investigate the effects of lanthanide ion doping on the pore structure and adsorption abilities of the TiO_2 catalyst, a set of nitrogen adsorption/desorption isotherm tests was carried out and the experimental results are presented in Fig. 5. The pore-size distribution of the different catalysts determined by the BJH method is expressed in Fig. 6.

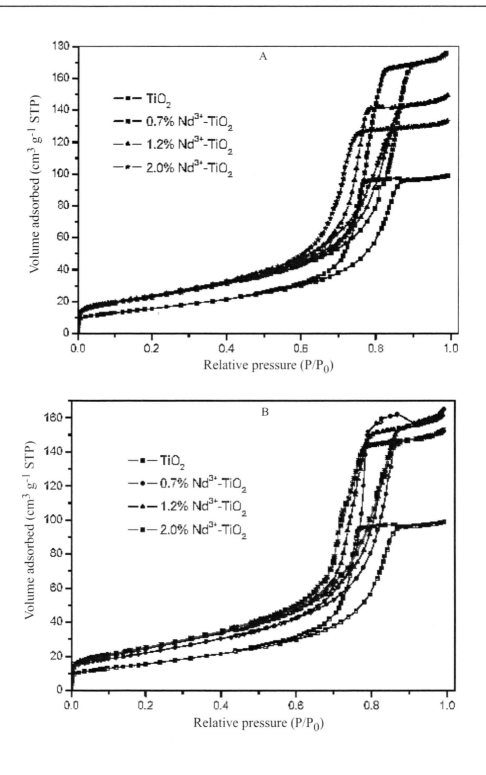

Fig. 5. Nitrogen adsorption/desorption isotherms of La^{3+}-TiO_2 powder (A) and Nd^{3+}-TiO_2 powder (B).

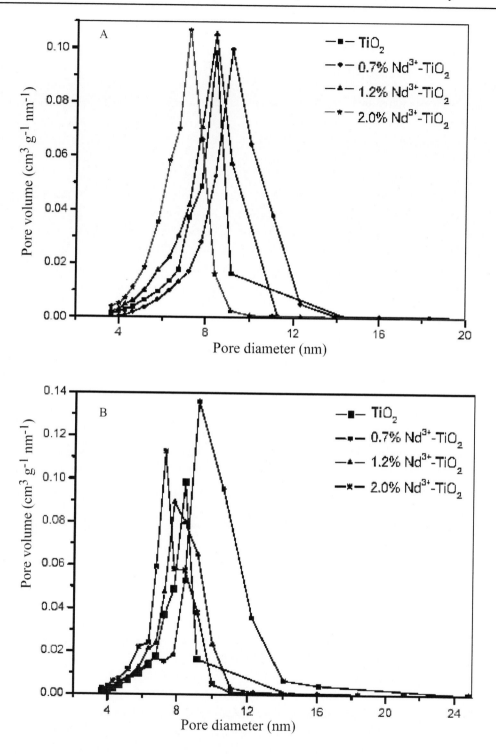

Fig. 6. Pore volume distribution of La^{3+}-TiO_2 powder (A) and Nd^{3+}-TiO_2 powder (B).

The adsorption isotherms in Fig. 5 demonstrated a pattern of Type IV curves [29], which is a typical feature of porous materials. It can be seen that all the lanthanide ion-doped TiO_2 catalysts had higher adsorption capacity than the TiO_2 catalyst. Among them, the 7%La^{3+}-TiO_2 and 7% Nd^{3+}-TiO_2 samples achieved the highest values. However, the La^{3+}-TiO_2 samples demonstrated that the adsorption ability decreased from its peak value clearly, when the La^{3+} dosage exceeded 0.7%. In the meantime, the well defined hysteresis loops in Fig. 5 confirmed that all the samples had a disordered mesoporous structure, which was attributable to pores formed between TiO_2 particles [30-32]. These hysteresis loops of the Ln^{n+}-TiO_2 demonstrated a curve pattern between Type H1 and Type H2 [29], while that of TiO_2 showed typical Type H2. Type H1 loops are often obtained with agglomerates or compactness of spherical particles of uniform size array while the distribution of pore size and shape might not be well defined for Type H2 loops. The results as shown in Fig. 6 demonstrated that the pore sizes of most catalysts were distributed in the range of 4-16 nm, in which the pure TiO_2 catalyst had a dominant pore size of 3.65-14.54 nm; the 0.7%, 1.2%, and 2.0%La^{3+}-TiO_2 samples had pore sizes of 4.01- 3.93 nm, 3.65-11.29 nm, and 3.65-9.15 nm; and the 0.7%, 1.2%, and 2.0% Nd^{3+}-TiO_2 samples had their pore sizes of 3.65-14.05 nm, 3.65-12.33 nm, and 3.65-10.01 nm, respectively. The analytical results demonstrated that the percentage of pore volume for TiO_2 with the sizes of 3.65-5.79 nm, 5.79-9.15 nm, and 9.15-14.54 nm was 4.3%, 77.1%, and 18.5%, respectively; the percentage of pore volume for 0.7% La^{3+}-TiO_2 with the sizes of 4.01-5.17 nm, 5.17-12.33 nm, and 12.33-16.01 nm was 8.0%, 90.4%, and 1.6%, respectively; the percentage of pore volume for 1.2%La^{3+}-TiO_2 with the sizes of 3.65-5.17 nm, 5.17-11.29 nm, and 11.29-16.01 nm was 3.0%, 95.4%, and 1.6%, respectively and the percentage of pore volume for 2.0%La^{3+}-TiO_2 with the sizes of 3.65-5.17 nm, 5.17-9.15 nm, and 9.15-16.01 nm was 7.3%, 89.7%, and 3.0%, respectively. Similar results were also obtained for the Nd^{3+}-TiO_2 powder catalysts. These results indicated that the Ln^{n+}-TiO_2 catalysts had a quite uniform pore size and their size distribution followed a normal distribution pattern like the Type H1 loop. Obviously, the 0.7% Ln^{n+}-TiO_2 powder samples had the highest pore size and the maximum pore volume.

PSD Analysis

Particle size of TiO_2 and Ln^{3+}-TiO_2 sol samples were analyzed by the light-scatting size analyzer and the particle size distributions of different catalysts are presented in Fig. 7. The results demonstrated that the P25 TiO_2 powder had a PSD in the range 148-208 nm with a mean value of 174 nm in its aqueous suspension and the pure TiO_2 sol had a PSD in the range of 13.8-35.3 nm with a mean value of 21.1 nm. These results indicated that all the sol catalysts were much smaller in size and had a single-modal distribution characteristic with more uniform PSD than the P25 TiO_2 powder catalyst. Furthermore, the results showed that the Nd^{3+}-TiO_2 sol had an average size of 8.5 nm and PSD from 4.6 to 16.4 nm; Eu^{3+}-TiO_2 sol had an average size of 3.5 nm and PSD from 3.5 to 17.2 nm; and Ce^{4+}-TiO_2 sol had an average size of 10.5 nm and PSD from 8.5 to 18.6 nm. These data confirmed that the particle size of TiO_2 sol was further reduced by doping with lanthanide ions.

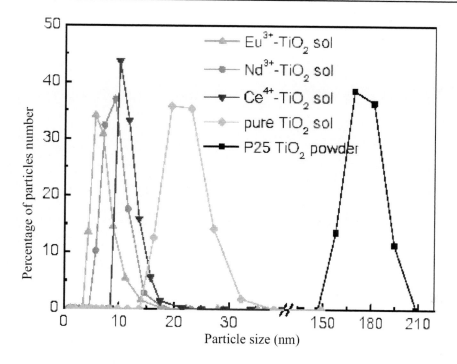

Fig. 7. PSD of P-25 powder and different sol catalysts

XPS Analysis

To better understand the chemical states of the Ln^{n+}-TiO_2 surface, the prepared catalyst samples were analyzed by XPS to determine the main elements on their surface. The Ti 2p XPS of TiO_2, 1.2%La^{3+}-TiO_2, 1.2% Nd^{3+}-TiO_2, and 1.2% Ce^{3+}-TiO_2 in Fig. 8 showed a slight deformation in the direction of lower binding energy, corresponding to the different oxidation states of titanium. Each contribution consisted of doublet, Ti $2p_{3/2}$ and Ti $2p_{1/2}$ peaks. Usually, an area ratio of A(Ti $2p_{1/2}$)/A(Ti $2p_{3/2}$) is equal to 0.5 and a binding energy difference of $\Delta E_b = E_b(Ti\ 2p_{1/2}) - E_b(Ti\ 2p_{3/2})$ is 5.7 eV [11]. In this study, the Ti $2p_{3/2}$ peak was fitted into two peaks of Ti^{4+} and Ti^{3+} at 458.70 eV and 457.69 eV, respectively. The binding energy, the full width at a half of the maximum height of peaks (FWHM), and the content percentage are listed in Table 3.

It can be seen in Table 3 that the amount of Ti^{3+} in the Ln^{3+}-TiO_2 catalysts increased with the increase of lanthanide ion dosage, while the amount of Ti^{4+} decreased accordingly. It might be explained that the charge imbalance, due to the titanium entering into the lattice of lanthanide oxide during heat treatment, reduced Ti^{4+} to Ti^{3+}. However, the Ti $2p_{3/2}$ XPS of TiO_2 showed only a very weak peak at 457.69 eV attributable to Ti^{3+} because residual carbon might reduce Ti^{4+} to Ti^{3+} during the heat treatment slightly. In the meantime, the binding energy of Ti^{3+} fitting peak was also drifting to a lower energy direction with the increase of lanthanide ion dosage. The O 1s XPS of Ln^{3+}-TiO_2 catalysts are shown in Fig. 9, in which the dominant peaks at 529.97, 530.03, 530.05, and 530.04 eV agreed with the O 1s electron binding energy for TiO_2, 1.2%La^{3+}-TiO_2, 1.2% Nd^{3+}-TiO_2 and 1.2% Ce^{3+}-TiO_2, respectively.

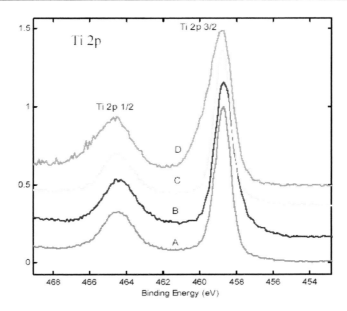

Fig. 8. Ti 2p XPS of TiO_2 (A); 1.2%La^{3+}-TiO_2 (B); 1.2% Nd^{3+}-TiO_2 (C); and 1.2% Ce^{3+}-TiO_2 (D)

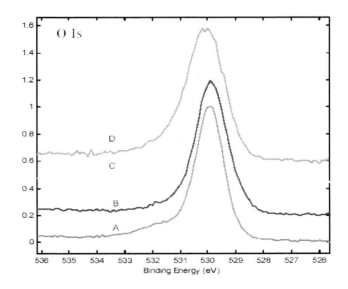

Fig. 9. O 1s XPS of TiO_2 (A); 1.2% La^{3+}-TiO_2 (B); 1.2% Nd^{3+}-TiO_2 (C); and 1.2% Ce^{3+}-TiO_2 (D)

The ratio of [O]/[Ti] obtained in the XPS analysis as listed in Table 3 increased with the increase of lanthanum ion or neodymium ion dosage, while that decreased with the increase of cerium ion dosage.

Table 3 Fitting Data of Ti 2p $_{3/2}$ and Atomic Ratio of Oxygen/Titanium in Ln^{n+}-TiO$_2$ catalysts

| Catalysts | Ti 2p 3/2 | | | | | | O/Ti |
| | Ti^{3-} | | | Ti^{4-} | | | |
	BE (eV)	FWHM(eV)	Area (%)	BE (eV)	FWHM (eV)	Area (%)	
TiO$_2$	457.69	1.13	0.16	458.70	1.08	99.86	2.11
0.7% La^{3-}-TiO$_2$	457.69	1.13	5.91	458.70	1.21	99.84	2.17
1.2% La^{3-}-TiO$_2$	457.63	1.14	7.41	458.70	1.21	94.09	2.70
2.0% La^{3-}-TiO$_2$	457.52	1.86	8.27	458.76	1.22	92.51	9.61
0.7% Nd^{3-}-TiO$_2$	457.49	1.13	1.35	458.70	1.03	98.65	2.46
1.2% Nd^{3-}-TiO$_2$	457.40	1.13	3.74	458.73	1.06	96.26	2.48
2.0% Nd^{3-}-TiO$_2$	457.05	1.28	12.98	458.75	1.21	87.02	10.8
0.7% Ce^{3-}-TiO$_2$	457.05	1.01	1.55	458.70	1.08	98.45	1.82
1.2% Ce^{3-}-TiO$_2$	457.43	1.03	5.64	458.70	1.08	94.36	1.73
2.0% Ce^{3-}-TiO$_2$	457.63	1.02	15.78	458.70	1.10	84.22	1.49

*FWHM: Full width at a half of the maximum height of peaks; BE: Binding energy; Area represents the percentage of Ti^{3+} or Ti^{4+}

DRS Analysis

To study the effect of neodymium ion doping on the optical absorption properties, UV-VIS DRS of the TiO$_2$ and Nd^{3+}-TiO$_2$ powder catalysts in the range of 200-800 nm were obtained as shown in Fig. 10. It can be seen that the pure TiO$_2$ had no significant absorption in the visible region (>400 nm), but Nd^{3+}-TiO$_2$ had several optical absorption peaks at 432, 464, 476, 515, 528, 586, 628, 684, and 747 nm and the intensity of absorption increased with the increase of Nd^{3+} dosage significantly. The positions of these absorption peaks accorded with the internal 4f transitions observed in corresponding Nd(III) complexes, which give rise to narrow absorption bands quite unlike normal band gap transitions, as reported by Hwang et al.[33], Mathur et al. [34], Xiang et al. [35], Kwag et al.[36], and Ripoll et al.[37]. The above absorption peaks were attributable to from the $^4I_{9/2}$ ground state to higher excited states as follows: $^2P_{1/2}+^2D_{5/2}$ (432 nm), $^2D_{3/2}+^4G_{11/2}$ (464 nm), $^2G_{9/2}+^2K_{15/2}$ (476 nm), $^4G_{9/2}$ (515 nm), $^4G_{7/2}$ (528 nm), $^4G_{5/2}$ (586 nm), $^2H_{11/2}$ (628 nm), $^4F_{9/2}$ (684 nm), and $^4F_{7/2}+^4S_{3/2}$ (747 nm). However, the 4f electrons of neodymium ion were shielded by the outer-shell 5s and 5p electrons, which made the Nd^{3+} energy levels independent of their surroundings. Hwang et al. [33] reported that the band gap energy of the photocatalysts, lanthanide titanites (Nd, La, Pr)$_2$Ti$_2$O$_7$, was highly dependent on the number of lanthanide 4f electrons (Nd^{3+} 4$f^4$6s^2; La^{3+} 4$f^0$5$d^1$6s^2; and Pr^{3+} 4$f^3$6s^2). This band gap was also observed for lanthanide tantalates (LnTaO$_4$) and layered perovskite tantalates (RbLnTa$_2$O$_7$) [38]. It was proposed that the corresponding photoexcited process attributed to 4f internal atomic transition should be not responsible for photocatalytic reaction, although Ebitani et al.[38] reported that the photoexcited state of lanthanide ion attributable to 4f-5d transition or f-f transition could have the capability of transferring their excited energy to other molecules in a gas phase or the adsorbed state. In this study, the absorption band edge of Nd^{3+}-TiO$_2$ catalysts in the range of 200-400 nm was highly similar to that of TiO$_2$. This implies that the direct electron transfers from Nd $4f$ to the conduction band should be impossible because of a larger inter-atomic distance. However, the occupied $4f$ band for Nd_2O_3 lies above the O $2p$ band. Nd $4f$ may interact with the O $2p$ that participates in deriving the conduction band through Ti-O-Nd interactions.

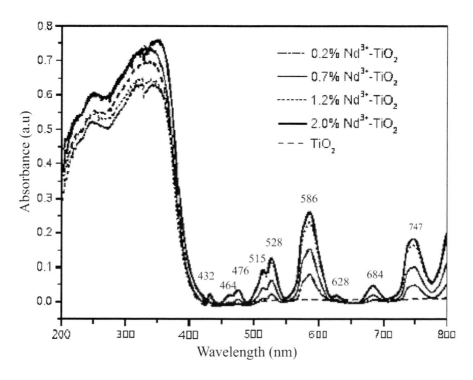

Fig. 10. UV-Visible diffusive reflectance spectra of TiO_2 and Nd^{3+}-TiO_2 catalysts.

To investigate the effect of cerium ion doping on the optical absorption properties of catalysts, the UV-Vis DRS of the TiO_2 and Ce^{3+}-TiO_2 catalysts in the range of 220-850 nm were examined and the results are shown in Fig. 11. The DRS results demonstrated that while TiO_2 had insignificant absorption in the visible region (>400 nm), Ce^{3+}-TiO_2 had considerable absorption between 400-500 nm and the absorption increased with the increase of cerium ion content. In the meantime, it can be seen that the optical absorption in the UV region was also enhanced. In fact, the enhanced absorption in the visible region for the Ce^{3+}-doped Y_2O_3, Lu_2O_3, ZrO_2 or La_2O_3 had been reported and the onset of the predominant Ce^{3+} absorption was found at about 460 nm [39, 40]. CeO_2 is an n-type semiconductor with a band gap of about 3.2 eV [41]. Therefore, the absorption at 400-500 nm by the Ce^{3+}-TiO_2 catalysts could not be attributed to CeO_2 but Ce_2O_3. In contrast to the closed shell Ce^{4+} ion ($4f^0$), Ce^{3+} ion possessed a single optically-active electron with the ground-state configuration in the $4f^1$ orbital. Within this configuration, there are only two electronic levels, an excited state of $^2F_{7/2}$ and a ground state of $^2F_{5/2}$. The $4f$-$4f$ transitions attributed to Ce^{3+} may only be observed in the infrared spectral region. However, Ce^{3+} has the first state configuration $5d^1$ that is rather close in energy. The electronic dipole transitions $4f^1 \leftrightarrow 5d^1$ may occur in either UV or visible region. Based on the valence band of Ce^{3+}-TiO_2 from XPS, it would be proposed that electron-hole pairs could be generated in both catalysts of Ce^{3+}-TiO_2 and Ce_2O_3.

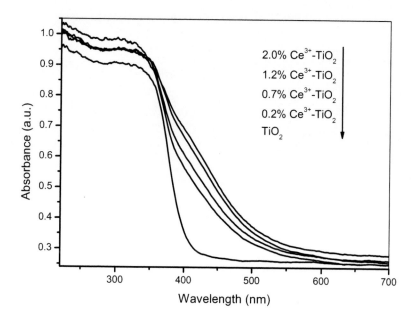

Fig. 11. UV-Visible diffusive reflectance spectra of TiO_2 and Ce^{3+}-TiO_2 catalysts.

Photocatalytic Degradation of MBT in Aqueous Ln^{n+}-TiO_2 Powder Suspension

Odor pollution has been of an increasing concern in urban environment. Odor is generally generated from sewage treatment works, solid waste transfer stations, sludge treatment plants and also many industries situated within urban areas. Main odor-causing compounds can be classified into three groups of (i) volatile organic compounds such as volatile fatty acids; (ii) sulfur compounds such as hydrogen sulfide and mercaptans; and (iii) nitrogen compounds such as ammonia and amines. Of the mercaptans, MBT is known as a widespread odorous pollutant and also found to be toxic and poorly biodegradable. In aquatic environment, the MBT has been detected in wastewater effluents from rubber additive manufacturers, tanneries and often found in wastewater treatment plant and surface water. The MBT can be transformed into benzothiazole (BT) in anaerobic media and into 2-hydroxy benzothiazole (OBT) and benzothiazole-2-sulfonate ($BTSO_3$) in aerobic conditions. Consequently, MBT, BT, OBT and $BTSO_3$ are frequently found in both of wastewater and surface water. These volatile organic compounds result in a lot of odor problems in wastewater treatment plants [26].

MBT Adsorption Isotherm

A set of MBT adsorption tests was carried out in the dark using different catalysts. On the basis of experimental data, the MBT adsorption isotherms on the different catalysts were calculated using the Langmuir adsorption model [27] as follows:

$$\frac{C_e}{\Gamma} = \frac{1}{\Gamma_{max}} \cdot C_e + \frac{1}{K_a \cdot \Gamma_{max}} \tag{1}$$

where C_e is the equilibrium concentration of the substrate in the solution in mol L^{-1}, K_a is the adsorption equilibrium constant in L mol^{-1}, and Γ_{max} is the saturated adsorption amount in mol g^{-1}.

The MBT adsorption isotherms on the different Ln^{3+}-TiO_2 catalysts are shown in Figs. 12A, 12B and 12C, respectively. It can be seen that the adsorption data were well fitted by the Langmuir model. The values of Γ_{max} and K_a against the dosage of lanthanide ion are also calculated and shown in Figs. 13A and 13B, respectively. These results demonstrated that the Ln^{3+}-TiO_2 samples had a higher adsorption capacity than the TiO_2 sample. While that of TiO_2 was 8.91×10^{-6} mol g^{-1}, the saturated adsorption amount (Γ_{max}) of 2.0%La^{3+}-TiO_2, 2.0% Nd^{3+}-TiO_2, and 2.0% Ce^{3+}-TiO_2 powders increased to 15.43×10^{-6}, 14.07×10^{-6}, and 19.08×10^{-6} mol g^{-1}, respectively. It is more important to see that the adsorption equilibrium constants (K_a) of 2.0%La^{3+}-TiO_2, 2.0% Nd^{3+}-TiO_2, and 2.0% Ce^{3+}-TiO_2 powders were 2.21, 1.73, and 1.89 times of that of the TiO_2 powder, respectively. This adsorption experiment demonstrated that the higher lanthanide ion dosage leads to the higher Γ_{max} and K_a values. Of them, the Ce^{3+}-TiO_2 catalysts achieved the highest Γ_{max}, while the La^{3+}-TiO_2 catalysts achieved the highest K_a. It is indicated that a higher Γ_{max} value may not be always accompanied by a higher K_a value. The factors leading to the enhanced adsorption ability could involve the variation of the physical and chemical properties of the catalyst surface owing to the lanthanide ion doping. Firstly, both the smaller crystallite size and larger specific surface area of Ln^{3+}-TiO_2 catalysts would be beneficial to achieve better physical adsorption of MBT in aqueous suspension. Secondly, a chemical complex (Ln^{3+}-SH) between the Ln^{3+}-TiO_2 catalysts and MBT in the aqueous suspension might be formed. Although a complex (Ti^{4+}-SH) could also be formed, the equilibrium constant for the formation of Ti^{4+}-SH is much lower than that of Ln^{3+}-SH [23].

Photocatalytic Degradation of MBT

To evaluate the photocatalytic activity of Ln^{n+}-TiO_2 powder catalysts, several sets of MBT photocatalytic degradation tests were carried out in the aqueous suspensions with an initial MBT concentration of 0.28 mmol L^{-1}, in which the Ln^{n+}-TiO_2 catalysts with different

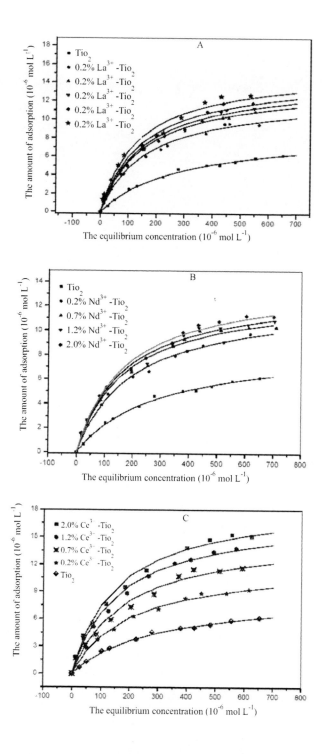

Fig. 12. MBT adsorption isotherms on different catalysts (A: La^{3+}-TiO$_2$; B: Nd^{3+}-TiO$_2$; and C: Ce^{3+}-TiO$_2$).

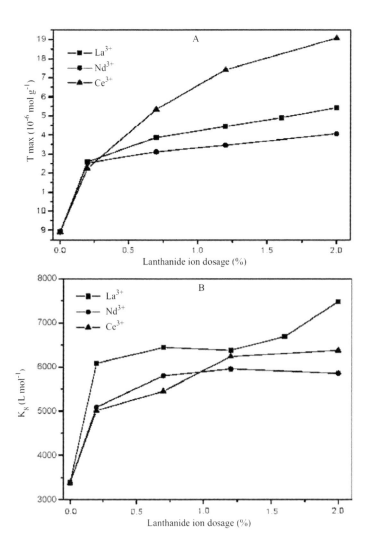

Fig. 13. Dependence of the saturated adsorption amount Γ_{max} (A) and the adsorption equilibrium constant K_a (B) on lanthanide ion dosage.

doping contents of 0%, 0.2%, 0.7%, 1.2%, 1.6%, and 2.0% were investigated. The experimental results using the La^{3+}-TiO_2, Nd^{3+}-TiO_2, and Ce^{3+}-TiO_2 catalysts are shown in Figs. 14A, 14B, and 14C, respectively. It is very clear that all the TiO_2 catalysts doped with Ln^{3+} achieved faster MBT photodegradation rates than the pure TiO_2 catalyst significantly. The enhancement of MBT photodegradation increased initially with the increase of Ln^{n+} content, but decreased while the Ln^{n+} content exceeded a certain level. It was found that the Ln^{n+}-TiO_2 catalysts containing 1.2% of Ln^{n+} achieved the best performance in this experimental condition, which was an optimal dosage for all three types of Ln^{n+}-TiO_2 powder catalysts.

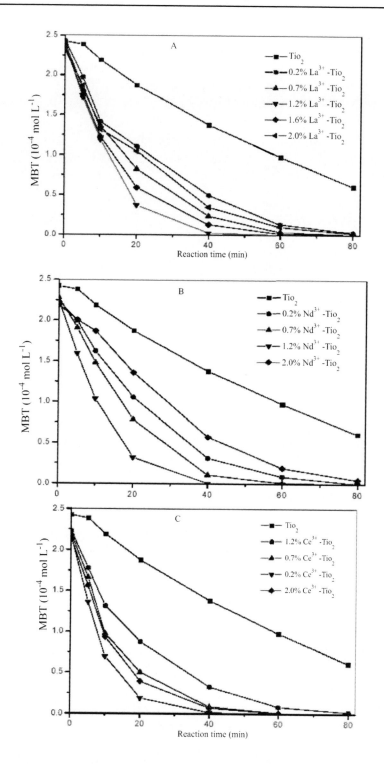

Fig. 14. MBT degradation using the Ln^{3+}-TiO_2 powders (A: Ln^{3+}-TiO_2; B: Nd^{3+}-TiO_2; and C: Ce^{3+}-TiO_2) under the experimental conditions of UV irradiation, pH 7.15, photocatalysts dosage: = 1 g L^{-1}, The initial concentration of MBT = 0.28 mmol L^{-1}

The TiO_2-based photocatalytic degradation of organics in aqueous suspension is a heterogeneous reaction and its kinetics can be usually described by the Langmiur-Hinshelwood (L-H) model. Very often, the L-H model is simplified into the first-order model, once the substrate concentration (C) is very low. However, it should be noted that if the adsorption constant (K_a) is significant to have a value of K_aC higher than 1, the L-H model should not be shorten to the first-order model, even the substrate concentration (C) is low. For examples, the K_aC value for the TiO_2 suspension in this study was 0.94, but those for any Ln^{3+}-TiO_2 catalysts were much higher than 1. It is suggested that the L-H model should be directly applied in its integral form as shown below:

$$Ln(C_0/C) + K_a \cdot (C_0 - C) = k_{ap} \cdot t \tag{2}$$

where $k_{ap} = k_r \cdot K_a$, k_{ap} is the apparent kinetic constant in min^{-1}, k_r is the photoreaction kinetic constant in mol L^{-1} min^{-1}, t is the reaction time in min, C_0 is the initial equilibrium concentration.

On the basis of experimental data from the MBT photodegradation tests, the kinetic constants (k_{ap} and k_r) were calculated by Equation 2, respectively, and are plotted versus the dosage of lanthanide ions as shown in Figs. 15A and 15B. The values of k_{ap} and k_r indicated that the MBT photodegradation using the 1.2% Ln^{n+}-TiO_2 catalyst achieved the best performance.

To over look the experimental results, the values of k_{ap}, K_a, and k_r for the different catalysts are summarized and compared in Table 4. The results showed that the apparent kinetic constants (k_{ap}) of 1.2%La^{3+}-TiO_2, 1.2% Nd^{3+}-TiO_2, and1.2% Ce^{3+}-TiO_2 were 6.89, 7.48, and 6.97 times of that of TiO_2; the adsorption equilibrium constants (K_a) were 1.89, 1.76, and 1.85 times; and the photoreaction kinetic constants (k_r) were 3.65, 4.25, and 3.77 times, respectively. These results indicated although the enhancement of MBT photodegradation resulted from both factors of the better adsorption ability and also the higher photocatalytic activity, it seems that the latter played a more significant role than the former comparatively.

Table 4 Ratios of Γ_{max}, K_a, k_{ap}, and k_r between Ln^{n+}-TiO_2 and TiO_2

Catalyst	Γ_{max} (Ln^{n+}-TiO_2) /Γ_{max} (TiO_2)	k_{ap} (Ln^{n+}-TiO_2) / k_{ap} (TiO_2)	K_a (Ln^{n+}-TiO_2)/ K_a (TiO_2)	k_r (Ln^{n+}-TiO_2) / k_r (TiO_2)
1.2% La^{3+}-TiO_2	1.62	6.89	1.89	3.65
1.2% Nd^{3+}-TiO_2	1.51	7.48	1.76	4.24
1.2% Ce^{3+}-TiO_2	1.96	6.97	1.85	3.77

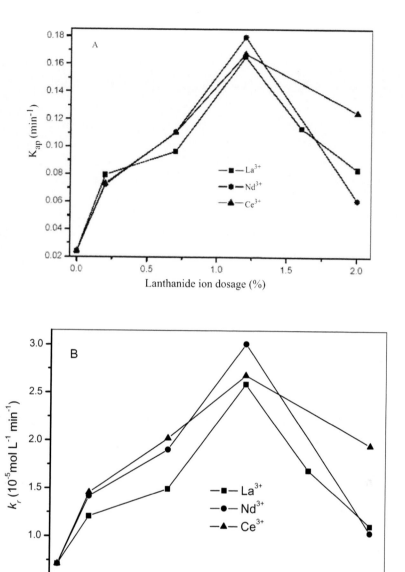

Fig. 15. Dependence of the apparent reaction kinetic constant k_{ap} (A) and the kinetic constant k_r (B) on lanthanide ion dosage.

Mineralization of MBT

A set of tests was carried out to determine the DOC conversion in the MBT photocatalytic degreadation. Each test with an initial DOC concentration of 20.18 mg L^{-1} lasted for 80 min, in which 7 samples were collected at the time intervals of 0, 5, 10, 20, 40, 60, and 80 min, respectively and filtered for the DOC analysis. The results of DOC variation during the MBT photocatalytic reaction are shown in Figs. 16A, 16B, and 16C. It was found that after 80 min reaction, DOC was removed by 41.9%, 53.0%, 56.2%, 61.1%, 58.6%, and 57.3% for TiO_2, 0.2%, 0.7%, 1.2%, 1.6%, and 2.0% La^{3+}-TiO_2, respectively; by 49.8%, 62.8%, 59.2%, and 54.5% for 0.2%, 0.7%, 1.2%, and 2.0% Nd^{3+}-TiO_2, respectively; and by 59.8%, 64.8%, 73.2%, and 68.6% for 0.2%, 0.7%, 1.2%, and 2.0% Ce^{3+}-TiO_2, respectively. The highest DOC removal of 73.2% was achieved by using the 1.2% Ce^{3+}-TiO_2 catalyst. From Fig. 16A, it can seen that the DOC concentration decreased significantly during the first 20 min, then slightly increased during the period of 20-40 min, and eventually further reduced to a lower level. This phenomenon might result from the easy desorption of some intermediates during the MBT photodegradation. On the basis of experimental results, it can be concluded that the MBT mineralization using the Ce^{3+}-TiO_2 catalysts was more complete than using the La^{3+}-TiO_2 and Nd^{3+}-TiO_2 catalysts relatively.

To evaluate the conversion of organic sulfur and organic nitrogen during the MBT photocatalytic degradation, three tests were carried out in the 1.2%La^{3+}-TiO_2, 1.2% Nd^{3+}-TiO_2 and 1.2% Ce^{3+}-$TiO_2$1 suspensions with the initial concentrations of MBT = 81.6 mg L^{-1}, organic sulfur = 31.22 mg L^{-1} and organic nitrogen = 6.83 mg L^{-1} for 240 min, in which 7 samples were collected at 0, 40, 80, 120, 160, 200, and 240 min, respectively in each test for determination of sulfate ion (SO_4^{2-}), ammonium ion (NH_4^+), and nitrate (NO_3^-) concentrations. The experimental results are shown in Fig. 17.

The experiment demonstrated that the SO_4^{2-}-S concentration in the 3 tests increased from 0 to 28.39, 27.8, and 29.66 mg L^{-1}, respectively; the NH_4^+-N concentration increased from 0 to 3.49, 3.88 and 4.01 mg L^{-1}, respectively; and the NO_3^--N concentration increased from 0 to 2.06, 2.33 and 2.26 mg L^{-1} during the MBT photodegradation. In these tests, the conversion of organic sulfur was achieved by 90.9%, 89.0%, and 95.0% for 1.2%La^{3+}-TiO_2, 1.2% Nd^{3+}-TiO_2, and 1.2% Ce^{3+}-TiO_2, respectively, while the conversion of organic nitrogen was achieved by 81.3%, 90.9%, and 91.8%. Although ammonium ion is a product of organic nitrogen in the MBT degradation, it should not be a final product. It is expected that if the experimental time lasted long enough, the ammonium ion would be eventually oxidized to nitrate ion as one of final products.

Photocatalytic Degradation of X-3B Azo Dye in Aqueous Ln^{n+}-TiO_2 Sol Solution

Textile dyeing and finishing industry in Hong Kong and also in many other cities of China has been playing an important role in economic development. However, as one of the main water pollution sources, dyeing and finishing processes generate a lot of effluents with high organic strength and colors. In general, conventional biological treatment processes have certain difficulties in degrading those dye chemicals causing high COD and color in the effluents. A significant remaining of about 40-70% of COD and color in textile effluents after conventional biological treatment requires an advanced treatment for further polishing its quality. The photocatalytic treatment of wastewater is a promising technology for further polishing dye wastewater effluents.

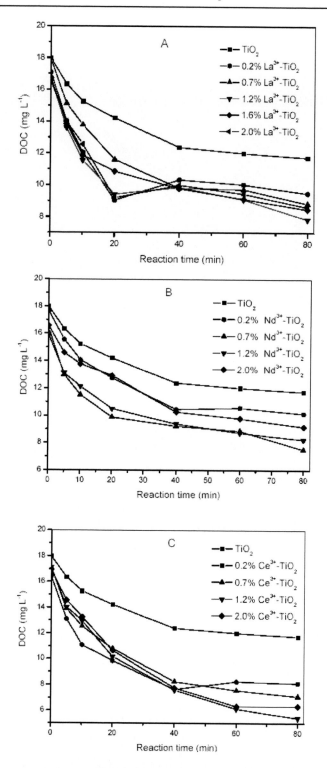

Fig. 16. DOC removal in MBT degradation using the Ln^{3+}-TiO_2 powders (A: La^{3+}-TiO_2; B: Nd^{3+}-TiO_2; and C: Ce^{3+}-TiO_2) under the experimental conditions of UV irradiation, pH 7.15, catalysts dosage = 1 g L^{-1}. the initial concentration of DOC = 20.18 mg L^{-1}

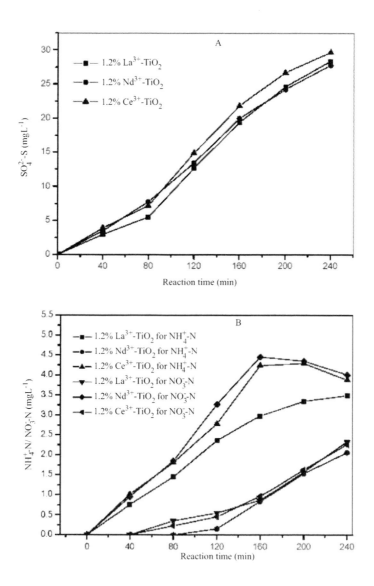

Fig. 17. Final products formation during the MBT degradation (A: SO_4^{2-}; B: NH_4^+, and NO_3^-).

X-3B Adsorption Isotherm

A set of X-3B adsorption tests in aqueous solution was carried out in the dark to determine the adsorption ability of the Ln^{n+}-TiO_2 sol catalysts. On the basis of experimental data, the X-3B adsorption isotherms on the different Ln^{n+}-TiO_2 catalysts were calculated using the Langmuir adsorption model (Equation 1). The experimental results are expressed by plotting C_e/Γ_{ads} versus C_e in Fig. 18. It can be seen that the adsorption data were well fitted by the Langumiur model in its linear form. The saturation adsorption capacity was determined to be 0.0579 mmol g^{-1} for the Nd^{3+}-TiO_2 sol, 0.0606 mmol g^{-1} for the Eu^{3+}-TiO_2 sol, 0.0500 mmol g^{-1} for the Ce^{4+}-TiO_2 sol, 0.0413 mmol g^{-1} for the TiO_2 sol, and 0.0345 mmol g^{-1} for the P25 TiO_2 powder, respectively. These results indicated that all the Ln^{n+}-TiO_2 sol exhibited higher adsorption capacity than both the TiO_2 sol and TiO_2 powder.

The Ln^{n+}-TiO_2 sol particles had finer particle size and larger surface area than the powders with much better dispersion in aqueous solution, which would result in better adsorption ability physically. Furthermore, the surface of Ln^{n+}-TiO_2 sol particles is positively charged due to the lanthanide ions banded on the TiO_2, while that of X-3B dye is negatively charged due to a $-SO_3Na$ group in its molecular structure. In this case, the Ln^{n+} ions could act as Lewis acid because of their partial unoccupied $4f$ atomic orbits and X-3B dye could act as Lewis base because of its π electrons conjugation structure. Consequently the formation of a Lewis acid-base complex of $RSO_3^- \cdots Ln^{n+}$-TiO_2 between lanthanide ion and X-3B dye in aqueous solution could enhance the interface adsorption chemically as well.

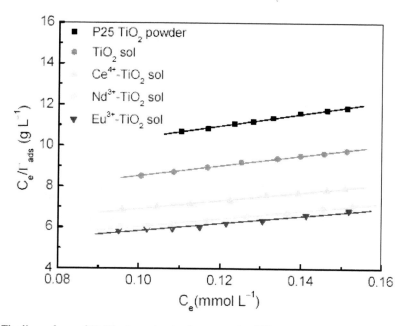

Fig. 18. The linear form of X-3B adsorption isotherms on the different catalysts.

Photocatalytic Degradation of X-3B under Visible Light Irradiation

To evaluate the photocatalytic activity of Ln^{n+}-TiO_2 sol catalysts, several experiments of X-3B photocatalytic degradation were carried out in either aqueous solution or suspension with an initial X-3B concentration of 100 mg L^{-1} and catalysts dosage of 1.0 g L^{-1}. Each experiment lasted for 120 min and samples were collected every 15 min for analysis to determine X-3B concentration by the UV/VIS spectrum. The experimental results are shown in Fig. 19. The results showed that X-3B concentration decreased under visible illumination remarkably. To determine the kinetics of X-3B degradation in this study, the L-H model was also applied similar to that in the MBT degradation study. However, It was found that the X-3B adsorption on the catalysts was not as strong as MBT adsorption, in which the K_aC_0 values were determined to be 0.1119 for TiO_2 powder, 0.1715 for TiO_2 sol, 0.2179 for Ce^{4+}-TiO_2 sol, 0.2792 for Eu^{3+}-TiO_2, and 0.2642 for Nd^{3+}-TiO_2, respectively. Since all the K_aC values were much lower than 1, the L-H model could be simplified into the first-order model as follows:

$$C = C_0 e^{-k_{ap}t} \tag{3}$$

where C is the X-3B concentration (mg L^{-1}) and t is the photoreaction time (min).

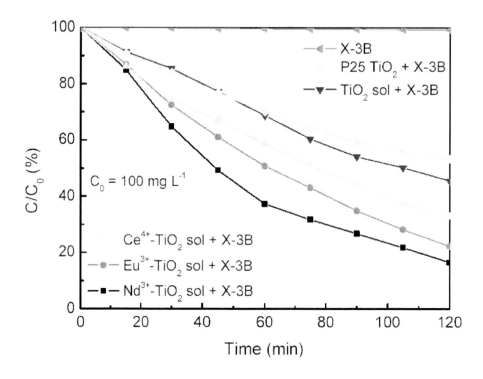

Fig. 19. Degradation of X-3B azo dye under visible light irradiation using different catalysts

The experimental data were well fitted by Equation 3 and the results of X-3B degradation using different catalysts are presented in Table 5. The reaction rates with different catalysts from high to low was ranked as Nd^{3+}-TiO_2 sol > Eu^{3+}-TiO_2 sol > Ce^{4+}-TiO_2 sol > TiO_2 sol > P25 TiO_2 powder. These results indicated all the sol catalysts performed faster degradation rates than the powder catalyst. Furthermore, all the lanthanide ion-doped TiO_2 sol catalysts performed better than the pure TiO_2 sol. Among them, the Nd^{3+}-TiO_2 sol catalyst achieved the highest X-3B degradation rate.

Table 5 Kinetic Parameters of X-3B Photodegradation under Visible Light Irradiation

Photocatalyst	K (min^{-1})	$t_{1/2}$ (min)	R
P25	0.00554	125.3	0.9977
TiO$_2$ sol	0.00667	103.9	0.9972
Nd^{3+}-TiO$_2$ sol	0.01499	46.2	0.9973
Eu^{3+}-TiO$_2$ sol	0.01246	55.6	0.9978
Ce^{4+}-TiO$_2$ sol	0.00729	95.1	0.9905

Photocatalytic Degradation of X-3B under UV Irradiation

The photocatalytic activity of Ln^{n+}-TiO$_2$ was also investigated under UV light excitation. All reaction conditions except for UV irradiation were applied as same as those in the visible light reaction. The experimental results are shown in Fig. 20. The results showed that X-3B dye was significantly degraded with all catalysts except for the control test without catalyst. Compared to the P25 TiO$_2$ powder, all sol catalysts demonstrated better performance in the X-3B degradation. The values of apparent reaction rate constant (k) using different catalysts are presented in Table 6, which were ranked from high to low as Eu^{3+}-TiO$_2$ sol > Nd^{3+}-TiO$_2$ sol > Ce^{4+}-TiO$_2$ sol > TiO$_2$ sol > P25 TiO$_2$ powder. These results indicated that the lanthanide ion modification could obviously improve the activity of TiO$_2$ sol particles. However, there was no great difference in photoactivity for three kinds of Ln^{n+}-TiO$_2$ sol catalysts. By the way, it can be seen that the efficiency of X-3B degradation under UV irradiation was significantly higher than that under visible light irradiation.

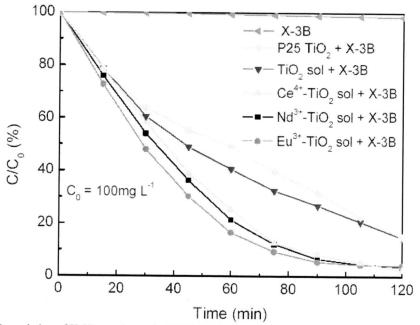

Fig. 20. Degradation of X-3B azo dye under UV light irradiation using different catalysts.

Table 6 Kinetic Parameters of X-3B Photodegradation under UV Light Irradiation

Photocatalyst	k (min^{-1})	$t_{1/2}$ (min)	R
P25	0.01432	48.4	0.9859
TiO$_2$ sol	0.01582	43.8	0.9962
Nd^{3+}-TiO$_2$ sol	0.02491	27.8	0.9942
Eu^{3+}-TiO$_2$ sol	0.02773	25.0	0.9961
Ce^{4+}-TiO$_2$ sol	0.02327	29.8	0.9902

Mechanism of Photosensitization

Ln^{n+}-TiO$_2$ with Visible Illumination

The experiments have demonstrated that both the MBT and X-3B in aqueous solution could be effectively degraded under visible light irradiation by using Ln^{n+}-TiO$_2$ catalysts. The significant red-shift found in the UV/Vis DRS of the Ce^{3+}-TiO$_2$ catalysts implies that lanthanide ions must have played a vital role in photosensitization from visible light. To study the photoresponse of the Ln^{n+}-TiO$_2$ catalyst under visible illumination, a set of photocurrent experiments was carried out by using different catalysts. The experimental results are shown in Fig. 21.

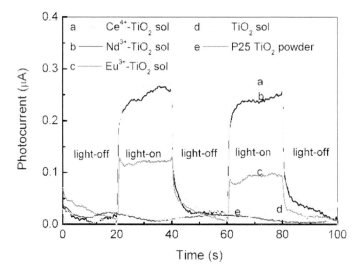

Fig. 21. Photocurrent response of ITO electrode under visible light irradiation-darkness impulse condition.

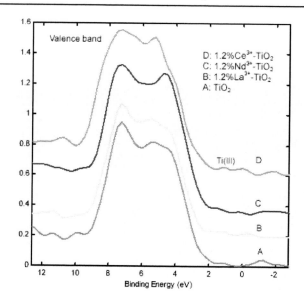

Fig. 22. Valence band XPS of Ln^{3+}-TiO_2 powders.

The experiments demonstrated that two samples of P25 TiO_2 powder and TiO_2 sol had no response under visible light irradiation in terms of photocurrent generation, but other three samples of Ln^{n+}-TiO_2 sol showed sharp responses. Once the visible light was switched on, the photocurrent intensity jumped rapidly from almost 0 to 0.245 μA for Nd^{3+}-TiO_2, 0.122 μA for Eu^{3+}-TiO_2, and 0.265 μA for Ce^{4+}-TiO_2, respectively without delay. However, once the light was off, the photocurrent intensity decreased to 0.02 μA drastically. These results clearly confirmed that visible light directly induced the Ln^{n+}-TiO_2 catalysts to generate photoelectrons.

Moreover, the valence band XPS of the TiO_2 and Ln^{n+}-TiO_2 catalysts were examined in the binding energy range of 3-10 eV and the analytical results are shown in Fig. 22. Relative to the Fermi level (E_F), the two peaks of a board one at 4.71-5.45 eV and a narrow one at 7.25-7.53 eV corresponded with π (nonbonding) and σ (bonding) of O $2p$ orbital, according to the results of Sanjinés et al. [42]. These XPS results indicated that an Ln $4f$ energy level might exist between the valence band and conduct band of TiO_2.

On the basis of the above results, a valence band structure of Ln^{3+}-TiO_2 catalysts is proposed in Fig. 23. It is suggested that electron-hole pairs could be generated under visible light in either Ln^{n+}-TiO_2 or Ln_2O_3 with three approaches of that electrons can be excited (1) from the valence band of Ln^{3+}-TiO_2 (if the band gap of Ln_2O_3 is less than 3.2 eV, such as Ce_2O_3) into Ln $4f$ level when the energy of photon is more than ($E_{Ln4f} - E_v$); (2) from the valence band of Ln_2O_3 into Ln $5d$ level when the energy of photon is more than ($E_c' - E_v'$); and also (3) from the valence band of Ln_2O_3 into Ln $4f$ level when the energy of photon is more than ($E_{Ln4f} - E_v'$). Therefore, the red-shift of absorption edge for Ln^{3+}-TiO_2 and Ln_2O_3 are expressed in Equations 4 and 5. It should be indicated that the Ln $4f$ and $5d$ levels might play a crucial role in generating electron-hole pairs under visible illumination.

$$Ln^{3+}\text{-}TiO_2 + hv \rightarrow e^- + h^+ \tag{4}$$

$$Ln_2O_3 + hv \rightarrow e^- + h^+ \tag{5}$$

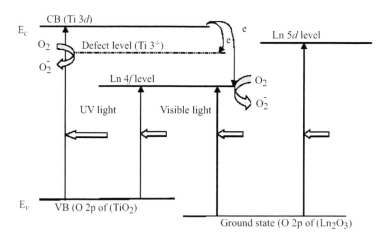

Fig. 23. Proposed mechanisms of photoresponse under visible light illumination

X-3B/Ln^{n+}-TiO$_2$ with Visible Illumination

The X-3B/TiO$_2$ hydrosol system has an entirely different mechanism of photo-excitation, since X-3B is a photosensitizer under visible illumination. The second set of photocurrent experiments was carried out under visible light irradiation and the results are shown in Fig. 24. The results showed that photocurrent intensity had no significant change in P25 TiO$_2$ powder suspension and TiO$_2$ sol solution without X-3B, while the visible light was on. However, photocurrent quickly rose to 0.352 μA in the X-3B /P25 TiO$_2$ powder system and to 0.495 μA in the X-3B/TiO$_2$ hydrosol system under visible illumination. Compared to the results in Fig. 21, these results confirmed that the photocurrent generation under visible light in this case resulted from the existence of dye but not the catalysts. In addition, the results demonstrated that X-3B was more sensitive than the lanthanide ions to generate photocurrent under visible illumination.

The third set of photocurrent experiments was carried out in the X-3B/Ln^{n+}-TiO$_2$ hydrosol systems under visible illumination. The experimental results are shown in Fig. 25. The results demonstrated that photocurrent intensity was generated up to the higher values of 0.634 μA for X-3B/Nd^{3+}-TiO$_2$ and 0.816 μA for X-3B/Ce^{4+}-TiO$_2$ during instant illumination time. Once light was off, the photocurrent quickly fell to 0.092 μA for X-3B/Nd^{3+}-TiO$_2$ and 0.062 μA for X-3B/Ce^{4+}-TiO$_2$, respectively. In this experiment, photocurrent generation had no decay when light was on and the photocurrent intensity was well maintained during the interval time of 20 seconds. When light was off, there was a quick falling of photocurrent intensity. However, in the Eu^{3+}-TiO$_2$ hydrosol system, the photocurrent instantly came into being when light was on and then gradually increased to a peak value of 0.565 μA after 20 seconds. Once light was off, it decreased to the initial value of 0.074 μA, but not as quickly as those in the Ce^{4+}-TiO_2 and Nd^{3+}-TiO_2 systems. The experimental results indicated that the photocurrent generation in the X-3B/Ln^{n+}-TiO_2 system was significantly stronger than that either Ln^{n+}-TiO_2 only or X-3B only.

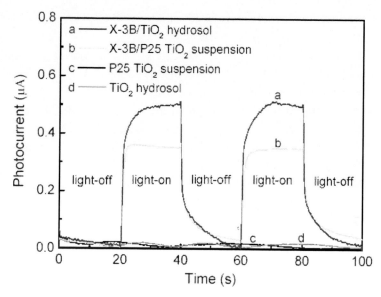

Fig. 24. Photocurrent response of ITO electrode under visible light irradiation-darkness impulse condition

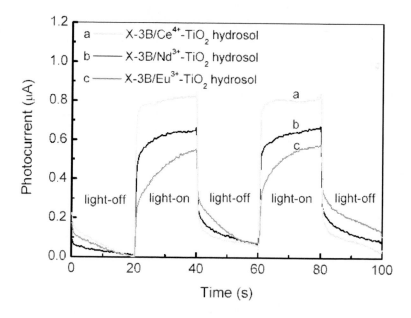

Fig. 25. Photocurrent response of ITO electrode in X-3B/Ln^{n+}-TiO_2 hydrosol under the visible light irradiation-darkness impulse condition.

The photocurrent intensity mainly depends on electron generation capacity and electron transfer efficiency between X-3B/Ln^{n+}-TiO_2 and the working electrode. The X-3B dye sensitization process involves the excitation of dye molecules by absorbing visible light photons and subsequent electron injection from excitation state dye to TiO_2 conduction band (CB). Then electrons underwent transfer process from CB to the working electrode (ITO conductive film) and finally formed an out-circuit. In this process, Ln^{n+}-TiO_2 particles act as a bridge-band connecting X-3B dye and working electrode. Meanwhile, the excellent light absorption ability of the X-3B/Ln^{n+}-TiO_2 system was contributed to the higher photocurrent generation. On the other hand, the lanthanide ions bonded on the surface of TiO_2 particles could act as good scavengers to trap photoelectrons, resulting in depressing photocurrent generation. As an overall result, only a small amount of electrons photogenerated can transfer to the working electrode to form an out-circuit. Comparing the photocurrent generation in three systems under the same experimental condition, the higher photocurrent intensity occurred in the X-3B/Ce^{4+}-TiO_2 solution might indicate that cerium ion had weaker electron-trapping capacity, while the lower photocurrent intensity occurred in the X-3B/Eu^{3+}-TiO_2 solution pointed out that europium ion had strong electron-trapping capacity. Therefore, Eu^{3+}-TiO_2 and Nd^{3+}-TiO_2 catalysts demonstrated better photocatalytic activity than Ce^{4+}-TiO_2 catalyst for X-3B degradation under visible light irradiation. It is a good agreement between the photocatalytic degradation experiments and photocurrent experiments.

In a dye/TiO_2 system, some key reactions are proposed in Equations 6-11. Dye can be excited under visible illumination (Equation 6). Then, the electrons of excited state dye molecule can inject into the conduction band of TiO_2 (Equation 7) and may be trapped by the electron scavengers of usually surrounding oxygen molecule (Equation 8). But it is also extremely susceptible for the recombination between cationic radicals and the electrons if the injection electrons accumulate in the CB of TiO_2. So, the electrons trapping and electrons transfer will be two key steps to inhibit electron-cationic radical recombination. The cationic radical ($dye^{+\bullet}$) produced by electron injection is less stable than the probe molecule in ground state (dye). As a result, unstable dye with cationic radicals can be directly degrade into its products by reacting with super-oxidizing anionic radials or other active oxygen ($HO\cdot$, $HO_2\cdot$, and $O_2^{\bullet-}$) (Equation 10). For a dye/Ln^{n+}-TiO_2 system, lanthanide ion may promote the transfer of excited electrons as shown in Equations 9 and 10. The mechanism of photosensitization in the dye/Ln^{n+}-TiO_2/VIS system can be proposed as shown Fig. 26, in which four key steps of electron excitation, injection, trapping, and transferring are well illustrated.

$$Dye + hv \rightarrow Dye^* \tag{6}$$
$$Dye^* + TiO_2 \rightarrow TiO_2\,(e^-) + Dye^+ \tag{7}$$
$$TiO_2\,(e^-) + O_2 \rightarrow O_2^- + TiO_2 \tag{8}$$
$$Ln^{n+} + TiO_2\,(e^-) \rightarrow Ln^{(n-1)+} + TiO_2 \tag{9}$$
$$Ln^{(n-1)+} + O_2 \rightarrow O_2^- + Ln^{n+} \tag{10}$$
$$O_2^- + Dye^+ \rightarrow Intermediates\ or\ products \tag{11}$$

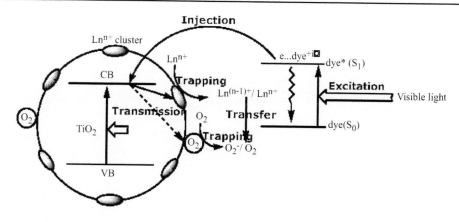

Fig. 26. Proposed mechanisms of photosensitization in dye/Ln^{n+}-TiO_2 /Vis system

Mechanism of the Elimination of Electron-Hole Recombination

Wang and his co-workers had proven the more efficient separation of electron-hole pairs in the lanthanide ion-doped TiO_2 including La^{3+}, Nd^{3+}, Pr^{3+}, Sm^{3+}, and Eu^{3+} than that in pure TiO_2 [46, 47]. Interfacial charge transfer should be a determining-rate step for photocatalytic reaction [48]. The PL emission spectra are useful to disclose the efficiency of charge carrier trapping, immigration and transfer, and to understand the fate of electron-hole pairs in semiconductor particles because PL emission results from the recombination of free carriers [49, 50]. To better understand the effect of lanthanide ion doping on the separation of electron-hole pairs, the PL emission spectra of TiO_2 and different Ln^{3+}-TiO_2 catalysts were examined in this study. The PL emission spectra of TiO_2 and Ce^{3+}-TiO_2 catalysts at the lower temperature of 77 K were also examined in the range of 370-700 nm and the analytical results are shown in Fig. 27A. It can be confirmed that the PL intensity of TiO_2 was significantly higher than that of the Ce^{3+}-TiO_2 samples. The lower PL intensity would indicate the less recombination of electron-hole pair. In addition, the main PL peak of TiO_2 occurred at 524 nm, while those of Ce^{3+}-TiO_2 turned up at 538, 539, 541, and 551 nm, respectively. These results indicated that the position of PL peaks gradually shifted to the red direction with the increase of cerium ion dosage from 0.2% to 2.0%. This red shift of PL emission agreed with the red shift of UV-visible absorption spectra.

Then the PL emission spectra of the TiO_2 and three 1.2% Ln^{3+}-TiO_2 catalysts were examined in the range of 370-700 nm at 77 K and the analytical results are shown in Fig. 27B. It is obvious that the PL emission intensity at 77 K is much stronger than that at room temperature. Similarly, the PL emission intensity of TiO_2 was more significantly stronger than that of Ln^{3+}-TiO_2. In the meantime, the PL emission peak for TiO_2 was located at 520 nm, but those for 1.2%La^{3+}, 1.2% Nd^{3+}, and 1.2% Ce^{3+}-TiO_2 located at 525, 522, and 538 nm, respectively, attributable to the recombination of the host charge carrier. If we agree that the PL emission mainly results from the recombination of excited electron and holes, the lower PL intensity may indicate a lower recombination rate of electron/holes and higher separation efficiency. Frindell group [51] proposed a model for energy transfer involving relaxation to defect states on TiO_2 and then to the lanthanide ions for a lanthanide ion-doped

TiO_2 system, in which the defect states played an important role in energy transfer and electron transfer between host (TiO_2) and guest (Ln^{3+}). In present study, the Ti^{3+} content increased with the increase of Ln^{3+} dosage. The PL emission spectra imply the fact that electron was transferred from TiO_2 to Ln^{3+} crystal field states.

For the Ln^{n+}-TiO_2 catalysts, Ln $4f$ level plays an important role in interfacial charge transfer and elimination of electron-hole recombination. Lanthanide ions could act as an effective electron scavenger to trap the CB electrons of TiO_2. Lanthanide ions (Nd^{3+}, Eu^{3+}, and Ce^{4+}), as a Lewis acid, apparently was superior to the oxygen molecule (O_2) in the capability of trapping CB electrons [52, 53]. The electrons trapped in Ln^{n+}/$Ln^{(n-1)+}$ sites were subsequently transferred to the surrounding adsorbed O_2. The presence of Ln^{n+} on TiO_2 surface may promote following processes as Equations 9 and 10. The formation of •OH might be proposed as Equation 12 and photogenerated electron was transferred efficiently.

$$O_2^{\bullet-} + 2H^+ + 2e^- \rightarrow \bullet OH + OH^- \tag{12}$$

The effect of lanthanide ions depend also on the standard redox potentials of lanthanide ion pairs (Ln^{n+}/$Ln^{(n-1)+}$) which greatly influenced the photocatalytic activity and photocurrent intensity of Ln^{n+}-TiO_2. Concerning the energy level, electrons were permitted to transit from TiO_2 CB to lanthanide ions (Nd^{3+}, Eu^{3+}, Ce^{4+}). So, these oxidation state ions can effectively trap electrons. The europium and neodymium ions could realize recycle application by subsequent electron transfer from Eu^{2+} and Nd^{2+} to oxygen. However, the standard reduction potential of Ce^{4+}/Ce^{3+} was more positive than that of O_2/O_2^- ($E^0(Ce^{4+}/Ce^{3+}) = +1.76V$, $E^0(O_2/O_2^-) = +0.338V$). So, it was forbidden to realize electron transfer from deoxidization state ion (Ce^{3+}) to molecular oxygen (O_2). Therefore, it was more effective for Eu^{3+}-TiO_2 and Nd^{3+}-TiO_2 to photogenerate superoxide of anionic radicals than that for Ce^{4+}-TiO_2, which caused the difference in photocatalytic activity of Ln^{n+}-TiO_2 catalysts.

On the other hand, Ti^{3+} can also form a defect level and act as hole traps to promote the charge transfer as shown in Fig. 23. These defects on the TiO_2 surface or in the bulk can suppress the recombination of electron-hole pairs and hence extend their lifetime. The mechanism of interfacial charge transfer can be expressed in Equations 13 and 14 [54, 55].

$$Ti^{4+}\text{-}O\text{-}H + e^- \rightarrow Ti^{3+}\text{-}O\text{-}H \tag{13}$$

$$Ti^{3+}\text{-}O\text{-}H^- + h^+ \rightarrow Ti^{4+}\text{-}{}^\bullet O\text{-}H \tag{14}$$

However, to certain degree, the higher content of Ti^{3+} on the Ln^{3+}-TiO_2 surface compared to that of TiO_2 would accelerate the interfacial charge transfer and enhance the photocatalytic activity. But the content of Ti^{3+} should have an optimal percentage. In present study, the Ti^{3+} content increased with the increase of Ln^{n+} dosage. Beyond the optimal amount, defect level will become the recombination center of electron-hole pairs and that lead to the decrease of photocatalytic activity when Ti^{3+} content is excessive.

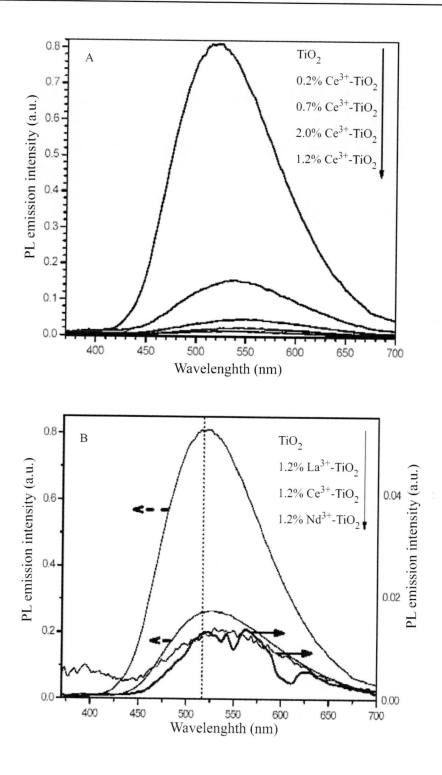

Fig. 27. Photoluminescence emission spectra of TiO_2 and Ce^{3+}-TiO_2 at 77 K (A), and TiO_2 and 1.2% Ln^{3+}-TiO_2 at 77 K (B) using 325 nm laser as an excitation.

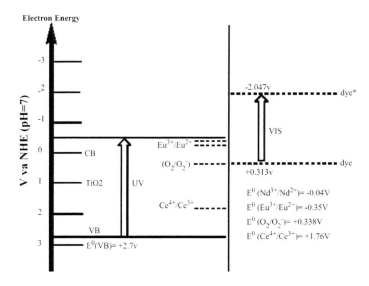

Fig. 28. Schematic illustration of valence and conduction band potentials of TiO_2 and excitation and ground state potentials of X-3B molecule along with the standard reduction potentials of lanthanide ion pairs

Conclusions

This study demonstrated that both the MBT and X-3B photocatalytic degradation in aqueous solution could be enhanced by using Ln^{n+}-TiO_2 catalysts due to the improvement of adsorption ability and photocatalytic reaction kinetics. The crystalline sol catalysts in aqueous solution had higher overall photocatalytic efficiency than the powder catalysts in an aqueous suspension. The enhancement of photocatalytic activity was crucially attributable to the elimination of the separation of electron-hole pairs and partially attributable to the improvement of the organic substrate adsorption. The formation of two sub-energy levels (defect level and Ln 4f level) in Ln^{n+}-TiO_2 might be a critical reason to eliminate the recombination of electron-hole pairs and to enhance the photocatalytic activity under UV and visible light. Both of lanthanide ions and dye all play vital role in visible photosensitization and charge transfer.

References

[1]　Hoffmann, M. R.; Martin, S. T.; Choi, W.; Bahnemann, D. W. 1995. Environmental applications of semiconductor photocatalysis. *Chem. Rev.* 95, 69-96.

[2]　Kamat, P. V. 1993. Photochemistry on nonreactive and reactive (semiconductor) surfaces. *Chem. Rev.* 93, 267-300.

[3]　Fujishima, A., Rao, T.N., Tryk, D.A., 2001. Titanium dioxide photocatalysis. *J. Photochem. Photobiol.* C Rev. 1, 1-21.

[4]　Herrmann, J. M., 1999. Heterogeneous photocatalysis: fundamentals and applications to the removal of various types of aqueous pollutants. *Catal. Today* 53, 115-129.

[5] Malato, S., Blanco, J., Vidal, A., Alarcon D., Maldonado, M.I., Caceres, J., Gernjak, W., 2003. Applied studies in solar photocatalytic detoxication: an overview. *Sol. Energy* 75, 329-336.

[6] Li, X. Z.; Li, F. B. 2001. Study of Au/Au^{3+}-TiO_2 photocatalysts toward visible photooxidation for water and wastewater treatment. *Environ. Sci. Technol.* 35, 2381-2388.

[7] Xu, Y.; Langford C. H. 2001. UV- or visible-light-induced degradation of X3B on TiO2 nanoparticles: The influence of adsorption. *Langmuir* 17, 897-902.

[8] Li, F. B.; Gu, G. B.; Huang, G. F.; Gu, Y. L.; Wan, H. F. 2001. TiO_2-assisted photocatalysis degradation process of dye chemicals. *J. Environ. Sci.*-China 13, 64-68.

[9] Choi, W., Termin, A., Hoffmann, M. R., 1994. The role of metal ion dopants in quantum-sized TiO_2: correlation between photoreactivity and charge carrier recombination dynamics. J. *Phys. Chem.* 98, 13669-13679.

[10] Litter, M.I., 1999. Heterogeneous photocatalysis: transition metal ions in photocatalytic systems. *Appl. Cataly.* B Environ. 23, 89-114.

[11] Yu, J. G., Yu, J. C.; Cheng, B.; Zhao. X. J. 2002. Photocatalytic activity and characterization of the sol-gel derived Pb-doped TiO_2 thin films. *J. Sol-Gel Sci. Technol.* 2002, 24, 39-48.

[12] Li, F. B., Li, X. Z., 2002. Photocatalytic properties of gold/gold ion-modified titanium dioxide for wastewater treatment. *Appl. Catal. A Gen.* 228, 15-27.

[13] Shah, S. I., Li, W., Huang, C.-P., Jung, O., Ni. C., 2002. Study of Nd^{3+}, Pd^{2+}, Pt^{4+}, and Fe^{3+} dopant effect on photoreactivity of TiO_2 nanoparticles. *PNAS.* 99, 6482-6486.

[14] Kamat, P. V.; 2002. Photophysical, photochemical and photocatalytic aspects of metal nanoparticles. *J. Phys. Chem.* B 106, 7729-7744.

[15] Jakob, M.; Levanon, H.; Kamat, P. V.; 2003. Charge distribution between UV-Irradiated TiO_2 and gold nanoparticles: determination of shift in the fermi level. *Nano Lett.* 3, 353-358.

[16] Bae, E.; Choi, W. 2003. Highly enhanced photoreductive degradation of perchlorinated compounds on dye-sensitized metal/TiO_2 under visible light. *Environ. Sci. Technol.* 2003, 37, 147-152.

[17] Yamakata, A.; Ishibashi, T.; Onishi, H. 2001. Water- and oxygen-induced decay kinetics of photogenerated electrons in TiO_2 and Pt/TiO_2: A time-resolved infrared absorption study. *J. Phys. Chem.* B 105, 7258-7262.

[18] Li, X. Z., Li, F. B., Yang, C.L., Ge, W.K., 2001. Photocatalytic activity of WO_x-TiO_2 under visible light irradiation. *J Photochem Photobiol A: Chem,* 141, 209-217.

[19] Dhananjeyan, M.R.; Mielczarski, E.; Thampi, K.R.; Buffat, Ph.; Bensimon, M.; Kulik, A.; Mielczarski, J.; Kiwi, J. 2001. Photodynamics and surface characterization of TiO_2 and Fe_2O_3 photocatalysts immobilized on modified polyethylene films. *J. Phys. Chem.* B 105, 12046-12055.

[20] Reddy, B. M.; Sreekanth, P. M.; Reddy, E. P.; Yamada, Y.; Xu, Q.; Sakurai, H.; Kobayashi, T. 2002. Surface characterization of La_2O_3-TiO_2 and V_2O_5/La_2O_3-TiO_2 catalysts. *J. Phys. Chem.* B 106, 5695-5700.

[21] Ikeda, S.; Sugiyama, N.; Pal, B., Marcí, G.; Palmisano, L.; Noguchi, H.; Uosaki, K.; Ohtani, B. 2001. Photocatalytic activity of transition-metal-loaded titanium(IV) oxide

powders suspended in aqueous solutions: correlation with electron-hole recombination kinetics. *Phys. Chem. Chem. Phys.* 3, 267-273.

[22] Xu, W., Gao, Y., Liu, H. Q., 2002. The Preparation, Characterization, and their photocatalytic activities of rare-earth-doped TiO_2 nanoparticles. *J. Catal.* 207, 151-157.

[23] Ranjit, K. T., Willner, I., Bossmann, S. H., and Braun, A. M., 2001. Lanthanide oxide doped titanium dioxide photocatalysts: effective photocatalysts for the enhanced degradation of salicylic acid and t-cinnamic acid. *J. Catal.* 204, 305-311.

[24] Ranjit, K. T., Willner, I., Bossmann, S. H., Braun, A. M., 2001. Lanthanide oxide-doped titanium dioxide photocatalysts: novel photocatalysts for the enhanced degradation of p-chlorophenoxyacetic acid. *Environ. Sci. Technol.* 35, 1544-1549.

[25] Watson, S. S., Beydoun, D., Scott, J.A., Amal, R., 2003. The effect of preparation method on the photoactivity of crystalline titanium dioxide particles. *Chem. Eng. J.* 95, 213-220.

[26] Fiehn, O.; Wegener, G.; Jochimsen J.; Jekel. M. 1998. Analysis of the ozonation of 2-mercaptobenzothiazole in water and tannery wastewater using sum parameters, liquid- and gas chromatography and capillary electrophoresis. *Wat. Res.* 32, 1075-1084.

[27] Li, X. Z.; Liu, H.; Cheng, L. F.; Tong, H. J. 2003. Photocatalytic oxidation using a new catalyst - TiO_2 microsphere - for water and wastewater treatment. *Environ. Sci. and Technol.* 37, 3989-3994.

[28] Matsuda, A., Kotani, Y., Kogure, T., Tatsumisago, M., Minami, T., 2000. Transparent anatase nanocomposite films by the sol-gel process at low temperatures. J. *Am. Ceram. Soc.* 83 (1), 229-231.

[29] Gregg, S. L., Sing, K. S. W., 1982. *Adsorption, Surface Area and Porosity*, Academic Press, London.

[30] Yu, J. G., Yu, J. C., Leung, M. K.-P., Ho, W. K., Cheng, B., Zhao, X. J., Zhao, J. C., 2003a. Effect of acidic and basic hydrolysis catalysts on the photocatalytic activity and microstructure of bimodal mesoporous titania. *J. Catal.* 217, 69-78.

[31] Yu, J. G., Yu, J. C., Cheng, B., Hark, S. K., Iu, K., 2003b. The effect of F⁻-doping and temperature on the structural and textural evolution of mesoporous TiO_2 powders. *J. Solid State Chem.*, 174, 372-380.

[32] Yu, J. C., Yu, J. G., Ho, W. K., Zhang, L. Z., 2001. Preparation of highly photocatalytic active nano-sized TiO_2 particles via ultrasonic irradiation. *Chem. Commun.*, 1942-1943.

[33] Hwang, D. W., Lee, J. S., Li, W., Oh, S. H., 2003. Electronic band structure and photocatalytic activity of $Ln_2Ti_2O_7$ (Ln = La, Pr, Nd). *J. Phys. Chem.* B, 107, 4963-4970.

[34] Mathur, S., Veith, M., Shen, H., Hufner, S., Jilavi, M. H., 2002. Structural and optical properties of $NdAlO_3$ nanocrystals embedded in an Al_2O_3 matrix. *Chem. Mater.* 14, 568-582.

[35] Kwag, G., Lee, H., Kim, S., 2001. First in-situ observation of pseudoliving character and active site of Nd-based catalyst for 1,3-butadiene polymerization using synchrotron X-ray absorption and UV-visible spectroscopies. *Macromolecules*, 34; 5367-5369.

[36] Xiang, Q., Zhou, Y., Lam, Y. L., Chan, Y. C., Kam, C. H., Ooi, B. S. H., Zhang, X., Buddhudu, S., 2000. Up-conversion emission in violet from yellow in Nd^{3+}: SiO_2-TiO_2-Al_2O_3 sol-gel glasses. *Materials Research Bulletin*, 35, 1571-1578.

[37] Ripoll, J., Bausa, L. E., Terrile, C., Sole, J. G., Diaz, F., 1997. Optical spectroscopy of Nd^{3+}-doped $KGd(WO_4)_2$ monocrystals. *Journal of Luminescence*, 1997, 72-74, 253-254.

[38] Ebitani, K., Hirano, Y., Morikawa, A., Rare earth ions as heterogeneous photocatalysts for the decomposition of dinitrogen monoxide (N_2O). *J. Cata.* 157, 262-265.

[39] Orera, V. M.; Merino, R. I.; Pena, F. 1994. $Ce^{3+}\leftrightarrow Ce^{4+}$ conversion in ceria-doped zirconia single crystals induced by oxido-reduction treatments. *Solid State Ionics.* 1994, 72, 224-231.

[40] Yen, W. M.; Raukas, M.; Basun, S. A.; Schaik, W. V.; Happek, U. 1996. Optical and photoconductive properties of cerium-doped crystalline solids. *Journal of Luminescence.* 69,287-294.

[41] Elidrissi, B.; Addou, M.; Regragui, M.; Monty, C.; Bougrine, A.; Kachouane, A. 2000. Structural and optical properties of CeO_2 thin films prepared by spray sprolysis. *Thin Solid Films.* 379, 23-27.

[42] Sanjinés, R.; Tang, H.; Berge. H.J. 1994. Electronic structure of anatase TiO_2 oxide. *Appl. Phys.* 1994, 75, 2945-2952.

[43] Diebold, U. 2003. The surface science of titanium dioxide. *Surf. Sci. Reports* 48, 53-229.

[44] Morris, D.; Dou, Y.; Rebane, J.; Mitchell, C. E. J.; Egdell, R. G.; Law, D. S. L.; Vittadini, A.; Casarin, M. 2000. Photoemission and STM study of the electronic structure of Nb-doped TiO_2. *Phys. Rev.* B 61, 13445-13457.

[45] Mullins, D.R.; Overbury, S.H.; Huntley, D.R. 1998. Electron spectroscopy of single crystal and polycrystalline cerium oxide surfaces. *Surf. Sci.* 409, 307-319.

[46] Wang, Y. Q., Cheng, H. M., Hao, Y. Z., Ma, J. M., Li, W. H., Cai, S. M., 1999. Photoelectrochemical properties of metal-ion-doped TiO_2 nanocrystalline electrodes. *Thin Solid Films*, 349, 120-125.

[47] Wang, Y. Q.; Cheng, H. M.; Hao, Y. Z.; Ma, J. M.; Li, W. H.; Cai, S. M. 1999. The photoelectrochemistry of Nd^{3+}-doped TiO_2 nanocrystalline electrodes. *J. Mater. Sci. Lett.* 1999, 18, 127-129.

[48] Liu H., Li X. Z., Leng Y.J., Li W. Z. 2003. An alternative approach to ascertain the rate-determining steps of TiO2 photoelectrocatalytic reaction by electrochemical impedance spectroscopy. *J. Phys. Chem.* B 107, 8988-8996.

[49] Kelly, J. J., Kooij, E. S., Meulenkamp, E. A., 1999. Luminescence studies of semiconductor electrodes. *Electrochimica Acta*, 45, 561-574.

[50] Chamarro, M., Gourdon, C., Lavallard, P., 1996. Photoluminescence polarization of semiconductor nanocrystals. *J. Lumin.*, 70, 222-237.

[51] Frindell, K. L., Bartl, M. H., Robinson, M. R., Bazan, G. C., Popitsch, A., Stucky, G. D., 2003. Visible and near-IR luminescence via energy transfer in rare earth doped mesoporous titania thin films with nanocrystalline walls. *J. Solid State Chem.* 172, 81-88.

[52] Xie, Y.B., Yuan C.W., 2003. Visible-light responsive cerium ion modified titania sol
      and nanocrystallites for X-3B dye photodegradation. *Appl. Catal. B: Environ.*, 46, 251-
      259.

[53] Coronado, J. M. Maria, A. J., Martínez-Arias, A.; Conesa, J. C., Soria, J., 2002. EPR
      study of the radicals formed upon UV irradiation of ceria-based photocatalysts. *J.
      Photochem Photobiol A: Chem.*, 150, 213-221.

[54] Szczepankiewicz, S. H., Moss, J. A., Hoffmann, M. R., 2002, Slow surface charge
      trapping kinetics on irradiated TiO_2. *J. Phys. Chem.* B. 106, 2922-2927.

[55] Szczepankiewicz, S. H., Moss, J. A., Hoffmann, M. R., 2002, Electron traps and the
      stark effect on hydroxylated titania photocatalysts. *J. Phys. Chem.* B. 106, 7654-7658.

In: Trends in Water Pollution Research
Editor: J. V. Livingston, pp. 75-93

ISBN 1-59454-328-3
©2005 Nova Science Publishers, Inc.

Chapter III

The Modification of Clay as a Coagulant and the Use of Modified Clay for Car-Washing Wastewater Treatment

J.-Q. Jiang[1,2], C. G. Kim[2], C.-H. Choi[3] and Z. Zeng[1]

[1]School of Engineering (C5), University of Surrey, Guildford, Surrey GU2 7XH, UK
[2]Department of Environmental Engineering, Hanbat National University,
Taejeon, 305-719, Korea
[3]Department of Industrial Engineering and Chemistry, Chungnam University,
Taejeon, 305-764, Korea

Abstract

The modification and use of clays as a new type of coagulants for the treatment of car washing effluent were investigated. The raw clays were montmorillonites K10 and KSF, and were modified by either polymeric Al or Fe species, or an Al/Fe mixing polymeric species, or the cationic polymer species. The performance of modified clay based coagulants was examined in comparison with aluminium sulphate, ferric sulphate and polyaluminium chloride. The quality parameters of the treated effluents evaluated were turbidity, suspended solids, total COD, and the oil contents (extracted with n-hexane), which were measured before and after treatment. The results demonstrated that after being modified with mixing polymeric Al/Fe species, two montmorillonite clays possessed greater properties to remove the particles (as suspended solids), organic pollutants (as COD), and oils from the car-washing wastewater.

Key words: Clay; Coagulation; Polymeric Al/Fe species; Car-washing wastewater treatment.

[2] Corresponding author: Fax: +44 (0)1483 450984, Email: J.Jiang@surrey.ac.uk

Introduction

In Korea, car-washing effluent is generated in the various car-washing sites at an approximately of $0.5 - 1$ m^3 per car par day. Such effluents contain a lot of synthetic detergent, waste anti-freezing agent, waste oils and heavy metals and cause a range of problems if they are not treated properly. For example, when the untreated car-washing wastewater is discharged into surface water, suspended materials will be accumulated, which interrupts the oxygen transfer and reduces the dissolved oxygen concentration and therefore deteriorates the surface water qualities. And also, the car-washing wastewater will block the discharge pipes and prevent oxygen transfer and thus interfere with the activated sludge process if it is discharged into the sewers and wastewater treatment plant directly.

The general processes for the treatment of car-washing wastewater in Korea include sand screen and oil/water separation, which can remove 35 - 50% oils (as n-hexane extracted compounds), and coagulation/sedimentation, which can remove 65% COD and suspended solids (SS). In some cases, filtration is used which can only remove 20% oils, 10% COD and 12% SS. Obviously, the treatment efficiency of car-wash wastewater is not very high and in most cases, the oil and SS concentrations in the treated effluent can exceed the waste discharge standards. An alternative process or new treatment chemical is required to be investigated in order to improve the general treatment performance of the car-washing wastewater.

The natural mineral clays have attracted a lot of research interests. The potential use of natural or modified clays as adsorbents or as coagulant aids has been investigated. By replacing the natural inorganic exchange cations with alkylammonium ions, clay surfaces are converted from being primarily hydrophilic to hydrophobic, which enable them to interact strongly with organic vapours and organic compounds dissolved in water [e.g., 1]. Also, The combination of the natural mineral clays with polymeric Al/Fe species [2] can produce somewhat the optimal properties and offer the comparatively great affinities for the organic compounds (e.g., phenol [3], humic acids [4]), and heavy metals [5].

In addition to being used as adsorbent, natural mineral clays have been used as coagulant aids to improve the settling performance when using metal-based coagulants to treat the low particle content water [6]. Preliminary study on the modification of clay for the production of new kind coagulant has been tried [e.g., 7] by inserting the Mn^{2+} ion into the clay layers. However, Mn^{2+} may not be the optimum cationic ion to be introduced into the clay layers. As stated previously, the polymeric Al/Fe species represented the best coagulating species, this study thus aims to evaluate the treatment performance of car washing wastewater with various modified and raw clays (montmorillonites KSF and K10) in comparison with conventional metal based coagulants (e.g., ferric sulphate and aluminium sulphate).

Principles of Clay Modifications for the Coagulation

Basic Structure of Clay

Fundamentally, clay exhibits a layered structure and can be subdivided into groups according to its underlying structure and layer's charge. An ideal structure of the most rigid clays is the 2:1-layered silicates [8]. The 2:1 notation means that the host layers consist of two tetrahedral silicate sheets sandwiching one octahedral sheet. The two other subclasses of clays have a 1:1 layer type and a 2:1 inverted ribbon structure, respectively (Fig. 1). At the central of the tetrahedral layers are silicon or aluminium ions, while the number of Al ions in tetrahedral sites determines the net negative charge of the host layer. Those oxygens form the tetrahedral bases border of the inter-layer gallery and are arranged in hexagonal rings that form a kagome lattice.

At the geometric mid-plane of each clay layer resides an atom octahedrally coordinated to those oxygens comprising the tetrahedron tips. In trioctahedral 2:1 clays such as vermiculite, all octahedral sites are filled, primarily with Mg^{2+}. The approximate chemical formula for the vermiculites is $(Mg_3(Si_3Al)O_{10}(OH)_2)(Mg_{0.5}(H_2O)_y)$; where the first set of brackets denotes the host layer, the second set denotes the guest layer, and the hydration state (y) is variable. The host layers in clays can adopt a number of arrangements to form ordered, partially ordered, or disordered three-dimensional structures. Particular clays are prone to form poly-types in which different stacking sequences are associated with lateral layer-to-layer shifts.

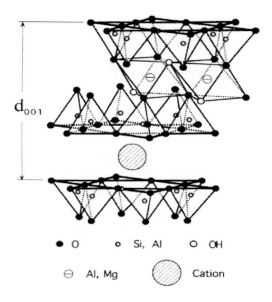

Figure 1. The structure of a typical 2:1 layered silicate clay. The basal spacing d001 is the smallest c-axis repeated distance [8]

Another interesting feature of clay is swelling [9], indicating that the gallery space of some clays can reversibly incorporate amounts of polar molecules such as water and co-intercalated guest cations. Whether clay swells depends on the layer charge and the concomitant strength of the Coulombic interaction between the guest and host layers.

Modification of Clays for the Coagulation

Modification of clay is to immobilize certain inorganic or organic groups to the external and/or internal surface of the layered clay particles by means of physical or chemical reaction. Hence, the modified surface will exhibit enhanced interaction between the contaminants and the clay particles. The driving force for the reactions between the modifiers and the host includes chemisorption, physisorption, ion-exchange, hydrogen-bonding, charge transfer, complex formation etc. In general, the modification methods can be summarized into three categories according to the predominant reaction feature:

- Adsorption: modifier molecules are adsorbed on the external surface of the clay by chemisorption and physisorption mechanism.
- Ion exchange: modifiers are bonded by ion exchange (mostly by cation exchange) reaction, while the structure of the host (such as interlayer spacing) is not changed.
- Intercalation: modifier molecules are inserted into gallery (interlayer) of the host, with maintaining the layered structural feature of the host.

Adsorption

Due to the layered structure, clay minerals offer a large specific surface area and hence possess the potential for adsorption. In order to improve their adsorption capability, clay can be modified by metal ions or organic molecules with special functions. The adsorbed ions sometimes act as a stock for ion exchange of toxic ions in solution [10], while the adsorbed organic molecules will be effective reinforcement for capturing ions or organic matters in water [11 – 13].

A wide variety of different substances can be adsorbed onto the surfaces of solids if such surface areas are large enough, while the affinity of an adsorbent to a given adsorbate is dominated by either van der Waals force (Physisorption) or molecules interaction (Cheimsorption). For adsorption of adsorbate from a solution, Langmuir equation is frequently used to assess the adsorption performance, which would be valid in the case of monolayer adsorption and suppose that there is no interaction between the adsorbates:

$$\frac{x}{m} = \frac{x_m \, ac}{1 + ac}$$

where, x: weight of adsorbate, m: weight of adsorbent, c: concentration of adsorbate at equilibrium, x_m: the monolayer capacity on the surface of 1g solid, and a: a constant

Another equation for dealing with adsorption is the Freundlich isotherm equation, based on the assumption that the adsorbent has a heterogeneous surface composed of different classes of adsorption sites, with adsorption on each of site:

$$\frac{x}{m} = kc^{\frac{1}{n}}$$

where k: a constant related to the adsorption capacity of the absorbent, and n: Freundlich constant, related to interaction between the adsorbate and adsorbent.

A third equation of very general applicability is the BET isotherm, which assumes that the adsorbent surface is composed of uniform, localized sites and that adsorption at one site does not affect adsorption at neighboring sites. Another assumption is that the energy of adsorption holds the first monolayer but the condensation energy of the adsorbate is responsible for adsorption of consecutive layers. The BET equation is written as follows:

$$\frac{x}{m} = \frac{ACx_m}{(C_s - C)\left[1 + (A-1)\dfrac{C}{C_s}\right]}$$

where C_s: saturation concentration of adsorbate, A: a constant to describe the energy of interaction between the adsorbate and the adsorbent surface.

All three equations have been applied successfully to analyse the adsorption data. In general the Langmuir and BET equations are not as good as Freundlich equation in dealing with mixing adsorbates and diluted solutions.

The adsorption of inorganic ions by clay would be influenced by a range of parameters: the nature and charge of the compensating cations, the ionic strength and pH of a solution, the concentration of adsorbate, and solution temperature and so on. Normally Freundlich isotherm has been found to fit experimental data well for levels of adsorption.

Previous study on proton adsorption-desorption of clay provided a model of adsorption sites on clay surface [14]. The model assumes that the structural negative charges and cation exchange sites are to be located on the surfaces of the clay particles. The model predicts that H^+ adsorption at high pH takes place mainly on variable charge sites. These sites become positively charged at pH lower than the pH where the charge is zero (iso-electric point, IEP), which is in agreement with kinetics measurements. Although this proton adsorption is high at low pH, it does not modify appreciably the net negative charge of the clay. This nearly constant charge induces a negative surface potential that is responsible for negative zeta potential of the particles. The negative surface potential also modifies the normal behaviour of the variable charge sites so that the IEP is predicted to change by changing the electrolyte concentration.

In the adsorptive modification, the main interactions between modifier and clay are chemisorption [11, 15] and physisorption [16]. In chemisorption, clay provides molecular complex sites for the modifiers (e.g., other cations), whilst in physisorption, the clay acts as a nucleation center to adsorb modifiers via van deer Walls force. In the case of organic modifier, the mechanism becomes more complicated due to the diversity of molecular conformation and their reaction with the host.

The adsorption mechanisms get more complicated when inorganic ions and organic polymer molecules coexist in the modifier's solution. The presence of aqueous metals (Al^{3+}, Pb^{2+}, Cu^{2+}, Mg^{2+}, and Ba^{2+}) significantly modified the adsorption of organic polymer on the silica surface. Three mechanisms [17] are proposed: metal ions may (1) modify the host surface, (2) interact with the polymer while in the aqueous phase, or (3) form an additional independent surface that can adsorb the polymer.

Ion Exchange

In clay minerals, the oxygen and hydroxyl valences at the planar surface of the structure are satisfied. However at the edges, there are aluminium, silicon, oxygen and hydroxyl ions that are not so satisfied. These unsatisfied valences, or "broken bonds", would be satisfied by external ions that do not combine with the structure, but merely act as counter-ions for electrical neutrality. These counter-ions, particularly the cations, are capable of being exchanged for other ions. This is one of the causes of cation exchange. In some disordered clay, additional balancing cations are present because of the lattice distortion. These additional cations also account for the great part of the cation exchange. For a given clay, the maximum amount of any one cation that can be taken up is a constant and is known as cation exchange capacity (CEC).

The exchange reaction can be expressed as follows:

$$X - clay + Y^+ \Leftrightarrow Y - clay + X^+$$

Normally clays are saturated by Na^+, Ca^{2+} and Mg^{2+}, and cation exchange appears to strongly change the surface activity of clay by varying the amount and nature of clay's surface acid sites. For example Al^{3+} and La^{3+} pillared clays were more active than the host, while a complete deactivation was observed for the K^+ pillared clay [18]. And Mn modified diatomite showed a higher tendency for adsorbing lead ions, due to increasing in the surface area and higher negative surface charge after modification [19]. In addition there are lots of investigations on changing the clay surface from hydrophilic to hydrophobic by ion-exchange method [20 – 22].

The ion exchange selectivity of clay for inorganic ions is primarily affected by the pH of the solutions [23], and also depends on the nature of the ions, the relative concentrations, the nature of the clay, and any secondary reactions if applicable. Even for the equivalent concentrations, some cations are adsorbed more strongly than others, in a lyotropic or Hofmerister series:

H > Al > Ba > Sr > Ca > Mg > NH_4 > K > Na > Li

A number of models of cation exchange have been proposed, which are based on common adsorption models, i.e., either Freundlich or Langmuir isotherm. These models show agreement with experimental results over a limited range of concentrations, but no universally applicable equation has been found. Many models satisfy for exchange between cations of same valence but break down when applied to cations with different valence.

Modification of clay with common inorganic anions leads to destruction of the crystalline lattice. The extent of the destruction, assessed on the basis of X-ray diffraction, infrared and differential thermal analysis studies [24], depends on the type of the anion used. Under the same concentration, destruction is greater for samples containing multivalent anions than for samples with monovalent anions (F^-, Cl^-, NO_3^-), and increases in the following order: $PO_4^{3-} <$ $SO_4^{2-} < BO_3^{3-}$. Samples modified with anions in an amount of 1.0 wt% exhibit about a 35% increase in adsorption capacity in comparison with the starting clay. Clays containing monovalent anions show a similar activity, while for clays with multivalent anions the activity decreases in the sequence $SO_4^{2-} >> PO_4^{3-} >> BO_3^{3-}$. This sequence is in agreement with decreasing electronegativity of the central atom.

Inorganic cations like Na^+ and Ca^{2+} on internal and external surface of the clays can also be exchanged by some quaternary ammonium type surfactants such as tetradecyltrimethyl ammonium bromine (TTAB), dodecyltrimethylammonium bromide (DTAB) [12], cetylpyridinium chloride (CPC) [25], octadecyldimethylchlorosilane [26], hexadecyl trimethylammonium (HDTMA) [27]. The modification equilibrium may be fitted to Freundlich model [28] or Langmuir model [27]. Organic modifier can change the surface property of clay from hydrophilic to hydrophobic, and then significantly enhance its affinity to organic contaminants, mostly due to their high charge density, special functional group (such as quaternary alkylammonium) in the interlayer [29].

One of the advantages of the organic modifiers is their special application owing to the diversity of organic functional group. An example of such organic modifiers is hexadecyl-trimethyl-ammonium (HDTMA) bromide that was used to modify the surface of clay minerals (e.g., kaolinite, montmorillonite). After modification by cationic surfactant, clay was found to adsorb considerable amounts of oxyanion of chromate, which is no affinity for unmodified clay due to the fact that both of them are negatively charged. Moreover by modifying clay surface with polyelectrolyte complex, it was possible to prepare a strongly cationic surface charge on clay particles [30]. There is a stronger affinity of the newly formed complexes to such contaminants as phenol [3].

The organic coating was found to exist as a rough layer on the surface of the clay grains, and to plug their pores. Both the natural and the synthetic surface modification resulted in steric and electrostatic stabilization of the clay particles, because of the highly charged, polyionic character of the surface-modifying organic matter [31]. And the conformation of the organic molecules, especially the macromolecules will be strongly affected by solution pH value [32], which is subject to the values of IEP; (i) Below the IEP), macromolecules unfold on the clay surfaces in response to electrostatic attractive interactions, a phenomenon that inhibits enzyme activity, (ii) near the IEP proteins are adsorbed with little modification of conformation and thus preserve their intrinsic properties, such as catalytic activities, and (iii) above the IEP the proportion of adsorbed macromolecules decreases due to electrostatic repulsive interactions, permitting the diffusion of macromolecules in the liquid-filled pore network of the clay.

Intercalation

Intercalation is the processing that certain molecules are inserted into interlayer space of clay particles. This insertion requires the presence of polar interactions between the guest and the host [33]. The motivation to study intercalation is that the properties of both the guest and the host would be leveraged by this reaction, and the new structure may be able to provide even better performance. On this basis intercalation compounds have been investigated extensively and a variety of host-guest system with unique structure has been presented [34]. Many different species such as organo-cations, organometallic complexes metal oxide sols and polycations have been investigated as intercalation reagents [35].

Intercalation with Inorganic Polycations

The inorganic intercalated clays, which are also called pillared clays (PILCS) have a virtually constant distance between the layers and therefore interlayer space. They are new stable micro and mesoporous materials available for adsorption [36], catalysis [37] and separation applications [27]. A number of pillaring candidates (e.g., Al, Fe, Zr, Cu, Cr, Mg, Si) have been used.

Preparation of the intercalated clay is dominated by hydrolysis of metal salts, thus a series of method controlling the metal hydrolysis may be applied: (a) addition of metal carbonates (Na, Mg etc) into $AlCl_3$ or $FeCl_3$ solution; (b) addition of metal hydroxides (Na, K etc) into Al/Fe solution; (c) addition of metal Al into HCl and/or $AlCl_3$; and (d) electrolysis of $AlCl_3$. And many factors such as concentration of the reactants, hydrolysis speeds (in term of addition rate of reactants), aging conditions will have significant effects on the final product [2].

Inorganic ion intercalation establishes their functionality dominantly by means of the structural modification. That means the pillared clays normally provide a customized mesoporous and microporous structure, which is prone to adsorb contaminants. The amount of polycation in an exchanging solution governed the interpillar distance in the pillared clay gallery without changing the diameters of the pillar [38]. Results from carbon and alumina intercalated montmorillonite [39] indicated that the framework of these adsorbents is made of alumina particles and clay sheets while the pyrolyzed carbon distributes in the space of interlayers and interpillars. The pores between the carbon particles, clay sheets, and alumina pillars are very narrow with very strong adsorption forces, leading to enhanced adsorption capacities. The composite adsorbents exhibit features similar to those of carbonaceous adsorbents. Meanwhile, ions can be doped into the adsorbents to additionally modify their adsorption properties [40]. Such flexibility in pore structure tailoring is a potential advantage of the composite adsorbents developed for their adsorption and separation applications.

And the adsorption potential can be increased by co-pillaring of Al, Zr, Mo, Cr, Cu and Ti, owing mainly to the better structural order in co-pillared clay [e.g., 41]. The incorporation of Zr into the Fe precursors leads to mixed Fe-Zr pillars with entirely new properties (pillar charge, pillar symmetry, etc.), creating a pillared clay with a different enhanced porosity [42].

An improved synthesis method of pillaring has been proposed by incorporating inorganic polycations and organic surfactants. This configuration is able to increase the intercalation capacity by overcoming the steric constraints at the interface between the intercalating solution and the delaminated clay [43]. Moreover the products exhibit higher adsorption capacities towards hydrophobic contaminates such as phenol [3], while the presence of surfactants will be helpful to have a more regular pillar distribution [44].

It should be noted that the effects of organic surfactants are not always positive. Their binding profile and conformation play an important role. FTIR frequency shifts for the $C_{12\text{-}14}E_5\text{-}Al_{13}$ complexes indicated that the surfactant binds to the polycation through the oxygen atoms of the ethylene oxide segment of the chain [45]. At low surfactant loadings the surfactant binds to the gallery Al_{13} ions and fills the microporous space between pillars, causing a dramatic loss of N_2 Brunauer-Emmett-Teller (BET) surface area. Increasing the surfactant loading resulted in additional surfactant binding to the gallery surfaces. In this second binding domain the surfactant acts in part as a pillaring reagent, causing an increase in basal spacing from 19 to 23 angstrom and the reappearance of micropores. At even higher loadings a third surfactant binding mode was observed in which the surfactant binds exclusively to external surfaces and blocks all micro- and mesopores. Surfactants greatly inhibited the hydrolysis of Al_{13} polycations in the clay galleries and dramatically improved the crystallographic ordering of the intercalate along the layer stacking direction.

Intercalation with Organic Molecules

There are two main methods of preparing intercalated organoclay: direct intercalation and intercalation by in situ polymerization of pre-intercalated monomers. The former is somewhat difficult because the kind of molecules that can be directly intercalated is limited, as a result the in situ polymerization route is more popular in fabricating organic-inorganic nanocomposites [46]. Nevertheless the in situ polymerization include a pre-intercalation procedure as well, which involves the same topics as those in direct intercalation. Moreover in water treatment processing, small size modifiers are preferred for maximizing the modification capacity [11], and actually the intercalation reaction itself can also be applied to remove contaminants from water [47].

The most popular organic modifier in this topic is organoammonium ions, such as alkylammonium, alkyltrimethylammonium, dialkyldimethylammonium (DMA), tetramethylammonium (TMA), tetrapropylammonium (TPA), tetrapentylammonium (TpeA), trimethylphenylammonium (TMPA) and alkylpyridinium. The hydrophobic interactions between the guest species and organoammonium ions are thought to be the driving force for the intercalation.

The basal spacing of the guest will be enlarged after intercalation, according to X-ray diffraction results [48]. The difference of basal spacing corresponds to the difference in the orientation of the alkyl chains. It has been known that excess amount of guest can penetrate in the interlayer space as a salt and this is called "intersalation". The increase in d value may be owing to the intersalation as well.

Experimental Methods

Modifying and Characterising Clays

The modification, characterisation and preparation of various clays were conducted at Environmental Engineering Laboratory of The University of Surrey, UK. The raw clays used in this study, i.e. montmorillonites K10 and KSF and the other chemicals were supplied by Sigma-Aldrich Chemicals Corporation UK. The polymeric Al/Fe modifiers were prepared following an established procedure [2]. The modification involved with the mixing of the given amount of clays with the polymeric metal species for four hours at $55^{\circ}C$ and then the mixtures were separated by filtration to obtain the solid phase of the modified clays. The chemical composition of the modified clays were analysed using X-ray Fluorescence (XRF), and the XRF data was collected on a Philips PW1480 XRF Spectrometer.

Procedures of Coagulation Experiments and the Effluent Quality Measurement

Car-washing wastewater samples were taken from the Garages of Yusoung, Taejeon City, and the coagulation jar test experiments were conducted at Department of Environmental Engineering Laboratory, Hanbat University of Korea. All coagulants used in this study were listed in Table 1. Except for the modified clay coagulants, other coagulants were ferric sulphate (FS), aluminium sulphate (AS), and polyaluminium chloride (PACl). The dosages of clays were 200, 400, 600, 800, 1000, and 1200 mg/l, respectively, and the dosage of AS , FS and PACl was in the range of 2-12 mg/l as Al, or as Fe, respectively. A standard jar test apparatus (Model PB-900, Phipps and Bird Co, USA) and a test procedure were used in the study, including a fast mixing at 250 rotations per min (rpm) for 1 min, a slow mixing at 45 rpm for 30min, and a settling time of 60min. The supernatant was taken for the quality measurement.

Water Quality Analysis

The measurement of turbidity, suspended solids, total chemical oxygen demand (COD_{Cr}) and the oil contents followed the Korean Standard Methods [49].

The coagulation results are presented as the percentage removal of suspended solids, COD_{Cr} and oil content. The percentage removal was calculated against the quality parameters of controlled samples, which were undergone the full coagulation procedures but no addition of any coagulants.

Table 1. The label of the coagulants used

Coagulant	Label
Raw montmorillonite K10	K10
Polymeric Fe modified montmorillonite K10	Fe-K10
Polymeric Al modified montmorillonite K10	Al-K10
Polymeric Al/Fe modified montmorillonite K10	Al/Fe-K10
Organic polymer modified montmorillonite K10	P7-K10
Raw montmorillonite KSF	KSF
Polymeric Fe modified montmorillonite KSF	Fe-KSF
Polymeric Al modified montmorillonite KSF	Al-KSF
Polymeric Al/Fe modified montmorillonite KSF	Al/Fe-KSF
Organic polymer modified montmorillonite KSF	P7-KSF
Aluminium sulphate	AS
Polyaluminium chloride	PACl
Ferric sulphate	FS

Results and Discussion

The XRF analysis results demonstrated that the mass ratio of the polymeric species fixed onto the clays to the total modifiers used in the modification was about 15%, and thus, the effective polymeric species in the modified clays was approximate 0.3 mmol per gram of clay.

The quality characteristics of raw car-washing effluent is shown in Table 2. The variation of quality characteristics of car-washing wastewater was due to the variations of the type of vehicles, personal preference in washing a car (e.g., the selection of the detergents) and the climate (e.g., raining) in the experimental period (March – May 2003).

Table 2. Quality characteristics of raw car-washing effluent

Parameter	Range	Mean Value
pH	6.9 – 7.1	7.0
Alkalinity (mg L^{-1} as CaCO$_3$)	110 - 160	135
Turbidity (NTU)	81 – 160	120
Total suspended solids (mg L^{-1})	44 – 116	80
COD$_{Cr}$ (mg L^{-1})	49 – 121	85
Oil contents (mg L^{-1} as haxane extractant)	76 – 150	113

Turbidity and Suspended Solid Removal

Fig. 2 (a-c) shows the percentage removal of suspended solids (SS) with modified clays and metal/polymer coagulants. For the KSF based clays, more than 90% SS was removed with the organic polymer (P7) and mixing Al/Fe modified clay coagulants at a dose of 800 mg/l. The raw KSF clay also achieved good SS removal. For the K10 based clays, polymeric iron modified clay achieved the best performance, 90% SS can be removed at a dose of 800 mg/l. Polymeric Al/Fe modified K10 also achieved adequately good performance. Among metal and polymer (P7) based coagulants, PACl can remove 90% SS at a low dose, 2 mg/l as Al.

COD$_{cr}$ Removal

Fig. 3 (a-c) shows the percentage removal of COD with modified clay and metal/polymer coagulants. For the KSF based clays, 80% and 90% COD removal were achieved with the polymer modified clay coagulant at the dose of 600 and 800 mg/l, respectively. The raw KSF can achieve about 67% COD removal at a low dose (400mg/l), but was not able to achieve >80% when the dose was greater than 1000mg/l. polymeric Fe and Al/Fe modified KSF performed similar to the raw KSF. Polymer modified KSF didn't perform well as other clays did.

For the K10 based clays, both polymeric iron and mixing Al/Fe modified clays achieved the best performance, 50% COD can be removed at a dose of 800 mg/l. Other three K10 based coagulants didn't perform well as Fe-K10 and Al/Fe-K10 did. Among metal and polymer based coagulants, PACl was able to remove 60% COD at a dose of 8 mg/l as Al, but all other three coagulants could not achieve such a high removal.

Oil Contents Removal

Figure 4 (a-c) presents the percentage removal of oil from the car-washing effluent with modified clay and metal/polymer coagulants. For the KSF based clays, polymeric iron modified KSF was able to achieve 90% more oil removal at a very low dose (200 mg/l), and polymeric Al/Fe modified KSF can achieve the similar removal performance at a high dose (1200mg/l). However, all other three KSFs can't achieve such a removal even at highest dose studied (1200mg/l).

For the K10 based clays, both polymeric iron and aluminium modified K10 clays achieved the best performance, >90% oil can be removed at a low dose of 200 mg/l. Other three K10 based coagulants didn't perform well as Fe-K10 and Al-K10 did. Among metal and polymer based coagulants, PACl can remove 80% oil at a dose of 2 mg/l as Al, all other three coagulants can't achieve such a high removal.

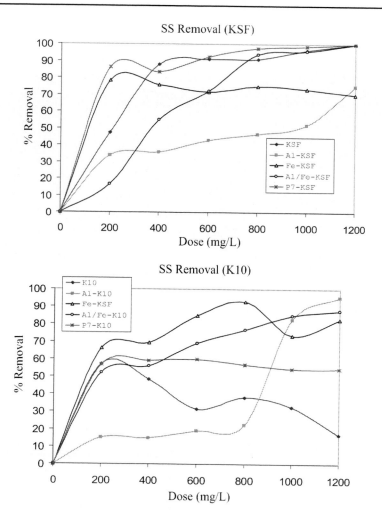

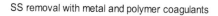

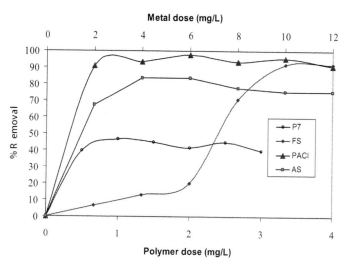

Figure 2. Suspended solids removal with (a) montmorillonite KSF based coagulants, (b) montmorillonite K10 based coagulants, and (c) metal and polymer coagulants

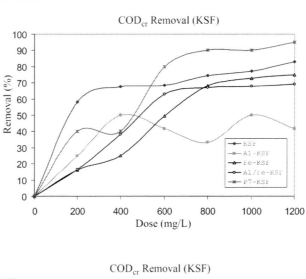

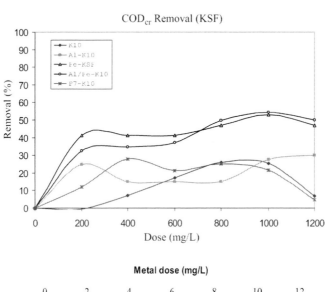

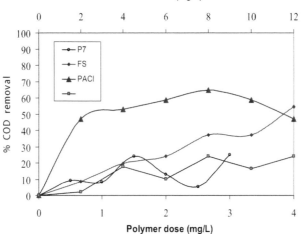

Figure 3. Chemical Oxygen Demand (COD) removal with (a) montmorillonite KSF based coagulants, (b) montmorillonite K10 based coagulants, and (c) metal and polymer coagulants.

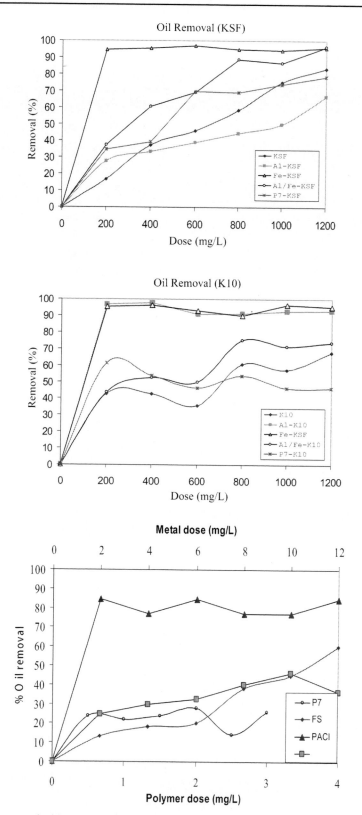

Figure 4. Oil removal with (a) montmorillonite KSF based coagulants, (b) montmorillonite K10 based coagulants, and (c) metal and polymer coagulants

Overall Discussion

This study demonstrated that polymeric iron modified KSF and polymeric iron or aluminium modified K10 possessed very high efficiency to remove the oil; 200 mg/l dose of which can remove more than 90% oil. Comparing to this, PACl can achieve the maximum 80% oil removal at a low dose of 2 mg/l as Al, but never could achieve > 90% oil removal. Since 200 mg/l modified clay is equivalent to 1.62 mg/l as Al or 3.36 mg/l as Fe, the modified clay coagulants can remove more oil than PACl at low doses.

Comparing the effectiveness in the removal of COD_{Cr}, polymer (P7) modified KSF coagulant performed better than all other coagulants, at a dose of 600 mg/l, P7-KSF can remove 80% COD. It is interesting to note that with P7 alone, it could only remove the maximum COD about 22%. The other good clay-based coagulants in terms of better COD removal were Al/Fe-KSF, raw KSF, Fe-K10, Al/Fe-K10 and PACl. For the clay based coagulants, a dose of 200 mg/l (equivalent to 1.62 mg/l as Al) can remove 40-50% COD whilst for PACl, a dose of 2 mg/l can achieve 50% COD. Therefore, lower dose required with clay based coagulants than the PACl in order to achieve the similar COD removal performance.

For the SS or turbidity removal, polymer (P7) or polymeric Fe or Al/Fe modified clays and PACl can remove more SS at low doses. It is interesting to note that the raw KSF clay can remove more SS and COD than the raw K10 clay and some other coagulants. This could be attributed to the KSF clay's acidity nature. The KSF is an acid-pretreated montmorillonite, and it will cause the pH drop down to 1-3 units when it was added into water (Figure 5). In contrast, all other modified KSF and K10 clays and metal coagulants can only cause pH go down 0.5-1 units. Lower pH might favour to the SS and COD removal, but is not the case for the oil removal. The advantage of using modified KSF and K10 coagulants is that the modified clays will not cause pH go down too low but still can achieve the best overall treatment performance.

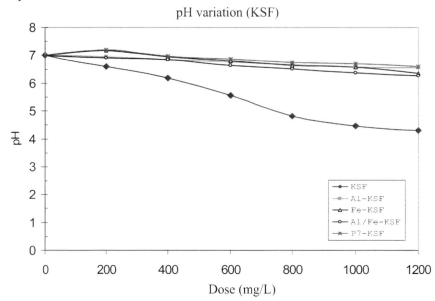

Figure 5. pH variation after sedimentation (montmorillonite KSF based coagulants)

As raw clays possess somewhat adsorption capacities, they could adsorb organic/inorganic molecules; this could be one of mechanisms of the clay modification. The adsorbed modifiers sometimes act as a stock for ion exchange of toxic ions in solution [50], or will be effective reinforcement for capturing ions or organic matters in water [e.g., 12]. In this study, the superior performance of modified clays in removing COD and oil suggests that there could be strong interactions between the pollutants and the modifiers, and the resulting "modifier-pollutant complexes" will be retained by the modified clays to enhance the coagulation performance. This assumption can be supported by a research where the modified clay behaved as a real coagulant [51].

Chemical coagulants are used widely internationally in the treatment of surface water for the supply of potable water and in sewage and industrial effluent treatment. They play an important role in the removal of particulate and dissolved pollutants. Such coagulants are predominantly inorganic salts of iron and aluminium. This study has demonstrated that a new, highly efficient and potential cost-effective, clay-based coagulant has been developed. Subsequently, this will make it to be competitive in the market of water treatment chemicals. However, in the use of modified-clay coagulant in the full-scale water and wastewater treatment, further work is need to assess its performance technically and economically by conducting various studies using different type of water and wastewaters.

Conclusions

Polymeric Fe-KSF, Fe- or Al-K10, and the PACl can achieve the highest oil removal efficiency. For a low dose of clay, 200 mg/l (equivalent to a metal dose of 0.06 mM as metal), the polymeric Fe-KSF and Fe- or Al-K10 can remove 95% oil but PACl can only achieve about 80% oil removal at a dose of 1.62 mg/l as Al (equivalent to a metal dose of 0.06 mM as Al). Polymer (P7) modified KSF coagulant can achieve the greatest removals of suspended solids and COD in comparison with the PACl and other clay-based coagulants. It can be concluded from this study that montmorillonites K10 and KSF can be modified by the mixing polymeric Al/Fe species or a cationic polymer with a procedure developed. The resulting modified clay coagulants possess the specific properties to react with particles, organic constitutes and oils, and can be used as coagulants for car-washing wastewater treatment. The treatment performance of modified clay coagulants was greater than that of conventional processes, i.e., sand screen with oil/water separation and coagulation/sedimentation. The modified clay coagulants are thus representing a new type of coagulants having high potentials in the treatment of various wastewaters.

Acknowledgements

The authors thank the UK Engineering Physics Science Research Council (EPSRC) for funding this international collaborative project.

References

[1]   Zhao, H. T., Vance, G. F. (1998) *Water Research*, 32 3710-3716.

[2]   Jiang, J. Q. (2001) *Separation and Purification Methods*, 30, 127-142.

[3]   Jiang, J. Q., Cooper, C. (2002) *Chemosphere*, 47 711-716.

[4]   Jiang, J. Q., Cooper, C. (2003) *Environ. Eng. Sci.*, 20, 581-587.

[5]   Cooper, C., Jiang, J. Q. (2002) *J. Chem. Technol. Biot.*, 77, 546-551.

[6]   Nemerow, N. L. Industrial Water Pollution: Origins, Chartacteristics, and Treatment, Addison-Wesley, *Reading*, 1978

[7]   Yu, Z. M., Sun, X. X., Song, X. X., Zhang, B. (1999). *Chinese Sci. Bull.*, 44, 617-620.

[8]   Brindley, G.W., Brown, G. Crystal structures of clay minerals and their X ray identification, London: *Mineral. Soc.* 1980, p 495.

[9]   van Olphen, H. *An introduction to clay colloid chemistry: for clay technologists, geologies.* 2nd edn., John Wiley and Sons, New York, 1977.

[10]   Sridhar, K., Naofumi, K., Rustum, R. (1998) *Journal of Materials Chemistry*, 8 (6), 1329-1331.

[11]   Shen, Y.-H. (2002), *Water Research*, 36, 1107-1114.

[12]   Pal, O. R., Vanjara, A. K. (2001) *Separation and Purification Technology*, 24, 167-172.

[13]   Casal, B., Merino, J., Serratosa, J. M., Ruiz-Hitzky, E. (2001) *Applied Clay Science*, 18, 245-254.

[14]   Adhikari, C., Proctor, A., Blyholder, G. D. (1997) *Journal of the American Oil Chemists Society*, 74, 1265-1268.

[15]   Nye, J. V., Guerin, W. F., Boyd, S. A. (1994) *Environmental Science and Technology*, 28, 944-951.

[16]   Specht, C. H., Kumke, M. U., Frimmel, F. H. (2000) *Water Research*, 34, 4063-4069.

[17]   Schulthess, C. P., Tokunaga, S. (1996) *Soil Science Society of America Journal*, 60, 92-98.

[18]   Geatti, A., Lenarda, M., Storaro, L., Ganzerla, R., Perissinotto, M. (1997) *Journal of Molecular Catalysis A-Chemical*, 121, 111-118.

[19]   Al-Degs, Y., Khraisheh, M. A. M., Tutunji, M. F. (2001) *Water Research*, 35, 3724-3728.

[20]   Skoutelas, A. P., Karakassides, M. A., Petridis, D. (1999) *Chemistry of Materials*, 11, 2754-2759.

[21]   Krysztafkiewicz, A., Werner, R., Lipska, L. K., Jesionowski, T. (2001) *Colloids and Surfaces A: Physicochemical and Engineering Aspects*, 182, 65–81.

[22]   Werner, R., Krysztafkiewicz A., Dec, A., Jesionowski, T. (2001) *Dyes And Pigments*, 50, 41-54.

[23]   Choi, M. H., Chung, I. J., Lee, J. D. (2000) *Chemistry of Materials*, 12, 2977-2983.

[24]   Sarbak, Z. (1994) *Materials Chemistry and Physics*, 39, 91-97.

[25]   Erim, F. B., Alemdar, I. (1998) *Fresenius Journal of Analytical Chemistry*, 361, 455-458.

[26]   Okutomo, S., Kuroda, K., Ogawa, M. (1999) *Applied Clay Science*, 15, 253-264.

[27]   Wibulswas, R., White, D. A., Rautiu, R. (1999) *Environmental Protection*, 77 (B2), 88-92.

[28] Krishna, B. S., Selvaraj, S., Mohan, B. V., Murty, D. S. R., Prakash, B. S. J. (1998) *Bulletin of Materials Science*, 21, 355-361.

[29] Bors, J., Dultz, S., Gorny, A. (1998) *Radiochimica Acta*, 82, 269-274.

[30] Oertel, U., Petzold, G., Buchhammer, H., Geyer, S., Schwarz, S., Muller, U., Ratzsch, M. (1991), *Colloids And Surfaces*, 57, 375-381.

[31] Tombacz, E., Szekeres, M., Baranyi, L., Micheli, E. (1998) *Colloids and Surfaces A-Physicochemical and Engineering Aspects*, 141, 379-384.

[32] Quiquampoix, H., Staunton, S., Baron, M. H. (1993) *Colloids and Surfaces A-Physicochemical and Engineering Aspects*, 75, 85-93.

[33] Li, X. C., Kang, T. Y., Cho, W. J., Lee, J. K., Ha, C. S. (2001) *Macromolecular Rapid Communications,* 22, 1306-1312.

[34] Ogawa, M., Kuroda, K. (1995) *Chemistry Review*, 95, 399.

[35] Michot, L. J., Pinnavaia, T. J. (1992) *Chemistry of Materials*, 4, 1433-1437.

[36] Breen, C., Watson, R. (1998) *Journal of Colloid and Interface Science*, 208, 422-429.

[37] Shimazu, S., Uematsu, T. (1993) *Journal of Synthetic Organic Chemistry* Japan, 51, 664-670.

[38] Yamazaki, T., Nakamura, Y., Ozawa, S. (2001) *Journal of Colloid and Interface Science*, 239, 440-446.

[39] Zhu, H. Y., Vansant, E. F., Lu, G. Q. (1999) *Journal of Colloid and Interface Science,* 210, 352-359.

[40] Zhu, H. Y., Lu, G. Q. (1998) *Journal of Porous Materials*, 5, 227-239.

[41] Bahranowski, K., Kielski, A., Serwicka, E. M., Wisla-Walsh, E., Wodnicka, K. (2000) *Microporous and Mesoporous Materials*, 41, 201-215.

[42] Heylen, I., Vansant, E. F. (1997) *Microporous Materials*, 10, 41-50.

[43] Bergaoui, L., Lambert, J. F., Franck, R., Suquet, H., Robert, J. L. (1995) *Journal of the Chemical Society-Faraday Transactions*, 91, 2229-2239.

[44] Montarges, E., Moreau, A., Michot, L. J. (1998) *Applied Clay Science*, 13, 165-185.

[45] Glinel, K., Laschewsky, A., Jonas, A. M. (2001) *Macromolecules*, 34, 5267-5274.

[46] Atwood, J. L., Davies, J. E. D., Macnicol, D. D., Vogtle, F. *Comprehensive Supramolecular Chemistry*, Pergamon, Oxford (1996).

[47] Gitipour, S., Bowers, M. T., Huff, W., Bodosi, A. (1997) *Spill Science and Technology Bulletin,* 4, 155-164.

[48] Ahmadi, M. F., Rusling, J. F. (1995) *Langmuir*, 11, 94.

[49] Korea Environmental Protection Agency, *Korean standard method for water and wastewater*, 2000.

[50] Sridhar, K., Naofumi, K., Rustum, R. (1998) *Journal of Materials Chemistry*, 8, 1329-1331.

[51] Nye, J. V., Guerin, W. F., Boyd, S. A. (1994) *Environ. Sci. and Technol.*, 28 944-951.

In: Trends in Water Pollution Research
Editor: J. V. Livingston, pp. 95-116

ISBN 1-59454-328-3
©2005 Nova Science Publishers, Inc.

Chapter IV

Removal of Ofloxacin and Propranolol from Water by Means of Ozonation and H₂O₂/UV System

Marisa Canterino, Marcella de Champdoré, Roberto Andreozzi[1] and Raffaele Marotta

Univ di Napoli "Federico II", Fac. di Ingegneria, Dip di Ingegneria Chimica
p.le V. Tecchio, 80 – 80125 – Napoli - Italia

Abstract

Relevant amounts of pharmaceuticals are daily released to the environment as the result of their massive use in human and veterinary medicines and of a poor removal in Sewage Treatment Plant (STP).

Ozonation and H₂O₂/UV photolysis are two of the most investigated AOP techniques which can be proposed to up-grade existing STPs to allow the removal of pharmaceuticals.

In this work, the reaction kinetics for the ozonation and H₂O₂/UV photolysis of two selected pharmaceuticals, propranolol (beta-blocker) and ofloxacin (antibiotic), are investigated.

For each single pharmaceutical, simplified mathematical models are developed and used to simulate the system behaviour for different pH values and -for H₂O₂/UV system- at varying initial concentrations of hydrogen peroxide. The ozonation and UV/H₂O₂ kinetics are validated in experimental runs with starting concentrations of two pharmaceuticals as low as 10 micrograms per liter.

Assessed reaction kinetics are used to predict the behaviour of propranolol and ofloxacin when they were submitted in the same mixture to ozonation and H₂O₂/UV oxidations, in bidistilled water or in synthetic STP effluents in presence of carbamazepine and clofibric acid.

[1] tel.+39-081-7682251; fax + 39-081-5936936; email: roberto.andreozzi@unina.it

Introduction

In recent years many works appeared in the specialized journals dealing with the presence of pharmaceutical compounds in Sewage Treatment Plant (STP) effluents [1, 2], surface and drinking waters [3-5]. Antibiotics, antiflammatory and antiarithmic drugs, blood lipid regulators, etc. have been widely found at concentrations ranging from nanograms to micrograms per liter depending on the type of analyzed water. These results are not surprising if one considers that hundreds of tons of pharmaceuticals are annually used in each European countries in clinical practise and animal breeding with many of these species being released – after the intake – unmodified to the sewer. Moreover many pharmaceutical compounds are characterized by a certain refractoriness to undergo biological degradation process within STP [6, 7] and are capable to persist for long times in the aquatic environment [8].

Although during last years many efforts have been devoted to this topic, up to now no clear proofs have been collected that these species-at low concentrations at which they are found in the environment- may have any adverse health effects on men and animals.

However mainly in the case of drinking waters the adoption of the precautionary principle imposes that these compounds have to be removed from supplied waters.

A more severe application of the above mentioned principle would also impose to completely prevent the discharge of these compounds into the environment due to their xenobiotic nature. But since this result appears to be hardly achievable for practical and economical reasons, other approaches have to be searched to minimize the risk of long term effects on living organisms which cannot be predicted on the basis of the present knowledge. An acceptable solution could be represented by the adoption of any actions to decrease the amounts of pharmaceuticals daily released to the environment.

A significant reduction of their inflow into the environment could be indeed obtained if already existing STPs would be up-graded by including a tertiary treatment section based on advanced oxidation processes (AOP). Previous investigations by some of the Authors [9,10] and by others [11, 12] demonstrated that two of most developed AOP techniques, namely ozonation and H_2O_2/UV photolysis, are suitable processes for pharmaceutical removal from waters.

In the present work the investigations are extended to assess the oxidation kinetics for propranolol (a β-blocker), and ofloxacin (an antibiotic) (two compounds found in STP effluents [13, 8]) by ozonation and H_2O_2/UV photolysis.

The oxidation of these two molecules is also studied in the presence of both carbamazepine and clofibric acid in bidistilled water and synthetic effluents.

Experimental

Chemicals: Hydrogen peroxide (30 % w/w, not stabilized). Adipic acid [124-04-9], Benzophenone [119-61-9], Caffeine [58-08-2], Carbamazepine [298-46-4] (fig.1), Clofibric acid [832-09-7] (fig.1), Octanoic acid [124-07-2], Ofloxacin [82419-36-1] (fig.1), Poly(ethylene glycol) 600 [25322-68-3], Propranolol [3506-09-0] (fig.1) and Vanillin [121-33-5].

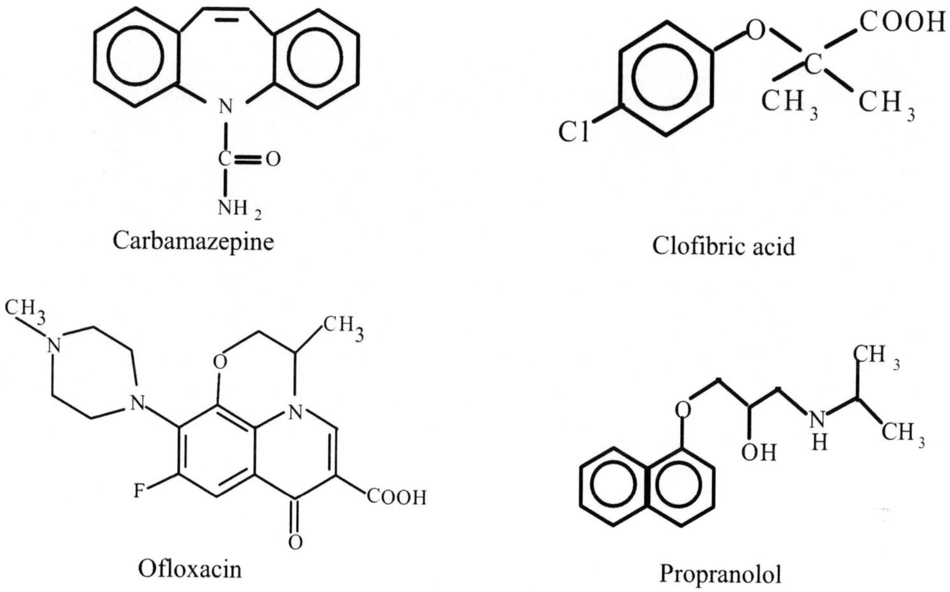

Fig. 1 – Molecular structures of the investigated pharmaceuticals

The ozonation runs of the aqueous solutions containing ofloxacin and propranolol at high concentrations ($1.0 \cdot 10^{-3} \div 2.5 \cdot 10^{-3}$ mol dm^{-3}) were carried out in a semicontinuous stirred tank Pyrex glass reactor (1.090 dm^3), thermostated at 298 K. The apparatus used for the investigations has been previously described [14]. An ozonised oxygen stream of 2 % by volume generated by an ozone-generator was fed at a flow rate of 36 dm^3 h^{-1} to the reactor containing the aqueous solution. The solutions were buffered at desidered pH with H$_3$PO$_4$, KH$_2$PO$_4$ and Na$_2$HPO$_4$. The ionic strength was adjusted at I = 0.1 mol dm^{-3} by adding to the solution a proper amount of NaCl salt. The ozone concentration in the outlet gaseous stream was monitored by continuous UV measurements at 253 nm by means of an UV spectrophotometer equipped with a quartz cell (optical length = $2.0 \cdot 10^{-2}$ dm).

Batch experiments were carried out for the ozonation of ofloxacin, propranolol, carmabazepine and clofibric acid at low concentrations (10 μg dm^{-3}). To the aqueous solutions (0.8 dm^3), buffered at pH = 5.5 and previously saturated with ozone by bubbling an ozonized gaseous stream ($[O_3]_{inlet}$ = $1.0 \cdot 10^{-5}$ mol dm^{-3}), a mixture of four selected pharmaceuticals was rapidly added. The reaction was quenched at the desired time by sparging the aqueous solution with a nitrogen stream. After the quenching the solution was recovered and concentrated to a final volume of 2.0 cm^3 for the HPLC analysis.

The UV/H$_2$O$_2$ experiments were carried out at 298 K in an annular glass reactor equipped with a low-pressure lamp with a monochromatic wavelength emission at 254 nm [15]. The radiation power ($2.51 \cdot 10^{-6}$ E s^{-1}) was measured by means of H$_2$O$_2$ actinometric measurements [16].

The aqueous solutions were regulated at desidered pH value with dilute HClO$_4$ and NaOH mixtures. Samples were taken at fixed reaction times and analysed. For photolytic experiments (at pH = 5.5) at low concentrations of selected pharmaceuticals (10 µg dm^{-3}) the oxidation runs were stopped by switching off the lamp and the solutions were recovered and concentrated by evaporation for the analyses as for the ozonation experiments.

The pharmaceuticals were analysed by HPLC (HP 1100 L, Hewlett Packard) equipped with a diode array detector and a Synergi C$_{12}$ 4u MAX-RP column. Two mobile phase solvents were used. Solvent A: 4 ml H$_3$PO$_4$ 85%, 50 ml methanol in 1 dm^3 HPLC water, Solvent B: CH$_3$CN.

Elution program was as follows: 0-2 min isocratic condition 75% solvent A and 25% solvent B; 2-3 min, linear gradient from 75% solvent A to 40% solvent A and from 25% solvent B to 60% solvent B; 3-4 min isocratic condition: 40% solvent A and 60% solvent B; 4-5 min linear gradient from 40% solvent A to 85% solvent A and from 60% solvent B to 15% solvent B. The flow rate was 1.0 mL min^{-1}, and the detection wavelengths were set at 200, 210, 220 and 300 nm respectively for clofibric acid, carbamazepine, propranolol and ofloxacin.

The pH of aqueous solutions was measured by using a pH-meter with a glass pH electrode. The total organic carbon was monitored by means of TOC analyzer (Shimadzu 5000 A).

The molar extinction coefficients of carbamazepine at 254 nm (6025 M^{-1} cm^{-1}), clofibric acid (380 M^{-1} cm^{-1}), ofloxacin (10970 M^{-1} cm^{-1}) and propranolol (1368 M^{-1} cm^{-1}) were determined at pH = 5.5 by means of a UV-VIS spectrophotometer.

The synthetic effluent was constituted by an aqueous mixture of adipic acid (1.70 µg dm^{-3}), benzophenone (0.64 µg dm^{-3}), caffeine (9.60 µg dm^{-3}), octanoic acid (4.92 µg dm^{-3}), poly(ethylene glycol) (274 µg dm^{-3}) and vanillin (1.92 µg dm^{-3}). The concentrations of these species are average values among those at which they are found in real STP effluents [25].

Results and Discussion

Ozonation

In fig. 2 the decays of the concentrations recorded in two experiments in which propranolol and ofloxacin were separately ozonized are shown. These results indicate that for adopted reaction conditions both the species are easily oxidized by ozone.

To assess the reaction kinetics proper experiments were planned and carried out. In fact, it is well known that in a gas-liquid reactor the oxidation process develops according to different regimes of absorption with reaction: kinetic, quasi-diffusive and diffusive regime.

Only for the first two regimes not-negligible sensitivities of the reaction rate with respect to kinetic parameters are found thus allowing their estimation. Therefore the operating conditions for kinetic runs were chosen in order to ensure the oxidation processes to proceed under these regimes.

The result of previous investigations for the oxidation of organic species in the same reactor indicated that these conditions were achieved at lower concentrations of the substrate with respect to those used in the runs of fig. 2.

Aqueous solutions of ofloxacin and propranolol at starting concentrations in the range of 1.5 ÷ 2.5 mM were thus used for these sets of experiments.

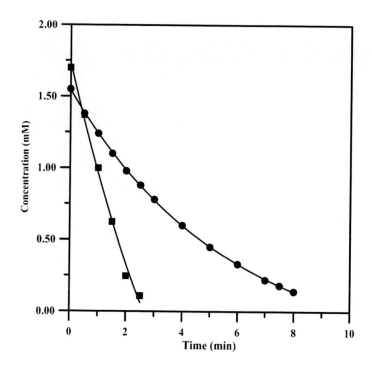

Fig. 2 – (●) ofloxacin and (■) propranolol decays during the ozonation at pH = 4.0

The kinetic analysis of the data collected during the ozonation runs was performed by means of some simplified models already used for clofibric acid [9] and carbamazepine [10], in which a fluidynamic submodel was coupled with an overall ozonation reaction:

$$\text{Pharmaceutical} \ + \ zO_3 \ \xrightarrow{\ k_{O3}\ } \ \text{products} \qquad (r_1)$$

For both the reacting species during the present investigation the most suitable regime of absorption with reaction was identified as the "quasi diffusive" one [17]. In this case, the complete mathematical model includes the differential mass balance equations for ozone in the bubbles ($[O_3]_B$) and freeboard ($[O_3]_F$) phases, each one considered as a well-mixed stirred reactor:

$$\frac{d[O_3]_B}{dt} = \frac{Q}{V_B} \cdot \left([O_3]_{in} - [O_3]_B\right) - \frac{k_L^o a \cdot E \cdot [O_3]_B \cdot \alpha}{V_B} V_L \qquad (1)$$

$$\frac{d[O_3]_F}{dt} = \frac{Q}{V_F} \cdot \left([O_3]_B - [O_3]_F\right) \qquad (2)$$

where the Enhancement factor (E) was calculated through the following formula:

$$E = \sqrt{1 + \frac{D_{O_3} \cdot k_{O_3} \cdot [S] \cdot z_{O_3}}{\left(k_L^o\right)^2}}$$

and the pharmaceutical rate consumption is given by:

$$\frac{d[S]}{dt} = -k_L^o a \cdot E \cdot [O_3]_B \cdot \alpha \tag{3}$$

In the table 1 the kinetic constants obtained for the ozonation of propranolol by using the above reported model and a proper optimization procedure [31] are shown along with the overall stoichiometric coefficients (z_{O3}) and percentage standard deviations (σ) on the components (ozone and propranolol) at varying the pH of the solution.

It is evident from the table that calculated σ values, are lower than 10%, that is of the same order of magnitude of those associated to the analytical determination of ozone in the freeboard and propranolol in the solution. Therefore it can be concluded that the employed model satisfactorily predicts the behaviour of the studied system.

In the case of the ozonation of ofloxacin (table 2), for pH < 6.0 the best results have been obtained by considering that the stoichiometric coefficient is a linear function of the reaction time (i.e. z_{O3} = a + b·t) with a = 1.0. For pH ≥ 6.0 poor results were obtained for a = 1.0 with very high values of σ_S (data not shown) whereas better results were found for a = 2.0 although σ_{O3} values still are a little higher than those calculated for pH < 6.0.

The data in the tables 1 and 2 indicate that the reactivity of propranolol is not influenced by the pH of the solution whereas that of ofloxacin increases by more than one order of magnitude when the pH changes from 3.0 to 7.0. This behaviour can be easily ascribed to the different capability of reacting with ozone of undissociated and dissociated ofloxacin forms:

pKa$_1$ = ~ 6.0,
pKa$_2$ = ~ 8.0 [18, 19]

the second being more reactive than the former. In the case of propranolol a negligible dissociation occurs in the investigated pH range (pKa = 9.50) [20].

In Fig. 3 the kinetic constants for propranolol and ofloxacin are compared with those already found for clofibric acid [9] and carbamazepine [10].

Table 1 Kinetic parameters for ozonation of propranolol calculated for different pH values by assuming a "quasi diffusive" regime.

pH	$[S]_o$ (mM)	k_{O3} ($M^{-1} s^{-1}$)	z_{O3}	σ_S (%)	σ_{O3} (%)
3.0	1.50	$6.72 \cdot 10^4$ $\pm$ $1.04 \cdot 10^4$	0.94 $\pm$ $1.62 \cdot 10^{-2}$	5.7	8.8
3.5	1.85	$6.95 \cdot 10^4$ $\pm$ $1.44 \cdot 10^4$	0.86 $\pm$ $2.12 \cdot 10^{-2}$	6.3	6.8
4.0	1.70	$8.56 \cdot 10^4$ $\pm$ $1.55 \cdot 10^4$	0.85 $\pm$ $1.87 \cdot 10^{-2}$	4.5	7.5
4.5	2.30	$5.85 \cdot 10^4$ $\pm$ $1.27 \cdot 10^4$	0.83 $\pm$ $2.07 \cdot 10^{-2}$	5.9	8.5
6.0	1.80	$8.93 \cdot 10^4$ $\pm$ $1.37 \cdot 10^4$	0.95 $\pm$ $1.77 \cdot 10^{-2}$	5.5	7.1

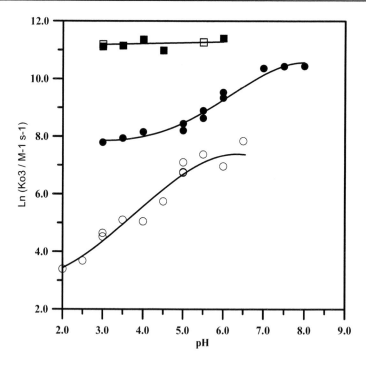

Fig. 3 - Rate kinetic constants of carbamazepine (□), clofibric acid (○), ofloxacin (●), propranolol (■) at different pH.

From the diagrams of the figure 3 the following order of reactivity is observed, for example at pH 5.0: carbamazepine ≈ propranolol >> ofloxacin >> clofibric acid. A qualitative explanation of the observed order of reactivity can partially found as follows. The double bond at 9-10 positions in carbamazepine has a non-aromatic character which makes it as reactive as an exhocyclic double bond such as, for example, that in styrene ($k_{O3} = 3.0 \cdot 10^5$ M^{-1} s^{-1} [21]) and stilbene molecules ($k_{O3} = 1.8 \cdot 10^4 \div 4.8 \cdot 10^4$ M^{-1} s^{-1}[22]). Although propranolol is an aromatic molecule it shows a reactivity towards ozone similar to that of carbamazepine as result of the presence of an activating –OR substituent. The possibility of an attack of ozone on the nitrogen atom can be easily ruled out in the adopted experimental conditions being the amino group in the protonated form. Similar arguments can be used for ofloxacin in which the ozone attack is mainly directed on the aromatic structure for pH values < 6.0. In fact, according also to the data reported by Hetzer *et al.* [32] for piperazine, in the case of ofloxacin it can be expected that nitrogen atom bond to the quinolonic ring has a negligible nucleofilic character, whereas the second, for pH < 6.0, is in a protonated form. When pH increases above 6.0 the latter deprotonates thus becoming itself a reactive center of attack of ozone in competition with the quinolonic ring.

Table 2 – Kinetic parameters for ozonation of ofloxacin calculated for different pH values by assuming a "quasi diffusive" regime.

pH	$[S]_o$ (mM)	k_{O3} $(M^{-1} s^{-1})$	$z_{O3} = a + b \cdot t$	σ_S (%)	σ_{O3} (%)
3.0	1.5	$2.42 \cdot 10^3 \pm 2.33 \cdot 10^2$	$a = 1, b = 0.365 \pm 1.71 \cdot 10^{-2}$	5.2	8.5
3.5	1.5	$2.80 \cdot 10^3 \pm 2.14 \cdot 10^2$	$a = 1, b = 0.435 \pm 1.57 \cdot 10^{-2}$	4.0	7.3
4.0	1.5	$3.47 \cdot 10^3 \pm 2.02 \cdot 10^2$	$a = 1, b = 0.521 \pm 1.32 \cdot 10^{-2}$	5.7	4.0
5.0	1.5	$3.65 \cdot 10^3 \pm 1.98 \cdot 10^2$	$a = 1, b = 0.512 \pm 1.14 \cdot 10^{-2}$	3.2	6.5
5.5	1.5	$5.60 \cdot 10^3 \pm 3.24 \cdot 10^2$	$a = 1, b = 0.625 \pm 1.33 \cdot 10^{-2}$	5.0	5.5
6.0	1.5	$1.13 \cdot 10^4 \pm 1.30 \cdot 10^3$	$a = 1, b = 0.879 \pm 3.16 \cdot 10^{-2}$	7.8	3.5
6.0	1.5	$1.37 \cdot 10^4 \pm 1.49 \cdot 10^3$	$a = 2, b = 0.367 \pm 2.00 \cdot 10^{-2}$	6.1	11.9
7.0	1.5	$3.17 \cdot 10^4 \pm 2.72 \cdot 10^3$	$a = 2, b = 0.349 \pm 1.21 \cdot 10^{-2}$	3.5	13.4
7.5	1.5	$3.38 \cdot 10^4 \pm 2.83 \cdot 10^3$	$a = 2, b = 0.333 \pm 1.12 \cdot 10^{-2}$	4.1	10.9
8.0	1.5	$3.42 \cdot 10^4 \pm 3.51 \cdot 10^3$	$a = 2, b = 0.344 \pm 1.38 \cdot 10^{-2}$	4.0	17.1

Therefore it can be supposed that higher percentage standard deviations for ozone in table 2 for pH $\geq$ 6.0 are due to some inadequancies of the simplified model, based on a single overall reaction (r_1) to account for the substrate removal in these conditions.

The simultaneously presence of more than two substituents with opposite effects on quinolonic ring and the possibility of activation, depending on the pH, of a second center of reaction hinder any direct comparison with the reactivity of other investigated compounds.

On the other hand it is clear that the chlorine substituent in clofibric acid molecule highly deactivates the aromatic ring with respect to the ozone attack, this species showing the lowest reactivity among studied pharmaceuticals.

UV/H$_2$O$_2$ System

A simplified kinetic model has been adopted to describe the oxidation of ofloxacin and propranolol in aqueous solutions irradiated with a lamp emitting at 254 nm and in the presence of hydrogen peroxide. The model considers the generation of HO radicals by the photolysis of hydrogen peroxide:

$$H_2O_2 \xrightarrow{\quad h\nu \quad} 2\ HO\cdot \qquad\qquad (r_2)$$

The HO radicals attack the substrate species (r_3), hydrogen peroxide itself (r_4) and all the intermediates and reaction products present in the solution (r_5):

$$HO\cdot \quad\begin{cases} S \xrightarrow{k_s} S\cdot & (r_3) \\ H_2O_2 \xrightarrow{k_h} H_2O + HO_2\cdot & (r_4) \\ S_i \xrightarrow{k_{p_i}} \text{products} & (r_5) \end{cases}$$

The hydroperoxyl radicals undergo a radical termination reaction to generate hydrogen peroxide:

$$2\ HO_2\cdot \xrightarrow{\quad k_t \quad} H_2O_2 + O_2 \qquad\qquad (r_6)$$

Therefore, by assuming that the presence in the aqueous solution of by-products can be neglected, the pharmaceutical and hydrogen peroxide degradation rates can be written as:

$$\frac{d[S]}{dt} = -k_s \cdot [HO^\cdot] \cdot [S] \tag{4}$$

$$\frac{d[H_2O_2]}{dt} = -\frac{\phi_{H_2O_2}}{V_{sol}} \cdot I_o \cdot \left[1 - \exp\left(2.3 \cdot l \cdot \left(\varepsilon_s \cdot [S] + \varepsilon_{H_2O_2} \cdot [H_2O_2]\right)\right)\right] \cdot f_{H_2O_2} +$$
$$- k_h \cdot [HO^\cdot] \cdot [H_2O_2] + k_t \cdot [HO_2^\cdot]^2 \tag{5}$$

The mass balances on HO and HO$_2$ radical species are:

$$\frac{d[HO^\cdot]}{dt} = 2\phi_{H_2O_2} \cdot \frac{W_{abs}}{V_{sol}} - k_h \cdot [HO^\cdot] \cdot [H_2O_2] - k_s \cdot [HO^\cdot] \cdot [S] \tag{6}$$

$$\frac{d[HO_2^\cdot]}{dt} = k_h \cdot [HO^\cdot] \cdot [H_2O_2] - 2k_t \cdot [HO_2^\cdot]^2 \tag{7}$$

with:

$$W_{abs} = I_o \cdot \left[1 - \exp\left(-2.3 \cdot l \cdot \left(\varepsilon_s \cdot [S] + \varepsilon_{H_2O_2} \cdot [H_2O_2]\right)\right)\right] \cdot f_{H_2O_2} \tag{8}$$

where

$$f_{H_2O_2} = \frac{\varepsilon_{H_2O_2} \cdot [H_2O_2]}{\varepsilon_S \cdot [S] + \varepsilon_{H_2O_2} \cdot [H_2O_2]}$$

By assuming the "steady-state" hypothesis for radical species [23], the stationary HO$\cdot$ and HO$_2^\cdot$ concentrations can be expressed as:

$$[HO]_{SS} = \frac{2\phi_{H_2O_2}}{V_{sol}} \cdot \frac{I_o \cdot [1 - \exp(-2.3 \cdot l \cdot (\varepsilon_{H_2O_2} \cdot [H_2O_2] + \varepsilon_s \cdot [S]))]}{k_h \cdot [H_2O_2] + k_s \cdot [S]} \cdot f_{H_2O_2} \tag{9}$$

$$[HO_2]_{SS}^2 = \frac{k_h}{k_t} \cdot \frac{\phi_{H_2O_2}}{V_{sol}} \cdot \frac{I_o \cdot [1 - \exp(-2.3 \cdot l \cdot (\varepsilon_{H_2O_2} \cdot [H_2O_2] + \varepsilon_s \cdot [S]))] \cdot [H_2O_2]}{k_h \cdot [H_2O_2] + k_s \cdot [S]} \cdot f_{H_2O_2} \tag{10}$$

and substituting in equations 4 and 5 gives:

$$\frac{d[S]}{dt} = -k_s \cdot \frac{2\phi_{H_2O_2}}{V_{sol}} \cdot \frac{I_o \cdot [1 - \exp(-2.3 \cdot l \cdot (\varepsilon_{H_2O_2} \cdot [H_2O_2] + \varepsilon_S \cdot [S]))] \cdot [S]}{k_h \cdot [H_2O_2] + k_s \cdot [S]} \cdot f_{H_2} \quad (11)$$

$$\frac{d[H_2O_2]}{dt} = -\frac{\phi_{H_2O_2}}{V_{sol}} \cdot I_o \cdot [1 - \exp(-2.3 \, l \, (\varepsilon_{H_2O_2} \cdot [H_2O_2] + \varepsilon_S \cdot [S]))] \cdot f_{H_2O_2} +$$

$$(12)$$

$$- k_h \cdot \frac{\phi_{H_2O_2}}{V_{sol}} \cdot \frac{I_o \cdot [1 - \exp(-2.3 \cdot l \cdot (\varepsilon_{H_2O_2} \cdot [H_2O_2] + \varepsilon_S \cdot [S]))] \cdot [H_2O_2]}{k_h \cdot [H_2O_2] + k_s \cdot [S]} \cdot f_{H_2O_2}$$

The kinetic constants for HO radical attack to ofloxacin and propranolol are thus calculated and reported in table 3 (absolute method).

Experimental runs at different pH values of the solutions allowed to conclude that this parameter does not influence the kinetics of HO radical attack to the substrate. Also for these two investigated species very similar values of kinetic constants were estimated as expected when aromatic molecules are submitted to H_2O_2/UV oxidation being HO$^\bullet$ addition to the ring the first and common reaction step.

The kinetic constants values for HO radical attack on both pharmaceuticals obtained by means of the previous described kinetic model have been compared with those evaluated by using a competitive kinetic method which takes carbamazepine as a reference compound.

Table 3 - Kinetic parameters for UV/H_2O_2 oxidation of ofloxacin and propranolol at pH 5.5.

k_s $(M^{-1} s^{-1})$	Ofloxacin	Propranolol
Absolute method	$2.48 \cdot 10^9$ $\pm$ $0.21 \cdot 10^9$	$2.85 \cdot 10^9$ $\pm$ $0.11 \cdot 10^9$
Competitive method	$2.14 \cdot 10^9$ $\pm$ $0.12 \cdot 10^9$	$2.56 \cdot 10^9$ $\pm$ $0.16 \cdot 10^9$

The competition kinetic experiments were carried out by submitting to UV/H_2O_2 process a solution containing the investigated pharmaceutical (S) and the reference substance (R). Under the same experimental conditions (pH 5.5, $[H_2O_2]_o$ = 20 mM) the rate expressions of disappearance for the species (S) and the carbamazepine (R) can be written as:

$$\frac{d[S]}{dt} = -k_s \cdot [HO] \cdot [S] \tag{13}$$

$$\frac{d[R]}{dt} = -k_r \cdot [HO] \cdot [R] \tag{14}$$

By dividing equation (13) by equation (14), and integrating between t = 0 and t, the following formula is obtained:

$$\ln \frac{[S]_o}{[S]_t} = \frac{k_s}{k_r} \cdot \ln \frac{[R]_o}{[R]_t} \tag{15}$$

Thus a straight line is expected by plotting $\ln [S]_o/[S]_t$ against $\ln[R]_o/[R]_t$ the slope being the ratio of kinetic rate constants k_s/k_r. As k_r is known ($2.56 \cdot 10^9$ M^{-1} s^{-1}, [24]), k_s can be determined for each compound (table 3).

The good agreement between the values found for the same species by two different methods indicate that the hypotheses put forward to develop the model (no influence of by-products on the oxidation kinetics and steady-state conditions for radical species) hold for adopted experimental conditions.

Kinetic Model Validation at Low Concentration

A validation of the reaction kinetics was attempted at the concentrations similar to those found in real effluents. To this purpose a suitable work-up procedure was used to render pharmaceutical concentrations in aqueous samples higher than the threshold limits of the adopted analytical technique. Therefore a set of kinetic experiments at low starting concentrations (10 µg dm^{-3}) was performed for ofloxacin and propranolol. As reported in the experimental section, the ozonation runs were carried out in the batch mode by firstly saturating a volume of water with ozone and rapidly injecting a proper amount of the single pharmaceutical in it. For both investigated species, experimental data were compared with those predicted by means of the following simplified model:

$$\frac{d}{dt}[S] = -k_{O3} \cdot [S] \cdot [O_3]_L \tag{16}$$

$$\frac{d}{dt}[O_3]_L = -z_{O3} \cdot k_{O3} \cdot [S] \cdot [O_3]_L \tag{17}$$

with $[S] = [S]_o$ and $[O_3]_L = 1.0 \cdot 10^{-5}$ M for t = 0.

For H_2O_2/UV system the model used was the same as that previously reported. In both the cases the values of the kinetic constants used in the prediction were those found in the experiments at higher starting concentrations.

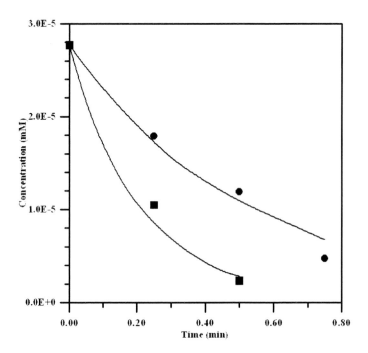

Fig. 4 - Comparison between experimental (solid lines) and predicted values (symbols) for UV/H_2O_2 (●) with $[H_2O_2]_o$ = 10 mM and batch ozonation (■) with $[O_3]_o$ = 0.01 mM of ofloxacin in bidistilled water. pH = 5.5.

In Fig 4 the results obtained with ofloxacin are shown. A good agreement is observed between experimental and calculated data. Similar results were obtained when aqueous solutions containing low concentrations of propranolol are submitted to ozonation or UV/H_2O_2 treatment (data not shown).

Once the reaction kinetics were validated for each single compounds a mixture of four drugs (carbamazepine, clofibric acid, ofloxacin and propranolol) was prepared by dissolving each species at starting concentrations of 10 micrograms per liter in bidistilled water. A part of this solution was submitted to ozonation and the remaining to H_2O_2/UV treatment.

For ozonation experiments the data were compared with those predicted by means of modified equations16 and 17:

$$\frac{d}{dt}[CAR] = -k_{O_3/CAR} \cdot [CAR] \cdot [O_3]_L \tag{18}$$

$$\frac{d}{dt}[PROP] = -k_{O_3/PROP} \cdot [PROP] \cdot [O_3]_L \tag{19}$$

$$\frac{d}{dt}[CA] = -k_{O3/CA} \cdot [CA] \cdot [O_3]_L \qquad (20)$$

$$\frac{d}{dt}[OFL] = -k_{O3/OFL} \cdot [OFL] \cdot [O_3]_L \qquad (21)$$

$$\frac{d}{dt}[O_3]_L = -\left(\begin{array}{c} z_{O3/CAR} \cdot k_{O3/CAR} \cdot [CAR] + z_{O3/CA} \cdot k_{O3/CA} \cdot [CA] + \\ z_{O3/OFL} \cdot k_{O3/OFL} \cdot [OFL] + z_{O3/PROP} \cdot k_{O3/PROP} \cdot [PROP] \end{array} \right) \cdot [O_3]_L \qquad (22)$$

The initial experimental conditions are $[CAR] = [CAR]_o$, $[PROP] = [PROP]_o$, $[OFL] = [OFL]_o$, $[CA] = [CA]_o$ and $[O_3]_L = 1.0 \cdot 10^{-5}$ M.

For UV/H$_2$O$_2$ system the mass balances equations for each single pharmaceutical and hydrogen peroxide were respectively re-written as:

$$\frac{d[CA]}{dt} = -\frac{\phi_{CA}}{V_{sol}} \cdot I_o \cdot \left[1 - exp\left(2.3 \cdot l \cdot \left(\begin{array}{c} \varepsilon_{CA} \cdot [CA] + \varepsilon_{PROP} \cdot [PROP] + \\ + \varepsilon_{CAR} \cdot [CAR] + \varepsilon_{OFL} \cdot [OFL] + \\ + \varepsilon_{H_2O_2} \cdot [H_2O_2] \end{array} \right) \right) \right] \cdot f_{CA} - k_{CA} \cdot [HO^\cdot]_{ss} \cdot [CA] \qquad (23)$$

$$\frac{d[PROP]}{dt} = -k_{PROP} \cdot [HO^\cdot]_{ss} \cdot [PROP] \qquad (24)$$

$$\frac{d[CAR]}{dt} = -k_{CAR} \cdot [HO^\cdot]_{ss} \cdot [CAR] \qquad (25)$$

$$\frac{d[OFL]}{dt} = -k_{OFL} \cdot [HO^\cdot]_{ss} \cdot [OFL] \qquad (26)$$

$$\frac{d[H_2O_2]}{dt} = -\frac{\phi_{H_2O_2}}{V_{sol}} \cdot I_o \cdot \left[1 - exp\left(2.3 \cdot l \cdot \left(\begin{array}{c} \varepsilon_{CA} \cdot [CA] + \varepsilon_{PROP} \cdot [PROP] + \\ + \varepsilon_{CAR} \cdot [CAR] + \varepsilon_{OFL} \cdot [OFL] + \\ + \varepsilon_{H_2O_2} \cdot [H_2O_2] \end{array} \right) \right) \right] \cdot f_{H_2O_2} + \qquad (27)$$
$$- k_h \cdot [HO^\cdot]_{ss} \cdot [H_2O_2] + k_t \cdot [HO_2^\cdot]_{ss}^2$$

where:

$$f_{H_2O_2} = \frac{\varepsilon_{H2O2} \cdot [H_2O_2]}{\varepsilon_{CA} \cdot [CA] + \varepsilon_{PROP} \cdot [PROP] + \varepsilon_{CAR} \cdot [CAR] + \varepsilon_{OFL} \cdot [OFL] + \varepsilon_{H2O2} \cdot [H_2O_2]} \qquad (28)$$

$$f_{CA} = \frac{\varepsilon_{CA} \cdot [CA]}{\varepsilon_{CA} \cdot [CA] + \varepsilon_{PROP} \cdot [PROP] + \varepsilon_{CAR} \cdot [CAR] + \varepsilon_{OFL} \cdot [OFL] + \varepsilon_{H2O2} \cdot [H_2O_2]} \qquad (29)$$

$$[HO]_{SS} = \frac{2\phi_{H_2O_2}}{V_{sol}} \cdot$$
$$\cdot \frac{I_o \cdot [1 - exp(-2.3 \cdot l \cdot (\varepsilon_{H_2O_2} \cdot [H_2O_2] + \varepsilon_{CA} \cdot [CA] + \varepsilon_{PROP} \cdot [PROP] + + \varepsilon_{CAR} \cdot [CAR] + \varepsilon_{OFL} \cdot [OFL]))]}{k_h \cdot [H_2O_2] + k_{CAR} \cdot [CAR] + k_{PROP} \cdot [PROP] + k_{CA} \cdot [CA] + k_{OFL} \cdot [OFL]} \cdot f_{H_2O_2}$$

$$(30)$$

$$[HO_2]_{SS}^2 = \frac{k_h}{k_t} \frac{\phi_{H_2O_2}}{V_{sol}} \cdot$$
$$\cdot \frac{I_o \cdot [1 - exp(-2.3 \cdot l \cdot (\varepsilon_{H_2O_2} \cdot [H_2O_2] + \varepsilon_{CA} \cdot [CA] + \varepsilon_{PROP} \cdot [PROP] + \varepsilon_{CAR} \cdot [CAR] + \varepsilon_{OFL} \cdot [OFL]))] \cdot [H_2O_2]}{k_h \cdot [H_2O_2] + k_{CA} \cdot [CA] + k_{PROP} \cdot [PROP] + k_{CARs} \cdot [CAR] + k_{OFL} \cdot [OFL]} \cdot f_{H_2O_2}$$

$$(31)$$

Due to the higher reactivity of carbamazepine and propranolol, any attempts to measure the decay of their concentrations during the ozonation runs failed. However in the case of ofloxacin and clofibric acid a good agreement was observed between experimental and predicted data (fig. 5).

A fairly good agreement is also recorded in the oxidation runs with H_2O_2/UV (fig. 6).

The investigations were further extended to evaluate the effects of the aqueous matrix on the system reactivity. According to Paxeus [25] a synthetic effluent was prepared by dissolving in bidistilled water six of the some relevant species (adipic acid, benzophenone, caffeine, octanoic acid, poly(ethylene glycol) and vanillin) among those found in STP effluents. The resulting solution was then employed for the preparation of the mixture of the four pharmaceuticals submitted to ozonation and oxidation by means of H_2O_2/UV system. No appreciable differences in the concentration decays were recorded with respect to those found in bidistilled water experiments (fig. 7 and 8). This result indicates that the adopted synthetic aqueous matrix does not significantly influence the development of the oxidation processes. Moreover the diagrams in figures 7 and 8 confirm the capability of developed kinetic models to successfully describe the behaviour of the investigated systems.

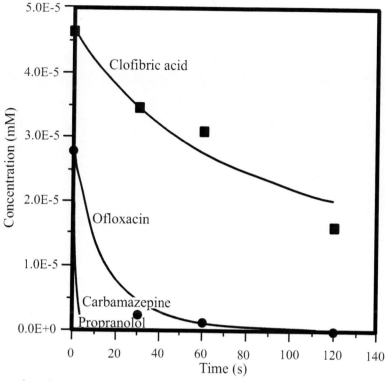

Fig. 5 - Comparison between experimental and predicted values for batch ozonation of (■) clofibric acid, (●) ofloxacin in bidistilled water. pH = 5.5 - $[O_3]_o$ = 0.01 mM.

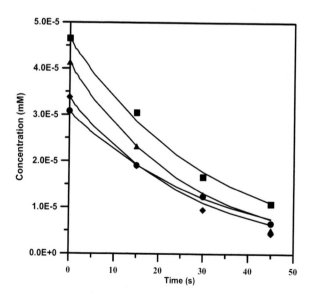

Fig. 6 - Comparison between experimental and predicted values for H_2O_2/UV oxidation of selected pharmaceuticals in bidistilled water. pH = 5.5 – $[H_2O_2]_o$ = 10 mM.
▲ carbamazepine, ■ clofibric acid, ● ofloxacin, ◆ propranolol

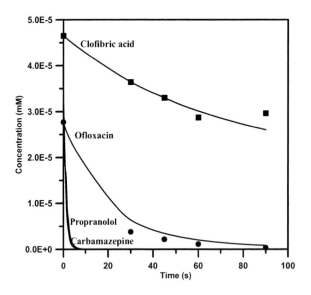

Fig. 7 - Comparison between experimental and predicted values for batch ozonation of selected pharmaceuticals in synthetic effluent. pH = 5.5 - $[O_3]_o$ = 0.01 mM.

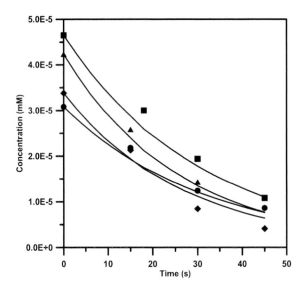

Fig. 8 - Comparison between experimental and predicted values for H_2O_2/UV oxidation of selected pharmaceuticals in synthetic effluent. pH = 5.5 – $[H_2O_2]o$ = 10 mM.
▲ carbamazepine, ■ clofibric acid, ● ofloxacin, ◆ propranolol

Conclusions

The reaction kinetics for the ozonation and H_2O_2/UV oxidation of propranolol and ofloxacin were assessed in the present work. To this purpose two different methods were used for H_2O_2/UV system. Ozonation kinetics for propranolol were found to be independent upon the pH of the solution whereas in the case of ofloxacin the kinetic of ozone attack increases by one order of magnitude for pH changing from 3.0 to 7.0.

Kinetic constants for HO radical attack were found to be $2.56 \cdot 10^9 \div 2.85 \cdot 10^9$ M^{-1} s^{-1} and $2.14 \cdot 10^9 \div 2.48 \cdot 10^9$ M^{-1} s^{-1} respectively for propranolol and ofloxacin.

These kinetics were successfully validated in experimental runs with starting concentrations as low as 10 micrograms per liter.

Assessed reaction kinetics were also used to predict the behaviour of propranolol, carbamazepine, clofibric acid and ofloxacin when they were submitted in the same mixture to ozonation and H_2O_2/UV oxidations, in bidistilled water and synthetic STP effluents.

A fairly good agreement is observed between predicted and experimental data in both cases.

References

[1.] Kummerer K. *Pharmaceuticals in the environment: sources, fate, effects and risks. Springer*-Verlag (2001) Klaus Kummerer editor 1st ed.

[2.] Heberer T. Occurrence, fate and removal of pharmaceutical residues in the aquatic environment: a review of recent research data. *Toxicology Letters* **131**: 5-7 (2002).

[3.] Halling-Sorensen B., Nielsen N. S., Lanzky P.F., Ingerslev F., Holten Lutzhoft H. C. and Jorgensen S. E. Occurrence, fate and effects of pharmaceutical substances in the environment. A review. *Chemosphere*, **36(2)**: 357 – 393 (1998).

[4.] Jones O.A., Voulvoulis N. and Lester J.N. Human pharmaceuticals in the aquatic environment: a review. *Environmetal Technology*, **22:** 1383 – 1394 (2001).

[5.] Drewes J.E., Heberer T. and Reddersen K. Fate of pharmaceuticals during indirect potable reuse. *Water Science and Technology*, **46(3)**: 73 –80 (2002).

[6.] Steger-Hartmann T., Kummerer K. And Hartmann A. Biological degradation of cyclophosphamide and its occurrence in sewage water. *Ecotoxicology and Environmental Safety* **36**: 174 – 179 (1997)

[7.] Kummerer K., Al-Ahmad A. and Mersch-Sundermann V. Biodegradability of some antibiotics, elimination of the genotoxicity and affection of wastewater bacteria in a simple test. *Chemosphere* **40**: 701 –710 (2000).

[8.] Andreozzi R., Marotta R. and Paxeus N. Pharmaceuticals in STP effluents and their solar photodegradation in aquatic environment *Chemosphere*, **50**: 1319 – 1330 (2003).

[9.] Andreozzi R., Caprio V., Marotta R. and Radovnikovic A. Ozonation and H_2O_2/UV treatment of clofibric acid in water: a kinetic investigation. *Journal of Hazardous Materials* **B103**: 233 – 246 (2003).

[10.] Andreozzi R, Marotta R., Pinto G. and Pollio A. Carbamazepine in water: persistence in the environment, ozonation treatment and preliminary assessment on algal toxicity. *Water Research*, **36(11)**: 2869 – 2877 (2002).

[11.] Lopez A., Bozzi A., Mascolo G. and Kiwi J. Kinetic investigation on UV and UV/H$_2$O$_2$ degradation of pharmaceutical intermediates in aqueous solution. *J. of Photochem. Photobiol A*: *Chemistry* **156**: 121 – 126 (2003).

[12.] Balcioglu I. A. and Otker M. Treatment of pharmaceutical wastewater containing antibiotics by O$_3$ and O$_3$/H$_2$O$_2$ processes, *Chemosphere* **50**: 85 – 95 (2003).

[13.] Ferrari B, Paxeus N., Lo Giudice R., Pollio A. and Garric J. Ecotoxicological impact of pharmaceuticals found in treated wastewaters: study of carbamazepine, clofibric acid and diclofenac. *Ecotoxicology and Environmental Safety*, *55: 359 – 370 (2003).*

[14.] Andreozzi R., Insola A., Caprio V. and D'Amore M. G. Quinoline ozonation in aqueous solutions. *Water Research* **26(5)**: 639 – 644 (1992).

[15.] Andreozzi R, Caprio V., Insola A. and Marotta R. The oxidation of metol (N-methyl-p-aminophenol) in aqueous solution by UV/H$_2$O$_2$ photolysis. *Water Research*, **34(2)**: 463 – 472 (1999).

[16.] Nicole I., De Laat J., Doré M., Duguet J. P. and Bonnel C. Use of UV radiation in watertreatment: measurement of photonic flux by hydrogen peroxide actinometry. *Water Research*, **24(2)**: 157-168 (1990).

[17.] Andreozzi R., Caprio V., Insola A. and Tufano V. Measuring ozonation rate constants in gas-liquid reaction under the kinetic-diffusional transition regime *Chemical Engineering Communication* **143**: 195 – 197 (1996).

[18.] Tolls J., Sorption of veterinary pharmaceuticals in soils: a review. *Environmental Science and Technology*, **35(17)**: 3397 – 3408 (2001).

[19.] Barbosa J., Berges R. and Sanz-Nebot V. Retention behaviour of quinolone derivatives in high-performance liquid chromatography. Effect of pH and evaluation of ionization constants, *J. Chromatogr. A*. **823**: 411-422 (1998)

[20.] Moriguchi I., Hirono S., Nakagome I. and Hirano H. Comparison of reliability of log*P* values for drugs calculated by several methods. *Chem. Pharm. Bull.* **42**: 976-978 (1994).

[21.] Hoigné J. and Bader H. Rate constants of reactions of ozone with organic and inorganic compounds in water. I. Non-dissociating organic compounds. *Water Research*, **17**: 173 – 183 (1983).

[22.] Henry H., Zador M. and Fliszar S. Quantitative investigation of the ozonolysis reaction. XVIII. Kinetic study of the ozone attack on phenylethylenes. *Canadian Journal of Chemistry*, **51**: 3398-3402 (1973)

[23.] De Laat J., Berger P., Poinot T., Vel Leitner N. K. and Dorè M. Modelling the oxidation of organic compounds by H$_2$O$_2$/UV. Estimation of kinetic parameters. *In Proc. of the 12th Ozone World Congress of the Int. Ozone Ass.*, Lille, May 1995, 373 – 384.

[24.] Vogna D., Marotta R., Andreozzi R., Napolitano A. and d'Ischia M. Kinetic and chemical assessment of the UV/H$_2$O$_2$ treatment of antiepileptic drug carbamazepine. *Chemosphere*, **54**: 497 – 505 (2004).

[25.] Paxeus N. Organic pollutants in the effluents of large wastewater treatment plants in Sweden. *Water Research*, **30(5)**: 1115 – 1122 (1996).

[26.] Buxton G.V., Greenstock C.L., Helman W.P. and Ross A.B. Critical review of rate constants for reactions of hydrated electrons, hydrogen atoms and hydroxyl radicals

(OH·/O·) in aqueous solution. *Journal of Physical Chemistry Ref. Data* **17(2)**: 513 - 886 (1988).

[27.] Bielski B.H.J., Cabelli D.E., Arudi R.L. and Ross A.B. Reactivity of HO_2/O_2^- radicals in aqueous solution. *Journal of Physical Chemistry Ref. Data* **14(4)**: 1041 - 1100 (1985).

[28.] Baxendale J.H. and Wilson J. A. Photolysis of hydrogen peroxide at high light intensities. *Transaction Faraday Society* **53**: 344 – 356 (1957).

[29.] Volman D.H. and Chen J.C. The photochemical decomposition of hydrogen peroxide in aqueous solutios of allyl alcohol at 2537 A. *Journal of American Chemical Society* **81**: 4141 – 4144 (1959).

[30.] Andreozzi R., Caprio V., Ermellino I, Insola A and Tufano V., Ozone solubility in phosphate buffered aqueous solutions: the effect of temperature, t-butyl alcohol, pH. *Ind. Eng. Chem. Res.*, **35**: 1467 – 1472 (1996).

[31.] Reklaitis G. V., Ravindran A. and Regsdell K. M. (1983) Engineering optimization, John Wiley & Sons, New York.

[32.] Hetzer H.B., Robinson R.A. and Bates R.G.. Dissociation consyitants of piperazinium ion and related thermodynamic quantities from 0 to 50° C *J. of Physical Chemistry*, **72(6)**: 2081 – 2086 (1968).

Legend

[CA]	Clofibric acid concentration, M.
[CAR]	Carbamazepine concentration, M.
D_{O3}	Diffusivity of ozone in water, $1.77 \cdot 10^{-7}$ dm^2 s^{-1} [30].
E	Enhancement factor, dimensionless.
f_{CA}	UV fraction absorbed by clofibric acid.
f_{H2O2}	UV fraction absorbed by hydrogen peroxide.
k_{CA}	Kinetic constant of the reaction between HO radical and clofibric acid, $2.38 \cdot 10^9$ M^{-1} s^{-1} [9].
k_h	Kinetic constant of the reaction between HO radical and H_2O_2, $2.7 \cdot 10^7$ M^{-1} s^{-1} [26].
k_L^o	Gas - liquid phase mass transfer coefficient without chemical reaction, $4.26 \cdot 10^{-4}$ dm s^{-1} [30].
$k_L^o a$	Gas - liquid phase volumetric mass transfer coefficient without chemical reaction, 0.045 s^{-1} [30].
k_{O3}	Rate constant of pharmaceutical ozonation, M^{-1} s^{-1} *estimated in the present work.*
$k_{O3/CA}$	Rate constant of clofibric acid ozonation, 1580 M^{-1} s^{-1} [9].
$k_{O3/CAR}$	Rate constant of carbamazepine ozonation, $7.8 \cdot 10^4$ M^{-1} s^{-1} [10].
$k_{O3/OFL}$	Rate constant of ofloxacin ozonation, M^{-1} s^{-1} *estimated in the present work.*
$k_{O3/PROP}$	Rate constant of propranolol ozonation, M^{-1} s^{-1} *estimated in the present work.*
k_{OFL}	Kinetic constant of the reaction between HO radical and ofloxacin, M^{-1} s^{-1} *estimated in the present work.*
k_{PROP}	Kinetic constant of the reaction between HO radical and propranolol, M^{-1} s^{-1} *estimated in the present work.*
k_s	Kinetic constant of the reaction between HO radical and the pharmaceutical, M^{-1} s^{-1} *estimated in the present work.*
k_r, k_{CAR}	Kinetic constant of the reaction between HO radical and carbamazepine, $2.56 \cdot 10^9$ M^{-1} s^{-1} [24].
k_t	Kinetic constant of the termination reaction between HO_2 radicals, $8.3 \cdot 10^5$ M^{-1} s^{-1} [27].
I	Ionic strength, 0.1 M.
I_o	UV-light intensity of the lamp at 254 nm, $2.7 \cdot 10^{-6}$ E s^{-1} [24].
l	optical pathlength of the reactor, 0.201 dm.

[OFL]	Ofloxacin concentration, M.
$[O_3]_B$	Ozone bubbles concentration, M.
$[O_3]_F$	Ozone freeboard concentration, M.
$[O_3]_L$	Ozone liquid concentration, M.
$[O_3]_{in}$	Initial ozone concentration, M.
[PROP]	Propranolol concentration, M.
Q	Gas flow rate, 0.01 $dm^3 s^{-1}$.
[S]	Pharmaceutical concentration, M.
V_B	Bubbles volume, 0.034 dm^3.
V_F	Freeboard volume, 0.20 dm^3.
V_L	Volume of solution for ozonation experiments, 0.80 dm^3.
V_{sol}	Volume of solution for H_2O_2/UV experiments, 0.42 dm^3.
z_{O3}	Stoichiometric ozone coefficient for reaction with pharmaceutical , dimensionless.
$z_{O3/CA}$	Stoichiometric ozone coefficient for the ozonation reaction of clofibric acid, 2 dimensionless [9].
$z_{O3/CAR}$	Stoichiometric ozone coefficient for the ozonation reaction of carbamazepine, 1 dimensionless [10].
$z_{O3/PROP}$	Stoichiometric ozone coefficient for the ozonation reaction of propranolol, dimensionless *estimated in the present work*.
$z_{O3/OFL}$	Stoichiometric ozone coefficient for the ozonation reaction of ofloxacin, dimensionless *estimated in the present work*.
W_{abs}	Radiation power absorbed by the solution.
α	Ostwald coefficient, 0.186 dimensionless [30].
ε_{H2O2}	molar extinction coefficients at 254 nm for hydrogen peroxide, 18.6 $M^{-1} cm^{-1}$.
ε_s	molar extinction coefficients at 254 nm for the substrate.
ε_{CA}	molar extinction coefficients at 254 nm for clofibric acid (380 $M^{-1} cm^{-1}$) [9].
ε_{CAR}	molar extinction coefficients at 254 nm for carbamazepine (6025 $M^{-1} cm^{-1}$) [24].
ε_{OFL}	molar extinction coefficients at 254 nm for ofloxacin (10970 $M^{-1} cm^{-1}$) *estimated in the present work*.
ε_{PROP}	molar extinction coefficients at 254 nm for propranolol (1368 $M^{-1} cm^{-1}$) *estimated in the present work*.
ϕ_{CA}	the primary quantum yield of the direct photolysis at 254 nm of clofibric acid, $1.08 \cdot 10^{-2}$ mol E^{-1} [9].
ϕ_{H2O2}	the primary quantum yield of the direct photolysis at 254 nm of hydrogen peroxide, 0.5 mol E^{-1} [28, 29].
σ_{O3}	standard deviation for ozone, %
σ_S	standard deviation for the substrate, %

In: Trends in Water Pollution Research
Editor: J. V. Livingston, pp. 117-136

ISBN 1-59454-328-3
©2005 Nova Science Publishers, Inc.

Chapter V

Catalytic Decomposition of Hydrogen Peroxide and Monosubstituted-Chlorophenol in the Presence of Modified Activated Carbons

Ming-Chun Lu[41] and Hsu-Hui Huang[2]

1. Department of Environmental Resources Management,
Chia Nan University of Pharmacy and Science
Tainan, Taiwan 717, R.O.C.
2. State-owned Enterprise Commission,
No.25, Pao-Chin Rd. Taipei 100, Taiwan, ROC.

Abstract

The objective of this research was to examine the heterogeneous catalytic decomposition of H_2O_2 and monosubstituted - chlorophenols (MCP) in the presence of activated carbons modified with chemical pretreatments. From the analysis of scanning electron microscope (SEM) and energy dispersive spectrometer (EDS), the surface characteristics of granular activated carbon (GAC) were modified significantly by the treatment of concentrated nitric acid. The decomposition of H_2O_2 was suppressed obviously by the change of surface properties including the decreased pHpzc modified with oxidizing agent and the reduced active sites occupied by the adsorption of MCP. The apparent reaction rate of H_2O_2 decomposition was dominated by the intrinsic reaction rates on the surface of activated carbon rather than the mass transfer rate of H_2O_2 to the solid surface. By the detection of chloride ion in the suspensions, the reduction of MCP was not only attributed to the advanced adsorption but also the degradation of MCP. Furthermore, the ratio of dechlorination to DOC loss for the 4-CP removal was much higher than that for 2-CP removal, implying that the reaction pathway and oxidative intermediates for

[4] Corresponding Author: Tel.: +886-6-2660489; Fax: +886-6-2663411, E-mail: mmclu@mail.chna.edu.tw

various MCP in this catalytic process would be different. Results show that the combination of H_2O_2 and GAC did increase the total removal of MCP than that by single GAC adsorption.

Key words: granular activated carbon, hydrogen peroxide, monosubstituted-chloro-phenol, heterogeneous catalysis, adsorption

Introduction

The presence of various refractory compounds may be a major obstacle to the use and reuse of water streams. Phenolic compounds can cause objectionable taste and odor problems in drinking water and can exert adverse effects on various biological treatment processes. The conventional wastewater treatment technologies for removing phenolic compounds in the past include both aerobic and anaerobic biodegradation, and adsorption process by activated carbon. However, in practice, there are several disadvantages for toxic compounds treated with biological system, such as the specialization of bacteria or the sensitivity of bio-system for the loading concentration. Application of the adsorption process conducts only phase transfer reaction rather than destruction of pollutants and requires more treatment for residual materials.

Advanced oxidation processes (AOPs) show the potential as one of the techniques for removing phenolic compounds. The application of Fenton-like chemical oxidation process for remediation of contaminated soils and treatment of wastewater has gained more attention in last decade (Ravikumar and Gurol, 1994; Kong et al., 1998; Lu et al., 2002). However, one of the disadvantages for Fenton process is that the homogeneous catalyst cannot be retained in the process thus causing additional water pollution. A number of researchers (Valentine and Wang, 1998; Miller and Valentine, 1999) with attempt to minimize the leaching of iron ion focused on the efficiency of heterogeneous catalysis for pollutant oxidation. Recently, considering the practical application of the oxidation process, supported iron oxides or granular solid catalysts, such as graphite and activated carbon, were also studied for their catalytic characteristics (Lucking et al., 1998; Chou and Huang, 1999). In addition, the potential for applying H_2O_2 to Fenton-like water treatment is primarily restricted to the supply and stability of H_2O_2. Therefore, understanding the fate of H_2O_2 is still an important topic (Lin and Gurol, 1998; Huang et al., 2001).

Granular activated carbon (GAC), used as a catalyst as well as adsorbent in this study, has been applied for a long time in the heterogeneous catalysis and adsorption for its enormous surface area, porous structure and characteristic flexibility (Francisco, 1998). A number of studies have been carried out on the interaction of oxidizing agents (e.g. H_2O_2 or O_3) with carbon and carbon-supported materials (Heisig et al., 1997; Khalil et al., 2001). These investigations were not only concerned with the factors affecting the catalytic rate, but also directed toward applying this type of reaction for practical purposes, especially in environmental impacts. Recent studies (Lucking et al., 1998; Lin and Lai, 2000) indicated that surface catalyzed reaction of GAC induced by oxidizing agent may lead to contaminant decay in aqueous system. Although GAC adsorption method is effective to the removal of organic compounds, the GAC can get saturated easily in the process, which requires regeneration or complete replacement. Combination of both adsorption and heterogeneous catalysis into a single process could offer an attractive alternative in the wastewater treatment. Due to the complex role of GAC, the catalytic decomposition of H_2O_2 and contaminants with GAC deserves further investigation.

In this study, we examined and compared the surface catalyzed transformation of the model pollutant, MCP, by H_2O_2 in the presence of GAC with different surface properties modified by various chemical processes. The factors including H_2O_2 concentration, GAC dosage, and GAC types affecting the decomposition behavior of H_2O_2 and MCP are discussed.

Materials and Methods

The activated carbon was Filtrasorb-300 GAC supplied by the Calgon Carbon with an average particle density of 0.8 g/cm^3 and particle diameter of 0.64 mm (sieved with 20×40 US Mesh size). GAC1 was the original carbon, which was washed several times with deionized water until most of the fines were removed. GAC2 and GAC3 were the products of GAC1 which was oxidized with concentrated H_2O_2 (1000 mg GAC1 in 10 ml, 9.8 M H_2O_2) and HNO_3 (1000 mg GAC1 in 10 ml, 13.9 N HNO_3 heated at 80 °C) solution for 24 hours, respectively. Prior to the oxidation experiment, GAC1 and GAC2 were treated with diluted HCl solution (1000 mg GAC in 10 ml, 1 N HCl) for 24 hours to reduce the metal ions contained in GAC. After the treatment, all the activated carbons were washed with deionized water several times until the pH of the supernatant was constant. In addition, the GAC treated with diluted HCl was washed with boiling deionized water twice more to minimize the interference of chloride ions desorbed from GAC during the oxidation experiment. All GAC were dried in an oven at 50 °C for preservation. Specific surface area and average pore diameter were calculated by N_2-BET meter (Micromeritics ASAP 2000). The value of pH_{pzc} was measured by the mass titration method (Noh and Schwarz, 1989). The morphology and surface components of activated carbons were examined using high-resolution scanning electron microscope and energy dispersive spectrometer (Hitachi S4700I).

The experiments were conducted in 250 ml flasks that were capped and shaken in a thermal oscillator tank at constant temperature of 30 °C. The ionic strength was kept at 0.05 M by the addition of $NaClO_4$. The kinetics of H_2O_2 decomposition was studied by examining the variables such as the concentration of H_2O_2 and GAC. The reactor was prepared by filling proper amount of GAC and adjusted to the desired pH value several times (equilibrium for one day); the reaction mixture was 150 ml; the reaction was initiated by the addition of H_2O_2. The range of the pH variance in the H_2O_2 decomposition experiment was less than unit. In the oxidation experiment of MCP, the reactor was prepared by introducing the proper amount of MCP and GAC; the reaction mixture was 200 ml. The adsorption equilibrium of the solution (GAC and MCP) was to be achieved for at last three days prior to the oxidation experiment. Samples taken from the reactor within certain time intervals were filtered through 0.45 μm membrane filters to separate GAC particles from the solution. H_2O_2 concentration was quantified by the peroxytitanic acid method with the addition of $Ti(SO_4)_2$ test solution (Schumb et al., 1955). Residual MCP was measured by an HPLC (Water LC module 1) with a reverse phase 3.9×150 mm Nova-Pak C_{18} column (Waters). Total dissolved organic carbon (DOC) was determined using a TOC analyzer (Shimadzu 5000A). Concentration of chloride ion was measured with a chloride analyzer (Cole-Parmer U27502-13 plus WTW pH340/ion meter).

Results and Discussions

Characteristics of Catalysts

The properties of the three activated carbons are shown in Table 1.

Table 1. Characteristics of modified granular activated carbons

Catalyst	Specific surface area (m^2/g)	Micropore volume (cm^3/g)	Average pore size (Å)	pH_{pzc}	Element composition (wt %)			
					C	O	Fe	others
GAC1	983	0.28	17.1	4.2*	82.8	1.5	12.2	3.5
GAC2	1023	0.27	17.0	3.5*	96.7	1.2	0.3	1.8
GAC3	555.7	0.11	18.1	3.2	90.7	6.4	0.6	2.3

* : after the treatment of diluted HCl and washing process

The total specific surface area of GAC was increased slightly after the treatment with concentrated H_2O_2 solution, but reduced significantly by the heating treatment of concentrated HNO_3 solution. The difference among activated carbons modified by different treatments can also be verified via the SEM diagram (shown in Figure 1). The oxidation treatment by concentrated H_2O_2 has a moderate impact on the texture of the activated carbon, while the treatment by hot nitric acid makes the surface morphology quite different with that of the original activated carbon. This may be due to the strong corrosive property of hot nitric acid, which made the pore walls thinner resulting in a widening of the microporosity and consequently a diminishing of surface area. The atoms of C, O, Fe and other metal ions were detected on the surface of activated carbons by EDS, which are also represented in Table 1. It should be noted that the values of elemental analysis are not the absolute mass but the relative weight percentage of the surface element. However, from the analysis, we still can observe the change of element composition. The washing treatment by diluted HCl solution could not extract the metal ions effectively (e.g. GAC1), but the oxidation treatment by H_2O_2 and nitric acid removed a large amount of the ferric ions from the surface of GAC2 and GAC3. Moreover, the higher weight percentage of oxygen was observed for GAC3, indicating that the functional group containing oxygen is higher on its surface than that of the other activated carbons. It was reported that acidic oxygen surface complexes would be introduced predominantly onto activated carbons when they were treated by strong oxidation processes (Figueiredo, 1999). In addition, the values of pH_{pzc} are much smaller than the general range of pH_{pzc} (i.e. 9.8 to 10.2) reported for F-300 (Corapcioglu and Huang, 1987), indicating that the washing and chemical treatment used in this study has increased the

(a) GAC1

(b) GAC2

(c) GAC3

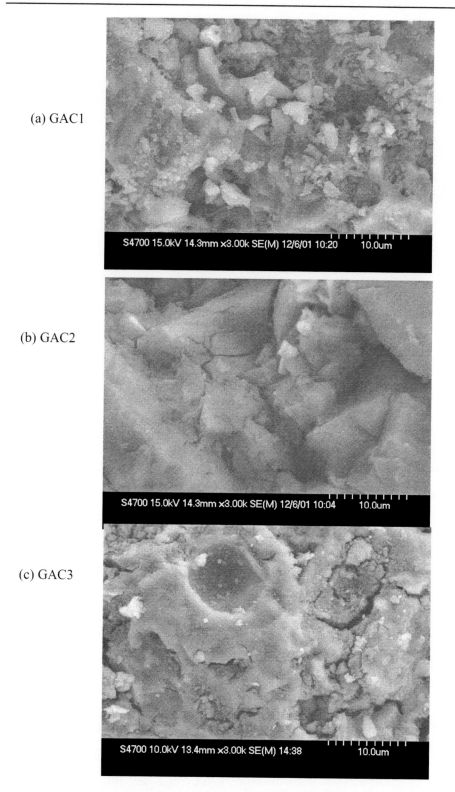

Figure 1 SEM images of modified activated carbons. (a) original. (b) modified by H_2O_2. (c) modified by HNO_3.

surface acidity of activated carbon. As the result, it could be concluded that the characteristics of activated carbon have been modified significantly either on the physical structure or on the surface chemistry properties.

Hydrogen Peroxide Decomposition

Comparison of Modified Activated Carbons.

The decomposition of H_2O_2 catalyzed by the activated carbons in the presence and absence of MCP (e.g. 2 and 4-CP) are shown in Figure 2 and 3. The reaction behavior followed a first-order rate expression with respect to the H_2O_2 concentration, which is consistent with the observation of the previous research (Khalil et al., 2001). In addition, the decomposition of H_2O_2 catalyzed by the activated carbon of which surface had been saturated with MCP in advance was still observed to follow a first-order rate even the reaction time was over 12 h. However, the decomposition rate was reduced largely in comparison with that in the absence of MCP. This was attributed to the MCP adsorption, which reduces the surface active sites available for the H_2O_2. Lucking et al. (1998) reported the similar results in their adsorption/oxidation system using GAC as the catalyst. However, a slight influence of organics adsorption on H_2O_2 decomposition was observed in the earlier researches using iron oxide as the catalyst. Those are due to the low affinity of organics with the metal oxide surface (Valentine and Wang, 1998; Huang et al., 2001).

A comparison of catalytic activity toward H_2O_2 decomposition for the activated carbons is shown in Table 2.

Table 2. The rate constant of k_{mass}, k_{suf} in the presence and absence of 4-CP

Catalyst type	$k_{mass}{}^a$	$k_{suf}{}^a$	$pH_f{}^a$	$k_{mass}{}^b$	$pH_f{}^b$
GAC1	6.71×10^{-6}	6.83×10^{-6}	~7.0^c	1.27×10^{-3}	~4.5
GAC2	4.87×10^{-6}	4.76×10^{-6}	~7.0^c	8.21×10^{-4}	~4.3
GAC3	1.17×10^{-6}	2.12×10^{-6}	~3.9	3.33×10^{-4}	~3.5

a: in the absence of 4-CP; $[H_2O_2]_0 = 5$ mM; catalyst dosage = 500 mg/L
b: in the presence of 4-CP; $[H_2O_2]_0 = 20$ mM; catalyst dosage = 1000 mg/L
c: with pH control; $[H_2O_2]_0 = 5$ mM; catalyst dosage = 500 mg/L
k_{mass}: min^{-1}(mg/L)$^{-1}$; k_{suf}: min^{-1}(m^2/L)$^{-1}$

The k_{mass} and k_{suf} are the first-order decomposition rate coefficients modified on the basis of the mass and total surface area of catalyst per unit volume of reaction mixture, respectively (Valentine and Wang, 1998). Apparently, no matter how the observed rate constant is modified with mass or surface area basis, the catalytic activity toward H_2O_2 decomposition is the highest for GAC1 and the least for GAC3 either in the presence or absence of 4-CP. In the majority of previous studies, H_2O_2 decomposition with activated carbon is considered to

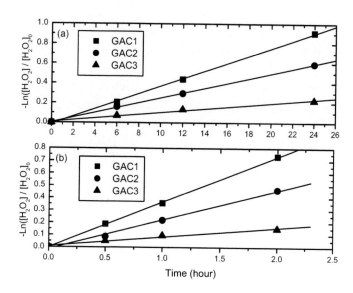

Figure 2 Change of H_2O_2 concentration in presence and absence of 4-CP. (a) 500 mg/L GAC with addition of 4-CP; (b) 1000 mg/L GAC without 4-CP ([H_2O_2]$_0$, 20 mM; temperature, 30 °C; Ionic strength, 50 mM $NaClO_4$)

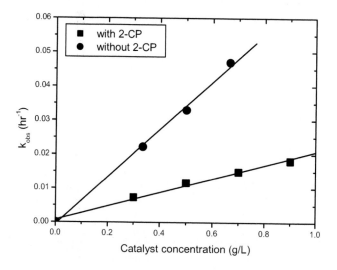

Figure 3 Effect of catalyst concentration on k_{obs} with and without 2-CP.

depend mainly on carbon porosity, slurry pH, and chemical properties of the surface (Khalil et al., 2001). Regarding the effect of porosity on the extent of H_2O_2 decomposition, the difference of micropore volume and pore size between GAC1 and GAC2 (Table 1) is insignificant. Moreover, the effect of pore diffusion (i.e. reaction rate reduced by pore diffusion) for GAC3 with larger pore size is expected to be less than those for GAC1 and GAC2. This indicates that the effect of porosity on H_2O_2 decomposition for the three activated carbons is not the major factor. The H_2O_2 decomposition is also generally dependent on the pH of the carbon slurry. The values of pH_f, pH at the end of the reaction, for the reaction mixtures containing GAC1 and GAC2 were controlled at the similar range from 6.8 to 7.2, signifying that the variance of rate constant in such an oxidation system was attributed not only to the medium pH but also the surface characteristic of GAC. Additional experiments without pH adjustment also show the same decline trend of catalytic activity toward H_2O_2 decomposition with the decreased pH_{pzc} of the activated carbons. It was reported that acidic oxygen surface complexes (e.g. carboxylic, phenolic, and lactonic groups) would be introduced predominantly onto activated carbons when they were treated with oxidizing agents such as H_2O_2 and HNO_3 (Castilla et al., 1995; Figueiredo et al., 1999). Therefore, the lower pH_{pzc} of the modified activated carbon shown in Table 1 is probably due to the formation of acidic function groups on the surface.

It has been widely suggested that catalytic decomposition of H_2O_2 by activated carbon could be initiated by the exchange of a hydroxyl group with a hydrogen peroxide anion as shown below (Khalil et al., 2001),

$$Carbon-surface)C\frac{H^+}{H}O...OH^- + H^+OOH^- \longrightarrow)C\frac{H^+}{H}O...OOH^- + H_2O \tag{1}$$

H_2O_2, meanwhile, can be thought as a weak acid ($pK_a = 11.6$) to proceed its dissociation to H^+ and OOH^-. The OOH^- anion, much less stable than H_2O_2 itself, decomposed readily. From the assumptions, it is reasonable to predict that the dissociation of H_2O_2 will be enhanced in alkaline medium. As the result, the acidic function groups of GAC2 and GAC3 treated with H_2O_2 and HNO_3 would retard the combination and dissociation of H_2O_2 resulting in suppressing the H_2O_2 decomposition rate considerably. Our results confirm again that the surface chemical nature of the GAC modified with oxidizing agent is the major factor in governing the catalytic action of GAC on H_2O_2 decomposition.

Decomposition Kinetics

The decomposition behavior was clarified with the consideration of the effect of H_2O_2 concentration and catalyst dosage. Consistent with general observation on the heterogeneous catalytic decomposition of H_2O_2 (Lin and Gurol, 1998; Huang et al., 2001), the experiments conducted with various catalyst dosages establish a linear relationship between the observed first-order rate constant and the mass of activated carbon. However, the observed rate constants of H_2O_2 decomposition conducted with various initial H_2O_2 concentrations ($[H_2O_2]_0$: from 4 to 30 mM) in the presence of GAC were found to decline with the increasing $[H_2O_2]_0$. The phenomenon seems different from other studies using metal oxides as the catalyst (Lin and Gurol, 1998; Huang et al., 2001) in which observed rate constant was independent of the $[H_2O_2]_0$. To analyze the catalytic kinetics of H_2O_2 decomposition, a modified Langmuir- Hinshelwood (L-H) rate model with the consideration of catalyst dosage is used to approach the experimental data conducted with various $[H_2O_2]_0$. The rate model is described as

$$R_H = -\frac{d[H_2O_2]}{dt} = \frac{k[catalyst][H_2O_2]}{1 + k_H[H_2O_2]} \qquad (2)$$

where k_H and k are the binding and rate constant, respectively. The inverse initial decomposition rate of H_2O_2 (R_{Hi}) versus $[H_2O_2]_0$ is plotted in Fig. 4. In this figure, the reciprocal of the R_{Hi} is directly proportional to the reciprocal of the $[H_2O_2]_0$ ($R^2 > 0.98$). Hence, it can be concluded that the reaction behavior of H_2O_2 decomposition with the GAC can be well described by the modified L-H model. L-H kinetic rate model has been used empirically to describe many heterogeneous catalytic surface reactions (Lin and Gurol, 1998). From the intercept and the slope of the regression line, the initial rate constant k and binding constant k_H are listed in Table 3. The rate constants obtained from the L-H model are found to be a little less than but still similar to the values of k_{mass} shown in Table 2, indicating that the rate model could be simplified as a second-order rate expression with respect to the H_2O_2 concentration and catalyst dosage when the products of k_H and $[H_2O_2]$ in the denominator are much smaller than unity.

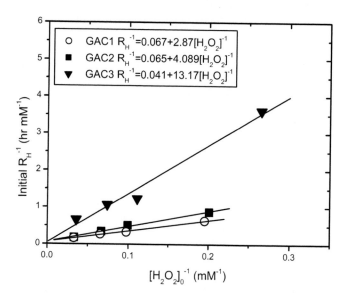

Figure 4 Reciprocal of initial rate versus reciprocal of initial H_2O_2 concentration. (GAC, 1000 mg/L; temperature, 30 °C; Ionic strength, 50 mM NaClO$_4$)

Table 3. The parameters of k and k_H in Langmuir- Hinshelwood model

Catalyst type	k (min^{-1})	k_H (mM^{-1})	pH$_f$
GAC1[a]	5.93×10^{-3}	2.33×10^{-2}	~ 7.0
GAC2[a]	4.11×10^{-3}	1.71×10^{-2}	~ 7.0
GAC3	1.25×10^{-3}	0.31×10^{-2}	~ 3.9

a : with pH control ;$[H_2O_2]_0 = 4 \sim 30$ mM; catalyst dosage = 1000 mg/L)

In addition, the binding constant k_H also follows the increased sequence of the catalytic activity for the activated carbons, implying the catalytic activity is dependent on the accessibility between the surface function groups and reactants. From the above discussion, it seems plausible that the surface phenomenon rather than mass transfer is the major factor, and the surface reaction is likely to control the overall reaction rate for the heterogeneous decomposition of H_2O_2 with GAC. In general, the apparent rate of a heterogeneous reaction is dominated by either the rate of intrinsic reaction on the surface or the diffusion rate of the reactant to the surface. The comparison of total molar flux can be used as a simple method to determine whether the film resistance or the surface reaction is the rate-controlling step. The maximum observed rate constant toward H_2O_2 decomposition for GAC1 is obtained as 1.19×10^{-4} sec^{-1}. Hence, the product (i.e. R_H) of maximum rate constant and H_2O_2 concentration (e.g. 5 mM) is 5.95×10^{-4} mMsec^{-1}. If the overall reaction rate were completely controlled by mass transfer, the surface concentration of the reactant would approach zero and the observed reaction rate could be calculated by the simplified rate equation (Satterfield, 1981)

$$R_H = \frac{6mk_cC_H}{\rho_p d_p} \qquad (3)$$

where k_c is mass transfer coefficient and can be estimated as 0.01 cm/sec which is a typical value in agitated water system, m is the catalyst dosage (g/cm^3), ρ_p is the particle density, and d_p is the particle diameter. Therefore, the observed rate estimated by equation (3) with the same H_2O_2 concentration ($C_H = 5$ mM) for GAC1 is 5.8×10^{-3} mMsec^{-1}. This is about 10 times of the fastest rate observed in our experiment, indicating that the H_2O_2 concentration gradient between bulk liquid and catalyst outside surface, i.e. film resistance, could be neglected in this system. Consequently, it is concluded that the catalytic reaction of H_2O_2 decomposition followed the L-H rate model, and the surface reaction is the rate-controlling step for the overall catalytic reaction.

Chlorophenol Oxidation

Adsorption of MCP by Modified Activated Carbon

The experiments of MCP oxidation were conducted with various modified activated carbons. To exclude the competing adsorption of MCP, which makes it difficult to differentiate the effect of adsorption and heterogeneous catalysis on the removal of MCP, the adsorption equilibrium of the solution is required prior to the oxidation experiment. Our preliminary experiment showed that the adsorption equilibrium of MCP with the modified activated carbons could be reached within 72 h. Table 4 lists the adsorption capacities of modified activated carbons toward 2-CP obtained from the adsorption isotherm experiment with pH control. In addition, the adsorption capacity toward 4-CP obtained from the adsorption isotherm without pH control is also listed in Table 5.

At the same pH, the adsorption capacity of GAC3 toward 2-CP and 4-CP was similar. The adsorption capacity of GAC3 for MCP was much smaller than those of the other activated carbons no matter on the base of mass or surface area, indicating that the adsorption property of activated carbon would be affected significantly by the surface modified pretreatment. Acidic oxygen-containing surface functional groups had been found to reduce the chemisorption of phenols on surface sites of activated carbons (Tessmer et al, 1997), which is also verified by our result of element analysis that higher oxygen content was observed on the surface of GAC3.

Table 4. The effect of modified GAC on the adsorption capacity of 2-CP with pH control

		GAC1	GAC2	GAC3
Adsorption capacity	Q (mmole/g)	1.57	1.65	0.73
	Q (mmole/m^2)	1.6×10^{-3}	1.61×10^{-3}	1.31×10^{-3}
	pH_f	3.8±0.2	3.8±0.2	3.8±0.2

adsorption isotherm for 72 h, $[2\text{-CP}]_0$=1.13 mM; [GAC]=500 mg/L; 30^0 C

Table 5. The effect of modified activated carbons on the adsorption capacity and removal efficiency toward 4-CP

		GAC1	GAC2	GAC3
Adsorption capacity [a]	Q (mmole/g)	1.66	1.61	0.77
	pH_f	5.7	4.7	3.8
Reduction [b]	E_R (mmole/mmole)	0.49×10^{-2}	0.63×10^{-2}	0.28×10^{-1}
	E_D (mmole/mmole)	0.41×10^{-2}	0.37×10^{-2}	0.12×10^{-1}
	pH_f	5.2	4.3	3.6

[a]: adsorption isotherm for 72 h, $[4\text{-CP}]_0$= 1.13 mM; catalyst dosage = 500 mg/L; 30^{0}C
[b]: catalytic oxidation for 24 h, $[H_2O_2]_0$= 20 mM; catalyst dosage = 500 mg/L; 30^0 C

Comparison of Modified Activated Carbons

The experiment of MCP oxidation was conducted with the modified GAC. To exclude the competing adsorption of MCP, which makes it difficult to differentiate the effect of adsorption and heterogeneous catalysis on the removal of MCP, the isotherm adsorption equilibrium of the MCP and GAC in reaction mixture is required prior to the oxidation experiment.

The result of the oxidation experiment conducted with different H_2O_2 concentrations after the adsorption equilibrium is shown in Figure 5. The trend of 2-CP loss including reduction and dechlorination increased with the increase of H_2O_2 concentration for the three modified activated carbons, implying that the amount of 2-CP reduced would be proportional to that of H_2O_2 added. In general, the decomposition behavior of H_2O_2 with activated carbons within a short time interval could be explained by a simple first-order relationship either in the absence or in the presence of MCP over a range of GAC dosages, but the loss of MCP was much more complex than anticipated. To evaluate the catalytic ability of the modified activated carbons toward MCP removal, two stoichiometric efficiencies, E_R and E_D, based on the hypothesis that the oxidation of pollutant could be proportional to the decomposition amount of H_2O_2 (Miller and Valentine, 1995; Valentine and Wang, 1998) and the relationship between 2-CP reduction and H_2O_2 concentration observed in our experiments, are defined individually as the ratios of the reduction and dechlorination amount of MCP to the decomposition amount of H_2O_2

$$E_R = \frac{\Delta[MCP]_R}{\Delta[H_2O_2]} \quad and \quad E_D = \frac{\Delta[MCP]_D}{\Delta[H_2O_2]} \tag{4}$$

where the $\Delta[MCP]_R$ and $\Delta[MCP]_D$ are the amount of MCP lost which are detected by HPLC and chloride analyzer, respectively. It should be emphasized that the term, reduction, in this study represents the loss of MCP attributed to the degradation and advanced adsorption (if occurred) of MCP during oxidation experiment.

For GAC3, in addition, the 2-CP loss was higher but the H_2O_2 consumption was quite lower than those of the other activated carbons, indicating that GAC3 has the highest activity in catalyzing 2-CP oxidation. Similar results were also observed for the 3-CP and 4-CP oxidation experiments. However, the removal efficiency of 4-CP was higher than those of 2 and 3-CP in the present of GAC3 in our experiment (data not shown here). The comparison of reduction efficiencies for different MCP will be discussed in our further study. Therefore, 4-CP was selected as the target pollutant for further experiments. The values of catalytic efficiencies of 4-CP for the three activated carbons with the addition of 20 mM H_2O_2 are shown in Table 5. GAC3 also shows the highest catalytic efficiency either in terms of reduction and dechlorination. However, the highest catalytic ability toward H_2O_2 decomposition for GAC1 cannot induce a relative high loss of 4-CP, resulting in a lower value of catalytic efficiency. Therefore, not only the adsorption capacity but also the catalytic efficiency of MCP would be affected significantly by the modification of activated carbon.

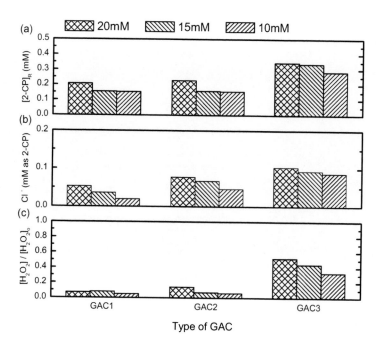

Figure 5 Effect of H_2O_2 concentration on reduction and dechlorination of 2-CP. (GAC= 500 mg/L; $[2\text{-CP}]_0$, 1.13 mM.; temperature, 30^0C.

The reduction and dechlorination efficiencies of 4-CP for GAC3 were 0.028 and 0.012 (mole/mole), respectively. This offers a comparable efficiency to those obtained from the other heterogeneous oxidation systems using metal oxides as catalyst. The majority of the efficiency reported earlier for catalytic oxidation of organics by H_2O_2 with iron oxide fell in the range of $10^{-2} \sim 10^{-4}$ (mole/mole) (Huang et al., 2001).

Furthermore, the loss of MCP could involve both heterogeneous and homogeneous catalytic reactions. Lucking et al. (1998) investigated the catalytic role of various activated carbons. Dissolved iron ions were observed to enhance the oxidation rate of 4-CP in the reaction volume during the oxidation experiment. To determine the importance of homogeneous reaction, the filtrate samples were aged for 24 h and the target pollutant concentration was monitored. No significant homogeneous loss was observed, which was attributed to the pretreatment of the GAC by strong acidic solution.

Sequential Oxidation Process

To further clarify the relative reactivity of each modified GAC, three sequential dosages of H_2O_2 were added into the reaction suspensions. The reduction of 4-CP and H_2O_2 concentration in the presence of GAC is shown in Fig. 6.

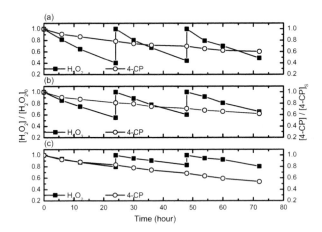

Figure 6 Change of 4-CP and H_2O_2 concentrations with three sequential additions of 20mM H_2O_2 in presence of activated carbons (GAC, 500 mg/L; $[H_2O_2]_0$, 20 mM; temperature, 30 °C; Ionic strength, 50 mM $NaClO_4$)

It should be noted that the starting concentration of 4-CP, $[4\text{-CP}]_S$, represents the 4-CP concentration remaining in the solution after the isotherm adsorption experiment. The effect of starting 4-CP concentration on catalytic efficiency will be discussed later. The overall reduction of 4-CP was obviously higher than that with the single dosage of H_2O_2, indicating that the loss of 4-CP increased with the increase of H_2O_2 decomposition. This is coincident with the hypothesis suggested by Miller and Valentine (1995) mentioned earlier. It is shown that the higher reduction of 52% occurred with GAC3, and similar loss of 40% occurred in the presence of GAC1 and GAC2. However, an inverse trend of H_2O_2 decomposition was observed; the smallest loss of H_2O_2 for GAC3, a medium loss for GAC2, and the largest decomposition of H_2O_2 occurred with GAC1. As the result, the surface characteristic of activated carbons could be considered as the major factor affecting the 4-CP degradation as well as the H_2O_2 decomposition discussed earlier. Figure 7 shows the accumulative reduction and dechlorination of 4-CP as the function of H_2O_2 decomposition for the sequential H_2O_2 dosage in the presence of GAC. The trend of dechlorination of 4-CP is similar to that of reduction but the efficiency of dechlorination (i.e. E_D) is general one-third of that of reduction (i.e. E_R). This phenomenon could be attributed to the uptake of chloride ion which decreased the real dechlorination amount of 4-CP. Chloride ion could form an outer-sphere complex outside the surface of the metal oxide (Stumm, 1992). Therefore, the detection of chloride ions cannot represent the total degradation of 4-CP. Nevertheless, it is apparent that the real catalytic efficiency of 4-CP falls in the range between the observed values of reduction and dechlorination.

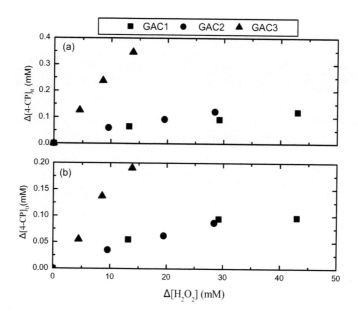

Figure 7 Relationship between loss of 4-CP and decomposition of H_2O_2 in presence of activated carbons (a) reduction; (b) dechlorination (GAC, 500 mg/L; $[H_2O_2]_0$, 20 mM; temperature, 30 ℃; Ionic strength, 50 mM $NaClO_4$)

Effect of Advanced Adsorption

Substances that adsorbed to aquifer sand surface could affect the degradation of H_2O_2 and organics (Miller and Valentine, 1995; Valentine and Wang, 1998). To examine the role of adsorption in the oxidation experiment, the relationships between the total reduction of MCP and DOC (dissolved organic carbon) in suspension are shown in Figures 8 and 9. The loss of DOC caused from the mineralization could be ignored for the weak catalytic activity toward the destruction of MCP in this system. Therefore, the decrease of DOC could be attributed to the advanced adsorption of MCP and its oxidation intermediates. In Figure 8, the decrease of DOC is similar to the total reduction for the three activated carbons, indicating that 2-CP and its oxidation intermediates were almost adsorbed further onto GAC surface. Figure 9 shows that the reduction of 4-CP was similar to that of 2-CP in the presence of the modified activated carbon. It should be noted that GAC3 showed a greatest catalytic activity but poor adsorption capacity toward 4-CP and its oxidation intermediates in comparison with that for 2-CP. Moreover, the percentage of dechlorination to DOC loss for the removal of 4-CP was much higher than that for 2-CP removal, implying that 4-CP was degraded to release more free chloride ion than that of 2-CP during the oxidation. It is assumed that the catalytic oxidation of 4-CP would undergo the reaction pathway via the substitution of chloride by radicals (i.e. dechlorination) rather than the attack on the ring structure. Therefore, the reaction pathway and oxidative intermediates for various MCP in this catalytic process would be different. Furthermore, the adsorption capacity of activated carbon toward phenolic compounds would be enhanced as the adsorption isotherm conducted in an oxidative coupling adsorption (Vidic et al., 1993). Under this condition, the oxygen produced from H_2O_2 decomposition in oxidation experiment would increase the adsorption capacity of activated carbon even the real adsorption equilibrium had been achieved. The portion of adsorption caused from different substances is difficult to be divided. However, from the data of the 4-CP removal in the presence of GAC3, even the decrease of DOC is entirely contributed from the oxidative-coupling adsorption, the total reduction of 4-CP is still much larger than that of DOC decrease, indicating that the catalyzed degradation of MCP did occur in this system. In addition, no matter how the reduction of 4-CP is attributed to the oxidative adsorption or catalytic oxidation, the combination of H_2O_2 and GAC has increased the total removal of MCP (adsorption plus reduction) than that by single GAC adsorption.

Reaction Mechanism

To explain why the three modified activated carbons exhibited different catalytic activity toward 4-CP oxidation, a general simplified mechanism proposed to describe the catalyzed organics with H_2O_2 is quoted as (Miller and Valentine, 1995)

$$H_2O_2 \xrightarrow{k_{1,surface}} I \xrightarrow{k_{2,surface}} O_2 + H_2O \tag{5}$$

$$I + Organics \xrightarrow{k_{3,solution}} Products \tag{6}$$

where I is intermediate (e.g. $\cdot OH$ or O_2^-) produced from the reaction of H_2O_2 with catalyst surface, $k_{1,\,surface}$ and $k_{2,\,surface}$ are the surface rate constants, and $k_{3,\,solution}$ is the rate constant in the reaction solution. In this study, the catalytic activity toward 4-CP loss is corresponded to the inverse sequence of that toward H_2O_2 decomposition for the three activated carbons. This phenomenon implies that the decrease of catalytic activity available for H_2O_2 (i.e. $k_{1,surface}$) by the oxidizing treatment would also reduce the surface activity ($k_{2,surface}$) to scavenge the intermediates of H_2O_2, and then induce to increase the collision probability for the effective radicals and organics (e.g. 4-CP). As discussed in H_2O_2 decomposition earlier, it could be concluded that the acidic functional groups would decrease the catalytic activity toward H_2O_2 and its intermediates but increase the degradation efficiency of 4-CP. Miller and Valentine (1995) found that the modified aquifer sand by acid-hydroxylamine decreased the rate of H_2O_2 decay while increased the degradation efficiency of quinoline significantly. Lin and Lai (2000) suggested an adsorption/ozonation mechanism that the destruction of organic was not only due to the direct ozonation but also the adsorbed pollutant oxidized catalytically on GAC surface.

Table 6. The comparison of dechlorination efficiency for each sequential H_2O_2 dosage

Parameter	GAC1 (20 mM)	GAC2 (20 mM)	GAC3 (20 mM)	GAC3 (15 mM)	GAC3 (10 mM)
$E_{D1}(\times 10^2)$	0.38	0.35	1.26	1.11	1.29
$E_{D2}(\times 10^2)$	0.32	0.32	1.65	1.11	1.06
$E_{D3}(\times 10^2)$	0.24	0.32	1.41	2.59	2.09
Average$(\times 10^2)$	0.31	0.33	1.44	1.60	1.47
pH range	5.6-3.9	4.9-3.6	3.9-3.3	3.8-3.2	3.9-3.4

catalyst dosage = 500 mg/L; $E_{D1,2,3}$ is the ratio of 4-CP loss to H_2O_2 loss in each H_2O_2 dosage

Some additional results conducted with various activated carbons and H_2O_2 concentrations are shown in Table 6. A similar average efficiency for the different addition of H_2O_2 concentrations (10 ~ 20 mM) is observed, indicating that the degradation efficiency of 4-CP is independent of the H_2O_2 concentration for the same starting 4-CP concentration. Furthermore, according to the mechanism (equation 6), it is plausible that the degradation efficiency of 4-CP should be the function of 4-CP concentration. If the 4-CP concentration in aqueous phase would affect the degradation efficiency, the decrease of efficiency should occur because of the decrease in 4-CP concentration at the time of each H_2O_2 addition during oxidation experiment. No obvious declining trend of dechlorination efficiency (i.e. $E_{D1,2,3}$) is observed for each H_2O_2 dosage in Table 6. The effect of pH should be taken into consideration. The variance of pH in oxidation experiment for GAC1 and GAC2 is larger than one, which could affect the degradation efficiency. However, with a small variance of pH, the effect of pH on degradation efficiency could be ignored in the presence of GAC3. Therefore, it could be concluded that the degradation efficiency toward 4-CP for GAC3 is independent of 4-CP amount remaining in aqueous phase. This unexpected result could be attributed to the excess concentration of 4-CP in comparison with the relative small amount of effective radicals, which is consistent with the low oxidation rate of 4-CP observed in this study.

Conclusions

The modified surface properties of the GAC by oxidizing agent indeed affect not only the decomposition of H_2O_2 but also the oxidation of MCP significantly. The catalytic activity toward H_2O_2 follows an increased sequence of pH_{pzc} for the three activated carbons. The decomposition kinetics of H_2O_2 over GAC can be well described by the Langmuir-Hinshelwood rate model. The rate constant increases with the increase of equilibrium constant (k_H), indicating the binding of H_2O_2 on the surface of catalyst could be an important factor on H_2O_2 decomposition. In comparison with the mass transfer rate, the reaction rate of H_2O_2 decomposition is mainly dominated by the surface reaction. The acidic functional group may play a major role in this catalytic oxidation system, which would decrease the catalytic activity toward H_2O_2 and its intermediates inducing the increase of the 4-CP degradation

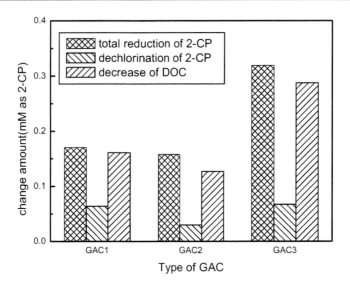

Figure 8 Total change of 2-CP and DOC in presence of activated carbons (GAC, 500 mg/L; [H$_2$O$_2$]$_0$, 20 mM; temperature, 30 ℃; Ionic strength, 50 mM NaClO$_4$)

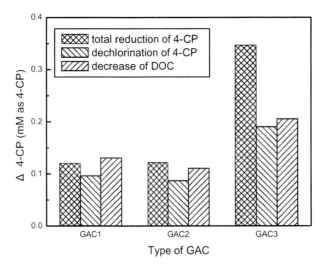

Figure 9 Total change of 4-CP and DOC in presence of activated carbons (GAC, 500 mg/L; [H$_2$O$_2$]$_0$, 20 mM; temperature, 30 ℃; Ionic strength, 50 mM NaClO$_4$)

efficiency. The degradation efficiency of 4-CP is independent of the initial H$_2$O$_2$ concentration, but the amount of 4-CP lost is proportional to the decomposition of H$_2$O$_2$. The efficiency relating 4-CP loss and H$_2$O$_2$ decay is independent of 4-CP concentration, which could be attributed to the small amount of effective radicals. The degradation efficiency of 4-CP for the modified activated carbon is comparable to those of the other oxidation systems using metal oxides as catalyst, suggesting an attractive alternative for the removal of organic pollutant in wastewater treatment.

Nomenclature

C_H H_2O_2 concentration in bulk solution (mM)

DOC dissolved organic carbon

d_p diameter of particle (cm)

E stoichiometric efficiency; E_R is the ratio for 4-CP reduction (loss) to H_2O_2 decomposition; E_D is the ratio for 4-CP dechlorination to the H_2O_2 decomposition

GAC granular activated carbon

k rate constant

k_c mass transfer coefficient (cm/s)

k_{mass} (observed rate constant) / (catalyst mass per unit volume of solution)

k_{suf} (observed rate constant)/(catalyst total surface area per unit volume of solution)

k_H equilibrium binding constant (mM^{-1})

m catalyst dosage (g/ cm^3)

pH_{pzc} point of zero charge

pH_f pH at the end of reaction

Q adsorption capacity

R_H decomposition rate of H_2O_2 (mM/time); R_{Hi} for initial decomposition rate

ρ_p particle density (g/cm^3)

[ ] concentration of solute in aqueous phase (mM); [ ]$_0$ denotes initial concentration; [4-CP]$_S$ is 4-CP concentration remaining in solution after isotherm adsorption.

References

Castilla, C.M., Ferro-Garcia, M.A., Joly, J.P., 1995. Activated carbon surface modifications by nitric acid, hydrogen peroxide, and ammonium peroxydisulfate treatments. *Langmuir* 11(11), 4386-4392.

Chou, S., Huang, C., 1999. Application of a supported iron oxyhydroxide catalyst in oxidation of benzoic acid by hydrogen peroxide. *Chemosphere* 38(12), 2719-2731.

Corapcioglu, M.O; Huang, C.P., 1987. The Surface Acidity and Characterization of Some Commercial Actibated Carbons. *Carbon* 25 (4), 569-578.

Figueiredo, J.L., Pereira, M.F.R., Freitas, M.M.A., 1999. Modification of the surface chemistry of activated carbons. *Carbon* 37(9), 1379-1389.

Francisco, R.R., 1998. Plenary lecture: The role of carbon materials in heterogeneous catalysis. *Carbon* 36(3), 159-175.

Heisig, C., Zhang, W., Oyama, T. 1997. Decomposition of ozone using carbon-supported metal oxide catalysts. *Applied Catalysis B: Environmental* 14(1-2), 117-129.

Huang, H.H., Lu, M.C., Chen, J.N., 2001. Catalytic decomposition of hydrogen peroxide and 2-chlorophenol with iron oxides. *Water Research* 35(9), 2291-2299.

Khalil, L.B., Girgis, B.S., Tawfik, T.A., 2001. Decomposition of H_2O_2 on activated carbon obtained from olive stones. *Journal of Chemical Technology and Biotechnology* 76(11), 1132-1140.

Kong, S.H., Watts, R.J. Choi, J.H., 1998. Treatment of petroleum-contaminated soils using iron mineral catalyzed hydrogen peroxide. *Chemosphere* 37(8), 1473-1482.

Lin, S.H., Lai C.L., 2000. Kinetic characteristics of textile wastewater ozonation in fluidized and fixed activated carbon beds. *Water Research* 34(3), 763-772.

Lin, S.S., Gurol, M.D., 1998. Catalytic decomposition of hydrogen peroxide of iron oxide: kinetics, mechanism, and implications. *Environmental Science and Technology* 32(10), 1417-1423.

Lu, M.C., Chen, J.N., Huang, H.H., 2002. Role of goethite dissolution in the oxidation of 2-chlorophenol with hydrogen peroxide. *Chemosphere* 46(1), 131-136.

Lucking, F., Koser, H., Jank, M., Ritter A., 1998. Iron powder, graphite and activated carbon as catalysts for the oxidation of 4-chlorophenol with hydrogen peroxide in aqueous solution. *Water Research* 32(9), 2607-2614.

Miller, C.M., Valentine, R.L., 1995. Hydrogen peroxide decomposition and quinoline degradation in the presence of aquifer material. *Water Research* 29(10), 2353-2359.

Miller, C.M., Valentine, R.L., 1999. Mechanistic studies of surface catalyzed H_2O_2 decomposition and contaminant degradation in the presence of sand. *Water Research* 33(12), 2805-2816.

Noh, J.S., Schwarz, J.A., 1989. Estimation of the point of zero charge of simple oxides by mass titration. *Journal of Colloid and Interface Science* 130(1), 157-164.

Ravikumar, J.X., Gurol, M.D., 1994. Chemical oxidation of chlorinated organics by hydrogen peroxide in the presence of sand. *Environmental Science and Technology* 28(3), 394-400.

Satterfield, C.N., 1981. Mass Transfer in Heterogeneous *Catalysis*. Robert E. Krieger Publishers, Florida.

Schumb, W.E., Satterfield, C.N., Wentworth, R.L., 1955. *Hydrogen Peroxide*. Chapman and Hall LtD., London.

Stumm, W., 1992. *Chemistry of the Solid-Water Interface*. Wiley-Interscience Publication, New York.

Tessmer, C.H., Vidic, R.D., Uranowski, L.J., 1997. Impact of oxygen-containing surface functional groups on activated carbon adsorption of phenols. *Environmental Science and Technology* 31(7), 1872-1878.

Valentine, R.L., Wang, H.C.A., 1998. Iron oxide surface catalyzed oxidation of quinoline by hydrogen peroxide. *Journal of Environmental Engineering* 124(1), 31-38.

Vidic, R.D., Suidan, M.T., Brenner, R.C., 1993. Oxidative coupling of phenols on activated carbon: impact on adsorption equilibrium. *Environmental Science and Technology* 27(10), 2079-2085.

In: Trends in Water Pollution Research
Editor: J. V. Livingston, pp. 137-165

ISBN 1-59454-328-3
©2005 Nova Science Publishers, Inc.

Chapter VI

Natural Adsorbent Materials for Effluent Treatment

Marco Aurélio, Zezzi Arruda, César Ricardo,
Teixeira Tarley and Geraldo Domingues Matos
Institute of Chemistry, Department of Analytical Chemistry, State University of
Campinas – Unicamp, P.O. Box 6154, Campinas, SP 13084-971, Brazil

Introduction

The disposal of heavy metals into aquatic systems has become a worldwide concern in recent decades due to their environmental impact on ecosystems. In addition, citizens have also become more worried about environmental subjects, not only due to environmental problems themselves but also due to the damage on the population's health. In addition, environmental laws are being improved, thus acting as another element of pressure for paradigm changes in the entire context. According to these facts, and connected to the real necessity for environmental research, there is an increase on those which involve effluent treatment in trying to overcome/minimize the environmental impact related to this subject. This fact can be attested to by the different approaches proposed for aqueous effluent treatments (Lee et al. 1998, Okieimen et al. 1988, Brown et al. 2000).

The most used processes for this task are based on neutralization/precipitation, ion exchange, activated carbon adsorption, membrane separation and electrochemical treatment based on electrolysis (Lacour et al. 2001, Hsieh and Teng 2000, Juang and Shiau 2000, Feng et al. 2004).

Although neutralization/precipitation processes can successfully be adopted for high effluent flow rates containing high metal ion concentrations, they present limitations mainly due to the solubility product of the formed salts, thus making the precipitation of those metals in the effluent difficult. The presence of organometallic compounds also reduces the efficiency of metal precipitation. Moreover, depending on the effluent composition, it is often necessary to make a prior reduction of the metal to a less soluble oxidation state, such as Cr (VI) to Cr (III).

Treatments based on ion exchange are also useful to decontaminate large amounts of effluent and the resins most commonly used (Dowex and Bayer 112-DG) can easily be regenerated. However, some limitations of this process include the cost of the resins and the necessity that suspended particles or oxidizing agents be eliminated from the effluent (Gaballah and Kilbertus 1998).

Regarding the application of activated carbon for metal removal from aqueous effluents, it is important to note that this adsorbent has undoubtedly been the most popular and most widely used (Hsieh and Teng 2000). In spite of its advantageous characteristics, such as efficient elimination of organic pollutants contained in the effluents, activated carbon remains expensive, mainly when high quality materials are required. Furthermore, for effluents containing metal ions, activated carbon requires chelating agents to enhance its performance, thus increasing treatment costs.

Separation by membranes is considered an efficient process for metal decontamination because the treated effluent generally presents low metal concentrations; however this process is not adequate for effluents that contain high metal concentrations as well as suspended particles, thus requiring a prior filtration step for its application (Juang and Shiau 2000).

Effluent treatment involving electrolysis, in which the metal ions are electroreduced, is convenient for effluents containing high metal ion concentrations, and it presents low operational costs. On the other hand, this process needs higher capital investment than other effluent treatment processes for heavy metal removal, although it provides lower purification limits, depending on the device employed (Henze et al. 1995).

Due to the problems previously mentioned, the development of new, cheap and environmentally friendly processes for aqueous effluent treatments has been intensified in recent years, thus receiving considerable attention in the literature. In this context, several alternative materials from natural sources have been proposed (Lee et al. 1998, Matos and Arruda 2003, Tarley and Arruda 2004).

The alternative adsorbents are generally divided into two classes, including the biosorbents where algae, fungi, bacteria and yeast are used as adsorbents and natural materials, namely such low-cost adsorbents such as, chitin/chitosan, seaweed, peat moss, red mud, clay, fly ash, natural zeolites, coal, materials rich in lignin, cellulose, including bark, corncobs, rice husks, peanuts, onions, soybeans and humic substances such as vermicompost (Bailey et al. 1999, Sag and Kutsal 2000, Pereira and Arruda 2002).

The term "low-cost" may only be attributed to an adsorbent when it does not require any processing, is abundant in nature, or is considered a by-product or waste from another industry (Bailey et al. 1999).

These materials are mainly constituted by macromolecules such as humic and fulvic substances, lignin, cellulose, hemicellulose and proteins, which present adsorptive groups such as carbonyl, carboxyl, amine and hydroxyl, thus making metal adsorption by complexation or ion exchange possible (Hervas et al. 1989).

In consonance with the context mentioned, the present contribution reports some examples in the literature relating to alternative materials for effluent treatment as well as pointing out some parameters that should be taken into account when effluent treatments are carried out, such as characterization (physical and chemical), adsorption isotherms, costs involved, and others.

As alternative application of natural material is demonstrated by the potential of loof sponge (*Luffa cylindrica*) for lead removal from laboratory effluents. The application of this material is due to its high porosity, negligible cost and abundance. For this contribution, in order to know its morphological characteristics and those chemical groups capable of lead uptake, spectroscopic analyses, using different techniques such as ^{13}C NMR (nuclear magnetic resonance) in the solid state, FT-IR (Fourier transform infrared), SEM (scanning electron microscopy) and others, were carried out. Adsorptive parameters, including pH of the sample and contact time, are evaluated to attain the best conditions for building adsorption isotherms. These were later fitted to the Langmuir isotherm model so that maximum adsorption capacity (MAC) was obtained. Afterwards, effluent treatment was successfully carried out for lead removal. According to the results, maximum adsorption capacity was found to be 9.20 mg g^{-1}. By performing effluent treatment, only 6 g of loof sponge, without prior physical or chemical treatment, was able to remove 98% of lead (10.2 mg L^{-1}) in 100 mL of effluent, thus attaining the maximum limit allowed by the legislation for heavy metals before water disposal.

Adsorption Processes

Adsorption process applications in the laboratory and on the industrial scale, as well as for environmental protection, are of paramount importance. For instance, adsorption of substrates is often the first stage in many industrial processes. Commonly, the adsorption process in the laboratory and in industry occurs between solids and liquids or gases this means that, this process takes place at the boundary between two phases.

The adsorption process is responsible for the transport of nutrients into the soil, assisting in plant and animal growth, chemical separation of proteins and enzymes, and industrial processes like purification of water, sewage and air.

Adsorption is a physical process in which dissolved species or small particles (the *adsorbate*) are attracted and become attached to the surface of something larger (the *adsorbent*). Depending on the type of phases in contact, this process can be considered in the following systems: liquid-gas, solid-liquid, solid-gas and liquid-liquid (Dabowski 2000).

The equilibrium between two phases may be established with regard to neutral or ionic species. If the adsorption process of one or several ionic species is accompanied by simultaneous desorption of an equivalent amount of ionic species, the process is considered as ion exchange or complexation.

The penetration by the adsorbate molecules into a liquid phase is determined as absorption. Adsorption should not be confused with this process. The term 'sorption', together with the terms 'sorbent' and 'sorbate', are used to denote both adsorption and absorption, when these processes occur simultaneously or cannot be distinguished.

The amount of material adsorbed depends on a number of factors including the degree of attraction, the surface area exposed to mobile particles, the concentration of the contaminants, and the pH and temperature of the liquid phase. Typically, the strongest adsorbents are microporous or finely divided solids. According to IUPAC, porosity is classified in three different groups: micropores are defined as pores of a width not exceeding 2 nm, mesopores are pores of a width between 2-50 nm, and macropores represent pores greater than 50 nm

(http:// www.iupac.org/reports/2001/ colloid_2001/ manual_of_s_and_t/node15.html#   sec: 1.1.5)

A great number of scientific studies are associated with adsorption of charged species on solid-liquid interfaces. The accumulation of organic or inorganic species at the solid-liquid interface is the basis of almost all surface reactions. Adsorption is often a process described in terms of isotherms, which represent the relationship between the concentration of a solute in solution and the quantity adsorbed at the solid phase surface at constant temperature. The isotherms are extremely important because can provide information on the adsorption strength, relative amount adsorbed and the maximum adsorption capacity of a given adsorbent. Adsorption isotherms generally exhibit several characteristic shapes, depending on the mechanism of sorption (Bajpai et al. 2004).

Adsorption Isotherms

Generally, adsorption is determined by the extent of species removal from solution, either in batch studies or in dynamic studies with columns of adsorptive materials.

A typical method is to supply a known concentration of adsorbate to a known mass of adsorbent. After both the solution and solid reach equilibrium, the solution concentration is then measured and the difference between the initial concentration and final equilibrium concentration adjusted for the solution volume is assumed to be the amount of adsorption per unit mass of adsorbent. This amount adsorbed is expressed as (Aldrich and Feng 2000):

$$Qe = \frac{(Co - Ce)V}{m} \qquad \text{Eq.(1)}$$

where Qe is the amount of species adsorbed per unit mass of adsorbent, Co and Ce are the initial concentration and equilibrium concentration, respectively, V is the experimental volume (expressed as liters), and m the adsorbent mass. Units for adsorption onto the solid phase depend on both concentration and mass units, however mg kg^{-1}, mmol kg^{-1} and μmol kg^{-1} are commonly used units for Qe. Sometimes the adsorption is expressed in terms of surface area, and the units are moles per m^2. In order to determine the solution concentration, the solid and solute must be separated. Decantation, centrifugation and filtration are commonly used.

Knowing the amount adsorbed per unit mass of adsorbent (Qe) and the equilibrium concentration (Ce), a plot of Ce vs Qe is constructed. This curve is called an *adsorption isotherm* because, typically, the measurements from an experimental run are carried out at a constant temperature during the adsorption process. Figure 1 depicts an example of an isotherm plot. In this example, the use of vermicompost as adsorbent material to remove metal ions was proposed. Experiments are performed by percolating a solution through a column packed with vermicompost (Matos and Arruda 2003). In this way, when the plateau region is reached, it means saturation of active adsorbent sites. From this region (at which the adsorbed mass is constant), it is possible to establish the maximum adsorption capacity of a material. Hence, a mathematical model may be employed to determine this value.

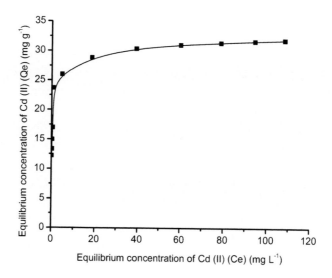

Figure 1. Adsorption isotherm plots of Cd (II) ions on vermicompost.

The mass transfer between the solution and the solid phase is modeled by several equations or concepts in both static and dynamic procedures. Adsorption isotherms show the distribution of solute between two phases.

Adsorption isotherms have proven useful for understanding the processes of adsorption. Two models of equilibrium adsorption isotherms are most frequently used: Langmuir and Freundlich. Using these models it is possible to calculate the adsorption capacity and also to indicate favorable adsorption of adsorbate onto adsorbent.

Langmuir Isotherm

The Langmuir equation was basically derived for the sorption of gases on a solid surface. Whenever a gas is in contact with a solid there will be an equilibrium established between the molecules in the gas phase and the corresponding adsorbed species (molecules or atoms) which are bound to the surface of the solid. This equilibrium will depend on factors such as the temperature of the system, pressure of the gas above the surface and the relative stabilities of the adsorbed and gaseous phases.

The Langmuir isotherm was developed by Irving Langmuir in 1916 to describe the dependence of the surface covered by an adsorbed gas on the pressure of the gas above the surface at a fixed temperature (Kim et al. 2004). This was later extended to liquid systems, where the equilibrium involved concentrations in solution. There are other types of isotherms (Temkin, Redlich-Peterson, Freundlich) that differ in one or more assumptions made in deriving the expression for surface coverage. The Langmuir model suggests that uptake occurs on a homogeneous surface by monolayer sorption without interaction between sorbed molecules. This model is described by equation below (Sag and Kutsal 2000):

$$Qe = \frac{aCe}{1+bCe}$$ Eq.(2)

where Ce is the non adsorbed species concentration at equilibrium (mg L^{-1}), Qe is the amount of species adsorbed per g of adsorbent (mg g^{-1}), a is a constant related to adsorption energy and b is the maximum adsorption capacity of the adsorbent (mg g^{-1}). Note that if $bCe \ll 1$, the equation is linear. The Langmuir equation obeys Henry's Law at low concentration, hence, at this condition the Langmuir isotherm appear to be nearly linear. The parameters a and b can be determined from the linearised form by plotting Ce/Qe vs Ce. These parameters are determined from the slope ($1/b$) and the intercept ($1/ab$). This linearisation can be made by rearranging Eq. (2) to the following linear form (Hsieh and Teng 2000):

$$\frac{Ce}{Qe} = \frac{1}{ab} + \frac{1}{b}Ce$$ Eq.(3)

This equation can also be used for dynamic systems (packed columns). The amount of species adsorbed onto the material (Qe) is calculated from the total amount of metal ion adsorbed ($Qtotal$) per g of adsorbent (X) at the end of a total flow time applied to the column, Eq. (4).

$$Qe = \frac{Qtotal}{X}$$ Eq.(4)

Ce in the column is calculated from Eq. (5):

$$Ce = \frac{m_{total} - Qtotal}{V_{eff}} 1000$$ Eq.(5)

where V_{eff} is the effluent volume (mL) and can be calculated from Eq. (6).

$$V_{eff} = Qtotal$$ Eq.(6)

Eq. (3) was used to obtain the linear curve, shown in Figure 2, from the data of Figure 1. The linear transformation and the maximum adsorption capacity value for Cd ions is then obtained. According to Eq. (3) the inverse of the slope of this curve corresponds to the maximum adsorption capacity for Cd (II) ions (33 mg g^{-1}). The value of constant a was found to be 0.5311.

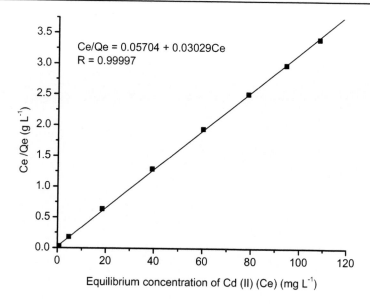

Figure 2. Langmuir isotherm adsorption plot of Cd (II) ions on vermicompost.

Another essential characteristic of the Langmuir isotherm equation can be expressed in terms of a dimensionless constant known as the separation factor or the equilibrium parameter (R_L), which predicts the adsorption efficiency of the process. This constant is given by Eq.(7):

$$R_L = \frac{1}{1 + aCo}$$ Eq.(7)

where Co is the initial concentration (mg L^{-1}) and a is the Langmuir isotherm constant. Values of $R_L < 1$ represent favorable adsorption and values greater than one represent unfavorable adsorption. Using the data already presented, the values of R_L were calculated to be between 0.02 and 0.94. These results indicate favorable adsorption of Cd (II) ions on vermicompost because all R_L values are between 0 and 1.

The Langmuir isotherm is probably the best known and most widely applied adsorption isotherm because it permits obtaining the maximum adsorption capacity at constant temperature.

Freundlich Isotherm

In 1906, Freundlich presented the earliest known sorption isotherm equation. This empirical model can be applied to non-ideal sorption on heterogeneous surfaces as well as to multilayer sorption, and it is expressed by Eq.(8) (Agrawal et al. 2004):

$$Qe = K_F Ce^{(1/n)}$$ Eq.(8)

where K_F is the adsorption capacity and $1/n$ is an arbitrary constant evaluated by linearizing the equation. K_F and n are the empirical constants dependent on several environmental factors and n is greater than one. If $1/n$ approaches 1, then the equation is linear. In addition, the Freundlich isotherm is an empirical expression used to access the linearity of adsorption capacity as a function of adsorbate concentration when adsorption data are plotted on a log-log scale. The linear Freundlich expression is presented as:

$$log\,Qe = log\,K_F + \frac{1}{n}log\,Ce \qquad\qquad \text{Eq.(9)}$$

A plot of log Qe against log Ce gives a straight line and the slope and intercept correspond to $1/n$ and log K_F, respectively. It is important to note that if the value of $1/n$ is within the range of 0.1 and 1.0 it indicates the favorable adsorption of the chemical species on the adsorbent. To make the discussion more didactic, the applicability of the Freundlich isotherm was analyzed using the experimental data from the previous section, according to Eq.(9). As one can see (Figure 3), the behavior of the experimental data is not in such good agreement, as it was in the case of the Langmuir isotherm, considering that the obtained in the linearised Langmuir equation is about 0.94666. The value of K_F and $1/n$ were calculated to be 18.49 mg g^{-1} and 0.13, respectively. As the value of 1/n lies between 0.1 and 1 the adsorption is favorable. In this particular case, the Langmuir isotherm was the best model. The agreement of the experimental data with the Langmuir model implied that there was monolayer adsorption under the experimental conditions used.

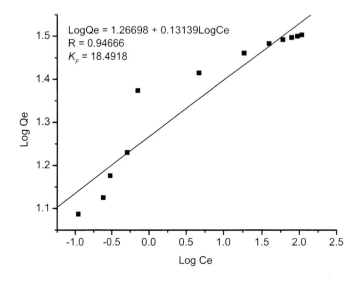

Figure 3. Freundlich isotherm adsorption plot of Cd (II) ions on vermicompost.

It is important emphasize that the Langmuir model assumes that adsorption occur at specific homogeneous sites within the adsorbent while the Freundlich equation deals with physicochemical adsorption on heterogeneous surfaces. The heterogeneous system is characterized by the heterogeneity factor $1/n$ and is not restricted to the formation of a monolayer. The Langmuir constant value (b) is associated to monolayer adsorption capacity while the Freundlich constant (K_F) represents a magnitude relative to multilayer adsorption capacity. From this comment, several inorganic species may to establishing interaction with solid phase material by both monolayer and multilayer. As an example, Acar and Malkoc (2004) reported the removal of Cr (VI) from aqueous solution using *Fagus orientalis* L. as adsorbent. In this study, both Langmuir and Freundlich models presented R values of 0.99. This implies that both monolayer adsorption and heterogeneous surface conditions existed under the experimental conditions used.

Uptake Mechanism

If one considers the expressive number of different natural materials as well as the amount of inorganic species capable of establishing favorable interactions with these related materials, the necessity to elucidate the main uptake mechanisms involved between metals ions and natural material surface is clear, in order to know the characteristics of each material. The complexity of natural materials implies that there are many ways for metal uptake on the material surfaces.

In general, the uptake mechanisms can be associated with active or passive interactions. In the active interactions, the metal ions play an important role in metabolism of the materials, so intracellular accumulation (transport across cell membranes) is characterized as the most important mechanism. This kind of transport affects the metabolism of living organisms (bacteria, algae, fungi and others) by changing respiration, ribosome synthesis and activity (Madrid and Cámara 1997).

Passive interactions, also called surface interactions, involve several kinds of uptake mechanisms and are not dependent on metabolism. It is generally fast, is affected by pH conditions but is less affected by temperature. The main metal retention mechanisms associated with passive interaction involve complexation and ion exchange. Chemical adsorption, such as covalent bonds between metal ions and the material surface, is not common when considering natural materials.

Although there is difficulty in establishing what kind of adsorption mechanism (complexation or ion exchange) is involved in metal removal, these processes should be reported.

Complexation mechanisms take place mainly on those materials rich in protein, lignin and polysaccharides, in which metal retention can occur through unidentate ligands or through chelation. Tsezos and Volesky (1981) showed that thorium and uranium retention by *Rhizopus arrhizus* takes place by complexation wherein the metals are coordinated with nitrogen from the cell wall. Similar behavior has been observed by Aksu et al. (1992) with respect to copper retention in *C. vulgaris* and *Z. ramigera*, thus showing that the uptake mechanism between copper and amino and carboxyl groups of cell wall polysaccharides occurs by complexation.

Recently, Pagnanelli et al. (2004) carried out a comparison of kinetics and acid-base properties as well as copper removal capacity studies employing a synthetic chelating resin based on bonded aminodiacetic groups and the bacteria *Sphaerotilus natans*. It was shown that the uptake mechanism involved in copper retention in the most bacteria occurs by metal complexation with mono-carboxylic groups.

Mechanisms based on ion exchange play a important role in metal uptake and can takes place in both microorganisms rich in polysaccharides and in mineral adsorbents. For example, alginates of marine algae commonly occur as natural salts of K, Na, Ca (II) and Mg (II). Therefore, this material works as an ion exchange resin when counter ions, such as Co (II), Cu (II), Zn (II) and others, establish contact with the material. Also, natural materials, such as polysaccharides, when submitted to a prior chemical treatment, for example, by employing alkaline solutions (NaOH, Ca(OH)$_2$ or KOH), acquire characteristics of ion exchange resins, as shown in Figure 4. In addition, chemical treatments with citric or phosphoric acids can be used for the same purpose (Marshall and Johns 1996, Marshall et al. 1999).

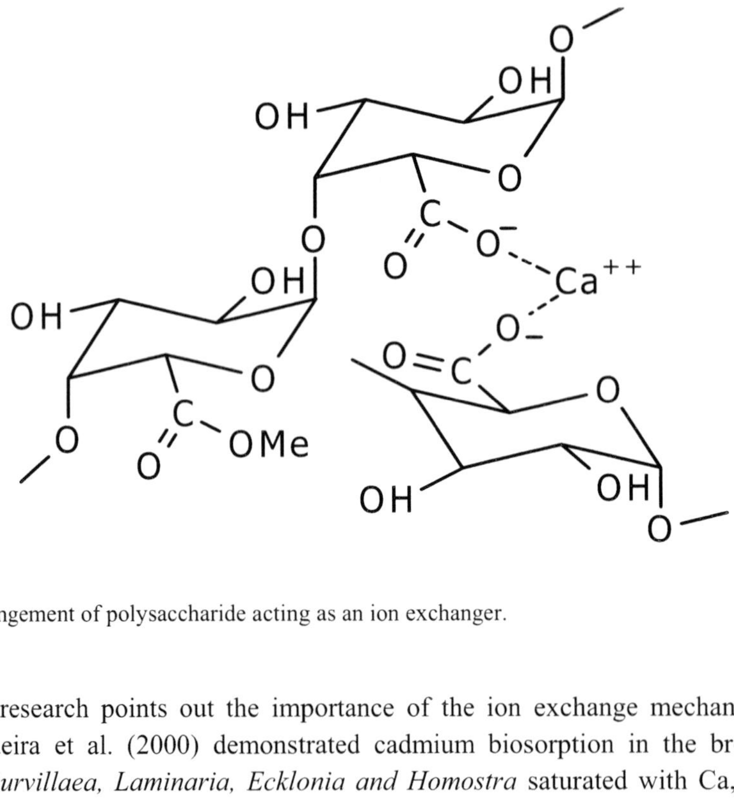

Figure 4. Arrangement of polysaccharide acting as an ion exchanger.

Related research points out the importance of the ion exchange mechanism on metal uptake. Figueira et al. (2000) demonstrated cadmium biosorption in the brown seaweed biomasses *Durvillaea, Laminaria, Ecklonia and Homostra* saturated with Ca, Mg or K by means of ion exchange. Kratochvil and Volesky (1998) have shown the biosorption of copper from water by ion exchange using *Sargassum* algal biomass. Ion exchange was also found to be responsible for copper biosorption by the fungi *Ganoderma lucidum* (Muraleedharan and Venkobachar 1990) and *Aspegillus niger* (Venkobachar 1990).

In regard to the mineral adsorbents, ion exchange is the most common mechanism related to these materials and it is explained due to three dimensional structures of majority components that undergo isomorphic transformation by replacement of higher oxidation state metals with ones having lower oxidation states, thus resulting in negatively charged sites. For instance, in zeolites the large channels contain negatively charged sites resulting from Al (III) replacement of Si (IV) in the tetrahedral linked by oxygen atoms. Therefore, positively charged exchangeable ions, such as Na, Ca (II) and Mg (II), occupy these spaces in the structure, and can be replaced with heavy metals (Bailey et al. 1999).

Classification and Application of Natural Adsorbents for Effluent Treatment

Biosorbents

Biosorbents are an important class of natural adsorbents because, unlike ion exchange resins, which are designed with single functionalities, the biosorbents contain an assortment of organic groups, including amino, carboxylate, hydroxide, imidazole, sulfate, phosphate and phenolic, thus providing higher adsorptive capacitive for metals than commercial synthetic adsorbents. Moreover, due to the diversity of active binding sites, biosorbents are less subject to interferences from alkali and alkali-earth metals than are ion exchange resins (Bag et al. 1998).

There are two broad categories of binding involving biosorbents, depending on whether metal uptake occurs in living or nonliving organisms. The first category, also known as passive binding, occurs in both living and dead organisms, and involves a fast interaction between cell surfaces and metals. The second category, active interaction, is more complex and consists of a fast initial surface binding followed by a second slower metal uptake, which involves biological process initialized by cell membrane binding, followed by transport of the metal across the membrane and chemical reactions such as methylation, reduction or oxidation. From these comments, living organisms that present active binding are not frequently indicated for metal removal because metal toxicity to these living organisms decreases the effectiveness of metal uptake and, thus, their usefulness in decontamination of aqueous effluents (Madrid and Cámara 1997).

The application of biosorbents for effluent treatment, especially those involving nonliving organisms, has been carried out successfully. Madrid et al. (1998) showed the potential of the bacteria *Spirula platensis* for removing chromium from leather industry wastewater. The experiments were performed using the batch method, where 0.2 g of *Spirula platencis* were added to 25 mL of wastewater containing 592 mg L^{-1} of chromium. After treatment, the resulting chromium concentration in the supernatant was only 9 mg L^{-1}, thus removing 97% of metal from the leather industrial wastewater. In another work, Dos Santos and Lenzi (2000) used aquatic macrophytes (*Eichhornia crassipes*) as a biological filter in lead removal from effluents of the battery industry. In this study, which was carried out at greenhouses, different parameters were evaluated, such as the relationship between the mass of macrophytes per volume of contaminated solution in liters, time of contact, pH and temperature. Before treatment, the effluent was neutralized to pH 7. A lead concentration of 4.45 mg L^{-1} was removed with 99% efficiency under optimized conditions.

An interesting work published by Stoll and Duncan (1997) showed the industrial applicability of yeast (*Saccharomyces cerivisiae*) immobilized on polyethylenimine:glutaraldehyde (PEI:GA) with respect to copper, cadmium, chromium, nickel and zinc removal from an electroplating effluent. The greatest importance of this study is attributed to the use of immobilized yeast as a bioreactor using a continuous-flow stirred which makes it possible to reduce the time involved in the treatment as well as the operational costs.

Mineral Adsorbents

Mineral adsorbents from natural sources such as clay and zeolite, as well as waste products from industrial operations, including red mud and fly ash, have been considered as alternative materials for metal removal from aqueous effluents. In general, these adsorbents have become promising materials because they present high surface areas and excellent ion exchange capacities.

Zeolites occur naturally as silicate minerals and clinoptilolite is the most abundant among 40 natural zeolites. In many countries, such as Italy, Mexico, Iran, Greece and the United Kingdom, there are large deposits of zeolites, thus being important sources of these materials for treatment of wastewater contaminated with heavy metals. In this sense, several applications for this purpose have been carried out (Babel and Kurniawan 2003). Recently, Chojnacki et al. (2004) proposed a method for removing mercury ions in industrial effluents from copper smelters and refineries at both the laboratory and full-plant scales. According to an adsorption isotherm based on the Freundlich model, a maximum adsorption capacity of 1.2 meq g^{-1} was achieved. In the laboratory as well as in full-scale tests performed in batch, the mercury concentration in the effluent after treatment was below to that indicated in environmental pollution directives for streams (0.2 mg kg^{-1}).

Ouki and Kavannagh (1999) evaluated the efficiency of two natural zeolites (clinoptilolite and chabazite) for treating effluents containing lead, cadmium, copper, zinc, chromium, nickel and cobalt. The results indicate higher adsorption capacities are achieved with chabazite than with clinoptilotile. In addition, the authors also reported that both materials evaluated presented good characteristics with respect to selectivity. For instance, the selectivity sequence for clinoptilotile was: Pb>Cu>Cd>Zn>Cr>Co>Ni while for chabazite was Pb>Cd>Zn>Co>Cu>Ni>Cr.

Overall, although zeolites have proven to be an alternative natural material for removing heavy metals, it is important to stress that the low permeability of these materials requires an artificial support when the assays are performed by the column method.

Clay is a material similar to zeolites, also being an important soil component. It is divided into three species: smectites (including montmorillonite), kaolinite and micas. If one briefly evaluates the cost, clay is generally twenty times less expensive than activated carbon. Countries such as Lithuania, Georgia and Kazakhstan, as well as the United States of America, have large deposits of clay (Babel and Kurniawan 2003). Therefore, a number of studies have been carried out using clay for metal removal. The performance of wollastonite, a natural clay, for Cr (VI) removal from wastewater and industrial effluents was evaluated by Sharma (2003). Several adsorptive parameters, such as coefficient of pore diffusion, coefficient of mass transfer, temperature and adsorption pH, as well as parameters associated to the adsorption isotherm, were studied.

Zinc decontamination from wastewater using clay was carried out by Singh et al. (1988). In this work, the clay employed was from the kaolinite group which basically consists of aluminosilicates. An advantage of kaolinite is that it does not swell in aqueous media, this being an important characteristic for effluent treatment. The maximum removal efficiency was found to be at pH 8.0, where an adsorption capacity of 1.25 mg g^{-1} was achieved.

Utilization of by-products from industry, such as red mud and fly ash, as unconventional adsorbents have successfully been tested by several researchers, aiming to remove metal ions from aqueous effluents.

Red mud is a waste from bauxite refining used for aluminum production and is basically comprised of SiO_2, Al_2O_3, Fe_2O_3, TiO_2, CaO, MgO, Na_2O and K_2O. Due to its composition and texture, red mud presents high surface reactivity, thus showing favorable conditions for metal removal. The application of red mud in effluent treatment is less expressive than zeolites because they are only locally available near to the relevant industries.

Apak et al. (1998) have shown an interesting application of red mud for cadmium, copper and lead removal from contaminated water. Red mud was evaluated in the natural form (only including a wash with water to a neutral pH value), treated with 10 % (v/v) HCl, and heated at 600 $^{\circ}$C during 4 h. It was found, from studies carried out by both column and batch methods at pH varying from 4.2 to 6.0, that higher adsorptive capacities were achieved with the column method, mainly for red mud in the natural form. In addition, higher adsorptive capacities were found for lead, cadmium and copper, respectively, as 161, 160 and 110 mg g^{-1}, in this situation. A notable reutilization of the red mud after being used with contaminated water was performed by its incorporation in Portland cement, thus hindering the leaching of metals from the solidified concrete blocks over long periods, with the exception of copper ions that presented a concentration of 0.4 mg L^{-1} after 8 months in water in an alkaline medium (pH 8-9). It is important to note that the chemical composition of red mud can change, depending on the source. As an example, López et al. (1998) showed the feasibility of red mud for treating effluents containing cadmium, copper, nickel and zinc by using batch and column experiments. The maximum adsorption capacities, obtained from fits of the Langmuir isotherm (attained after 48 h of contact time) were 19.72, 12.59, 10.95 and 10.57 mg g^{-1}, respectively, for copper, zinc, nickel and cadmium. The effectiveness of red mud for phosphorus removal at high concentration from effluents was also related in the referred work.

Fly ash is also considered an unconventional adsorbent and presents similar composition to red mud. This material is a coal combustion by-product from thermal power plants. As with red mud, fly ash has excellent surface reactivity for metals based on ion exchange mechanisms.

The removal of different kind of inorganic species such as copper and lead as well as phosphate and nitrate from wastewater treatment plants by using fly ash was demonstrated by Gupta and Torres (1998). In this work, the authors performed the effluent treatment by the batch method, shaking 150 mL of effluent with a known amount of fly ash for 4 h. After treatment, high percentage removals were achieved for copper (42%), lead (85%) and phosphate (88%) while a less expressive removal for nitrate was observed (18%). In addition, the effluent after treatment showed a significant increase in pH, above pH 8, thus reaching the limits established by the EPA (Environmental Protection Agency) for the pH of discharged wastewater (6-9).

Research aiming at mercury adsorption using fly ash was carried out by Sen and Arnab (1987). Using the Freundlich model, it was reported that fly ash can adsorb 2.82 mg of mercury per gram of material at pH varying from 3.5 to 4.5. Similar to red mud, fly ash loaded with metals can also be efficiently solidified, for example, in concrete, in order to prevent any metal leaching to the environment.

Lignocellulosic and Humic Adsorbents

Lignocellulosic materials include agricultural wastes, such as apple residues, corncobs, husks of soybeans, peanuts and rice. The principal humic material is vermicompost.

Lignocellulosic materials are basically composed lignin, cellulose and hemicellulose, with lower protein content. So, due to its composition, studies related to metal adsorption by these materials have demonstrated that both complexation and ion exchange mechanisms are involved in metal uptake. An interesting characteristic of these materials is that they can be used in their natural form or modified chemically, using different chemical agents such as phosphoric and citric acids and alkaline solutions. The chemical modification is usually made aiming to enhance the adsorptive capacity.

Lee et al. (1998) employed apple residues chemically modified with phosphate as an available adsorbent for copper, lead and cadmium removal from aqueous solution. Column as well as batch experiments were carried out, and influences of sample pH, shaking time and chemical treatment were evaluated. It was found from adsorptive studies under optimized conditions that maximum adsorption capacities were 8.0 mg g^{-1} for copper and lead and 6.0 mg g^{-1} for cadmium. In a similar work, Senthilkumaar et al. (2000) evaluated waste fruit residues (orange, apple, pineapple, dates, grape, etc). These materials, which contained processed skins, seeds and stems, were successfully used for mercury, lead, cadmium, copper, nickel and zinc removal from aqueous solutions.

Wafwoyo et al. (1999) performed a study aiming to compare the effectiveness of peanut shells modified with citric and phosphoric acids to that of commercial resins (Amberlite IRC-718 and Duolite GT-73) for copper, lead, cadmium, nickel and zinc adsorption. The results demonstrated that, in general, treatment with phosphoric acid is more promising than treatment with citric acid. Moreover, the metal uptake by peanut shells treated with acid was approximately one-half that of the commercial resins. Nevertheless, it seems that, due to the low cost of peanut shells and the fact that this material is biodegradable, its application may still justify its use. Marshall et al. (1999) also investigated the modification of soybean hulls with citric acid. The method was developed to enhance copper adsorption in soybean hulls for wastewater treatment. Similar to those work already mentioned, the modification of soybean hulls greatly enhanced adsorptive capacity, thus making it possible to retain about 108 mg of copper per gram of hulls.

In another study, Vaughan et al. (2001) modified corncobs with either citric acid or phosphoric acid, and the experiments were carried out aiming to enhance the adsorption efficiency of five metal ions (cadmium, copper, lead, nickel and zinc) from mixed solutions or from single solutions. The adsorptive results were compared to those from Amberlite IRC-718, Amberlite 200, Duolite GT-73 and caboxymethylcelulose (CMC) commercial resins. It was observed that modified corncobs generally showed lower adsorption capacities than commercial resins for the metals when experiments are carried out using single solution. On the other hand, when adsorption experiments with the five metals were performed in a mixed solution the results were only slightly different. The efficiency of modified corncobs was similar to Duolite GT-73 for cadmium and copper, and the same or higher than Amberlite IRC-718 for lead. These results imply that, depending on the metal ion and the presence or absence of co-existing ions, chemically modified corncobs present similar adsorption properties to the commercial resins evaluated.

Regarding lignocellulosic materials such as corncobs and husks of soybeans and peanuts, rice milling by-products and rice husks are the most promising alternative material for treating effluents. Its great advantage over the other materials is attributed to large available quantities, its chemical composition of lignin, cellulose, hemicellulose and silicon, and also because it is considered a significant waste disposal problem by agro-industry. Annual rice production in Brazil, for example, was about 12 million tons in 2002. Therefore, as rice husks represents 23% of the rice grains, *ca.* of 3 million tons of this material were disposed of in the environment that year (IBGE 2002). Even though rice husks that were traditionally used by the rice industry as an energy source for boilers, this procedure causes damage to workers' health because the burning of rice husks produces a black powder that, when inhaled, provokes silicosis, an illness that decreases the elasticity of the lung (Imagawa et al. 2000). Thus, rice husks are an alternative for effluent treatment because, in addition to contributing to metal removal from aqueous effluents it is another way to reuse this agricultural waste. Furthermore, it is important to note that, like mineral adsorbents, rice husks loaded with metals after effluent treatment may be used to reinforce material in the construction industry (in concrete, for example), because rice husks presents a high silicon content and have abrasive characteristics.

In this way, Tarley and Arruda (2004) pointed out the potentially of rice husks for heavy metal removal in laboratory effluents. In addition, these authors emphasized the morphologic characteristics of rice husks as well as the main chemical groups capable to take up metals by using several spectroscopic techniques. The experiments were carried out by a column method, in which parameters such as pH, particle size and sample flow rate (associated with the adsorptive performance of cadmium and lead) were evaluated. Under optimized conditions (pH 4, particle size ≤ 355 μm, sample flow rate 8 mL min^{-1}) the method was applied for treating laboratory effluents containing several metal ions and organic substances resulting from sample decomposition procedures. The cadmium and lead concentration in the effluent before treatment was, respectively, 22 and 12 mg L^{-1}, and after treatment with 30 g of rice husks the concentrations were 0.3 mg L^{-1} and < 0.7 mg L^{-1}, which is lower than limits established by EPA for water disposal containing heavy metals (0.48 mg L^{-1} for cadmium and 1.32 mg L^{-1} for lead). In addition, the effluent showed an increase in pH (from 4.0 to 5.2) after treatment, thus complying with Brazilian legislation (CONAMA) for the pH of discharged water samples (pH 5-9). Other metals, including aluminum, copper and zinc, were also evaluated, having removal percentages of 98, 88 and 89%, respectively.

Mishra et al. (1998) showed the uptake behavior of rice husks for Hg and Cr (III). Higher adsorption performance of these metals takes place at pH 10, where the maximum adsorptive capacities for mercury and chromium were 0.156 mg g^{-1} and 0.079 mg g^{-1}, respectively. Rice husks were used for chromium removal from industrial effluents containing several inorganic and organic species by Khalid et al. (1999). According to their results, for decontamination of

5000 liters of effluent having 11 mg L^{-1} of chromium, only 21 kg of rice husks need be used. Overall, the results demonstrate that rice husks may be considered nowadays a promising natural material for effluent treatment.

Humic substances, from vermicompost, on the other hand, have been less employed for metal adsorption even though presenting high adsorption capacity for metals due to their negatively charged functional groups, including phenolic groups, carboxylic acids and alcoholic hydroxyls from the lignin structure. The vermicompost produced by vermicomposting is a result of biological degradation and stabilization of organic matter when agricultural, industrial and urban wastes are decomposed by earthworms (Senesi 1989).

Matos and Arruda (2003) pointed out, in a pioneering work, the effectiveness of vermicompost as an inexpensive natural material for cadmium, copper, lead and zinc removal from laboratory effluents. The study was carried out by the column method, and several experimental parameters were evaluated in order to attain the highest adsorptive performance. According to these authors, applying the Langmuir adsorption isotherm, the maximum adsorption capacities of vermicompost for cadmium, copper, lead and zinc were 33.0, 32.6, 92.9 and 28.4 mg g^{-1}, respectively, thus emphasizing its potential as a natural adsorbent. The laboratory effluents were considered treated only after attaining the values established by EPA (0.48, 4.14, 1.32 and 2.87 mg L^{-1} for Cd, Cu, Pb and Zn, respectively) for metal disposal in water as well as the required pH. So, according to the results, only 2.5 g of vermicompost were necessary for treating 100 mL of effluent (containing, respectively, 25, 13, 12 and 28 mg L^{-1} of cadmium, copper, lead and zinc) while the pH was increased from 3.5 to 7.3.

Characterization and Application of Loof Sponge (*Luffa Cylindrica*) as an Alternative Material for Metal Adsorption: Case Study

As an example of the use of natural material for effluent treatment, the loof sponge (*Luffa cylindrica*) emphasizes the potentialities of these natural materials for this task.

Loof sponges are members of the *Cucurbitaceae* and have been cultivated for centuries in the Middle East and India, China, Japan, and Malaysia (Davis 1994). Nowadays, it is abundantly produced in several countries such as the United States of America and Brazil. Usually, loof sponges are only used for personal hygiene and household cleaning. Loof sponge is a natural material consisting of a fibrous network (see Figure 5) and presents high specific pore volumes, stable physical properties, biodegradability and non-toxicity. Due to its characteristics it has also been used as a support for microorganisms in bioreactors. Thus, considering all these characteristics, the proposal to use loof sponge as an alternative material for metal removal seems suitable, mainly by considering both the simplicity and the low cost that would be involved in metal removal from an aqueous medium. As an application, the potential of using loof sponge as an alternative lignocellulosic material for lead adsorption in an aqueous medium was evaluated.

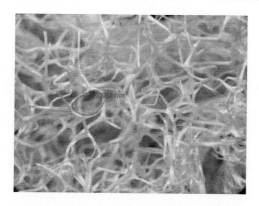

Figure 5. Aspect of loof sponge *in natura* (36 times magnification).

Therefore, before initialing this approach to an adsorbent for metal ions, loof sponge was first characterized by using several spectroscopic techniques in order to know the main chemical groups present to take up lead ions. After that, adsorptive experiments for lead ions were carried out by using a batch method, aiming to establish the best results for sample pH and shaking time. Finally, loof sponge was used for lead removal in laboratory effluents using a column method. All chemical characterizations as well as adsorptive assays were carried out by using loof sponge with particle sizes ≤ 355 μm. For treating effluent, loof sponge was used as its' *in natura* form, without prior chemical or physical treatment.

Techniques Used for Chemical Characterization of Loof Sponge

Loof sponge was characterized using several techniques. The ^{13}C NMR high resolution spectra of loof sponge samples were carried out with a frequency of 500 MHz using cross polarization and magic angle spinning (CP/MAS), on a Varian INOVA nuclear magnetic resonance spectrometer. A Perkin-Elmer FT-IR 1605 infrared spectrometer was used to elucidate the functional groups present in loof sponge. The experiments were made using KBr discs to prepare the loof sponge samples and the spectral range varied from 4000 to 500 cm^{-1}.

The X-ray diffraction spectra were obtained by using a Shimadzu XRD 6000 X-ray diffractometer. Samples were exposed to X-ray (λ = 1.54060 Å) with the 2θ angle varying between 5 and 50°. The applied voltage and current were 40 kV and 30 mA, respectively. For C, N and H determinations in the loof sponge samples a Perkin-Elmer PE 2400 elemental analyzer was used. The thermal behaviour of loof sponge was obtained by using a TA Instruments TGA 2950 thermogravimetric analyzer. About 10 mg of loof sponge were heated up to 950 °C in an oxidizing atmosphere at 20 °C min^{-1}.

The total metal content in loof sponge was quantified in a Perkin-Elmer Model Optima DV 3000 inductively coupled plasma optical emission spectrometer (ICP OES) as well as in a Perkin-Elmer Model Analyst 600 electrothermal atomic absorption spectrometer (ETAAS), equipped with Zeeman background correction. For measurements by ICP OES and ETAAS, loof sponge samples were decomposed with mineral acids using a microwave oven (QCI, QW-3000).

A JEOL JMT-300 scanning electron microscope (SEM) was additionally used to check the morphological characteristics of loof sponge. Samples were covered with a thin layer of gold and an electron acceleration voltage of 20 kV was applied.

Chemical Characterization of Loof Sponge

Results from elemental analyses (% m/m) showed a high carbon content, 45.19 ± 1.33, followed by hydrogen 5.76 ± 0.19 and nitrogen 1.20 ± 0.34. The remainder (47.85 %) is probability due to high oxygen content and, possibly, the presence of sulphur and moisture. The experimental results are in agreement with those obtained for other vegetable biomasses, which are basically composed of cellulose, hemicellulose and lignin (Juliano 1985).

An important tool used to obtain active sites in macromolecules, such as lignin, cellulose and hemicellulose, is solid state ^{13}C NMR. The presence of resonance lines associated to the lignocellulosic structure of loof sponge can be verified from the ^{13}C NMR spectrum (Figure 6). Basically, the ^{13}C NMR spectrum obtained from natural adsorbents such as vegetable biomass provides resonance lines attributed to repeating units of cellulose, hemicellulose and lignin. Thus, the signal intensity for cellulose was associated to resonance lines of glucose, which present different signals as follows: C-1 at 106 ppm, C-2, 3, 5 at 74 and 76 ppm; C-4 at 85 and 89 ppm: C-6 at 64 and 65 ppm. The splitting of the C-4 resonance lines is usually attributed to the presence of amorphous and crystalline cellulosic regions (Solum et al. 1995).

Related to lignin, the resonance lines were attributed to a guaiacyl unit, as seen in Figure 6 (structural unit – left side). It was also possible to identify the peak related to methoxyl groups at 57 ppm. In addition, some peaks due to aromatic carbon, ranging from 115 to 150 ppm, were also observed (Freitas et al. 1997).

Finally, the peaks for hemicellulose were attributed to acetate groups present in its structure. Signals at 22 ppm (methyl carbon) and 175 ppm (carboxyl carbon) were also observed, while others were not identified due to the superimposed cellulose resonance lines.

The identification of some characteristic functional groups capable of adsorbing metal ions was performed using Fourier transform infrared (FT-IR). As shown in Figure 7, the presence of OH groups on the loof sponge surface is confirmed by a broad band between 3000 and 3750 cm^{-1} (Kamath and Proctor 1998). This OH group stretching is associated with adsorbed water on the loof sponge surface. On the other hand, other OH groups bound to methyl radicals showed a signal between 2940 and 2820 cm^{-1}. These groups are common in the lignin structure (López Pasquali and Herrera 1997). The peaks located at 1730 and 1640 cm^{-1} are characteristic of carbonyl group stretching from aldehydes and ketones. These groups can be conjugated or non-conjugated to aromatic rings (1640 and 1730 cm^{-1}, respectively). The peaks associated with the stretching in aromatic rings were verified at 1511 cm^{-1} while deformations related to C-H and C-O bonds were observed from 1085 to 1030 cm^{-1}.

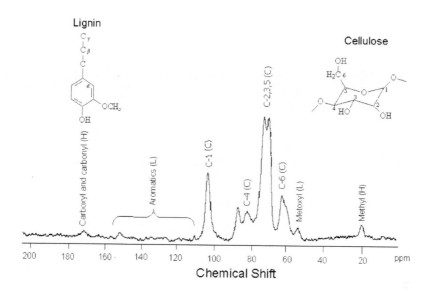

Figure 6. ^{13}C NMR spectrum of loof sponge. Peak labels refer to the typical building units associated with cellulose (C), lignin (L) and acetate groups in hemicellulose (H).

The behavior of the thermogravimetric curves indicates that mass loss is related to elimination of moisture and decomposition of cellulose, hemicellulose and lignin (Figure 8). Thus, a mass loss of 2.8% by heating the loof sponge up to 250 °C is due to the elimination of moisture retained in this material. Then, the second step of pyrolysis was obtained when the temperature was varied from 250 to 360 °C. In this step, a higher mass loss (*ca* 56%) was observed. The behavior of the pyrolysis curve at this temperature indicates hemicellulose and cellulose decomposition, as well as loss of the remaining adsorbed water (Teng and Wei 1998). Lignin decomposition occurs in the 360 to 525°C range, wherein 99.6 % of loof sponge is decomposed, thus indicating that this structure presents higher stability than hemicellulose and cellulose.

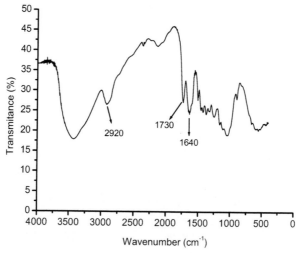

Figure 7. FT-IR spectrum of loof sponge.

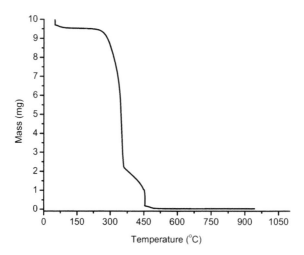

Figure 8. TG curve of loof sponge.

The X-ray diffraction spectrum of loof sponge is shown in Figure 9. Two broad peaks from 15 to 35° 2θ diffraction angles were obtained. The diffraction angles varying from 13 to 18° and 19 to 23° are, respectively, attributed to amorphous and crystalline cellulose.

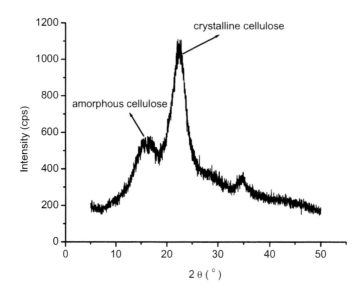

Figure 9. X-ray spectrum of loof sponge.

Metal concentrations in the loof sponge were determined by ICP OES and ETAAS after microwave assisted decomposition. Table 1 shows the quantitative analyses by ICP OES and ETAAS, in which the main macrocomponents were Ca and Mg. Low concentrations of Cd (II) were observed but other elements, such as Pb, Ni, Mn and K, were not identified in loof sponge. Hence, the low metal content in loof sponge can be considered a good characteristic for its application as a material for metal uptake.

Table 1. Metal concentrations in loof sponge determined by ICP OES and ETAAS (n=5).

Metals	Concentration ($\mu g\ g^{-1}$)
Al	46.9 ± 20.9
Ca[a]	1444 ± 106
Cd[b]	0.010 ± 0.0040
Cr	1.78 ± 0.50
Fe	1.02 ± 0.30
Mg	208 ± 15

[a] Results in mg g^{-1}; [b] Determined by ETAAS

Scanning electron micrographs of loof sponge are shown in Figure 10. As one can see, the morphological characteristic based on presence of irregularities on the surface of this material makes possible to conclude that loof sponge presents an adequate morphological profile to retain metal ions.

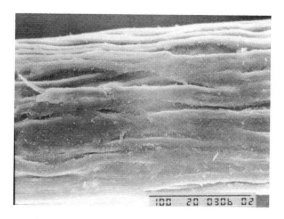

Figure 10. Scanning electron micrograph of loof sponge (≤ 355 μm) (500 times magnification). The bar indicates the magnification that is represented by the first number (in μm).

Adsorption Studies

Adsorption experiments were carried out in batch procedures at room temperature. Loof sponge samples of 50 mg were taken and stirred in closed polyethylene flasks with 50 mL Pb (II) solutions at 25 mg L^{-1} concentration.

Those variables associated with the adsorption profile of Pb (II) on loof sponge were evaluated (pH and shaking time, Figure 11) in order to obtain the optimum conditions for construction of adsorption isotherms.

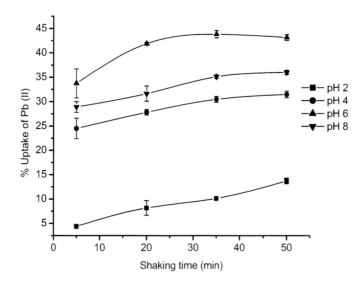

Figure 11. Pb (II) ion adsorption profiles on loof sponge at different pH and shaking times. Bars indicate the RSD for each condition (n=3).

As one can see, higher Pb (II) adsorption takes place at pH 6 and 8, while only slight variations of the results are observed after 20 min of shaking time. From these results, the optimum conditions for Pb (II) adsorption were studied by using a 3^2 factorial design using the best results obtained from the univariate method. Thus, the 4, 6 and 8 levels for pH were chosen while 20, 35 and 50 min levels for shaking time were employed. In Table 2, the levels used and the results obtained are summarized.

Table 2. Full factorial design (3^2) and the results obtained for Pb (II) adsorption on loof sponge

Runs	pH	Shaking time	% Uptake of Pb (II)
1	-1	-1	27.8 ± 0.6
2	0	-1	41.9 ± 0.3
3	1	-1	31.6 ± 1.6
4	-1	0	30.5 ± 1.8
5	0	0	43.8 ± 0.8
6	1	0	35.1 ± 0.4
7	-1	1	31.5 ± 0.7
8	0	1	43.2 ± 0.6
9	1	1	36.0 ± 0.4

Levels -1, 0 and 1 mean, respectively, the pH values 4, 6 e 8 and shaking time values 20, 35 and 50 minutes.

The 3^2 factorial design gives a quadratic model-function that represents the relationship between the variables and the responses. This strategy can be seen by using the mathematical treatment proposed by Mathias (1999), which provides the model-function and the response surface of a 3^2 factorial design. Therefore, the model-function (Eq.(10)) for Pb (II) adsorptions is:

Pb (II) adsorption (%) on loof sponge = 43.14 - 10.88 x pH^2 Eq.(10)

From this equation, it is evident that the effect of shaking time on Pb (II) adsorption is not significant while the pH of the sample plays an important role in the adsorption process, within experimental domain studied. Higher Pb (II) adsorptions are obtained at pH values between 6.0 and 8.0, while 20 min is enough to reach the equilibrium conditions of Pb (II) ions between the liquid and solid phases. At higher pH values (*i.e* pH 8.0) there was a small decrease (*ca.* 17%) of the adsorption, probably due to the formation of Pb(OH)$_2$. The optimum pH value (6.0) is shown by the response surface constructed from the model-function adsorption, as demonstrated in Figure 12.

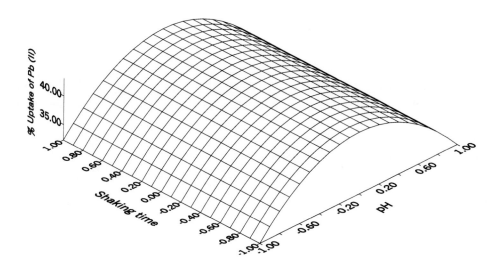

Figure 12. Response surface obtained from 3^2 factorial design. For respective values of pH and shaking time see Table 2.

Adsorption Isotherm

The adsorption capacity of loof sponge towards Pb (II) ions was determined after establishing the optimum conditions for pH and shaking time, pH 6.0 and 20 min, respectively, followed by measuring equilibrium isotherms. From adsorption isotherms of Pb (II) ions on loof sponge, a saturation condition of the surface for the material was obtained by increasing the metal ion concentrations (MAC). Thus, it was carried out using 50 mg loof sponge samples stirred in closed polyethylene flasks with 50 mL of Pb (II) solutions ranging in concentration from 1.3 to 300 mg L^{-1}. The isotherm shown in Figure 13 was then linearized according to the Langmuir adsorption isotherm model (Figure 14), to obtain the MAC. The Langmuir adsorption isotherm equation and the characteristics of this model have already been discussed (see Adsorption Process section).

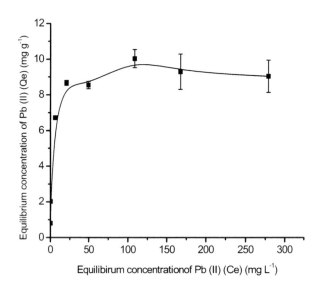

Figure 13. Adsorption isotherm plot for Pb (II) ions on loof sponge. Bars indicate the RSD for each condition (n=3).

As observed from Figure 14, the experimental data were well fitted by the Langmuir equation (R $\geq$ 0.999). Consequently, the adsorption process of metal ions on loof sponge follows the Langmuir isotherm model, where the metal ions are independently taken up on a single type of binding site so that the uptake of the first metal ion does not affect the adsorption of the next ion.

Considering the Langmuir model, the MAC can be obtained from the inverse of the angular coefficient of the linear curve, as already exemplified in the Langmuir Isotherm section. Therefore, the maximum amount (mg) of Pb (II) that is adsorbed, per gram of loof sponge, is 9.2.

Optimization of Column Experiments Using Loof Sponge for Pb (II) Ion Adsorption

Lead removal by loof sponge in effluent treatment was carried out only after optimization of the sample flow rate, which plays an important role in the retention of metals ions. This experiment was carried out in glass columns (30 x 3.4 cm) coupled to a peristaltic pump for controlling the column eluate flow rate. For checking the effect of flow rate on metal uptake, this parameter was varied (2, 4, 6 or 8 mL min^{-1}). For these experiments, 100 mL of a solution at pH 6.0 (as the same obtained in batch procedure), containing Pb (II) at 100 mg L^{-1}, was passed through a packed column containing 2 g of loof sponge.

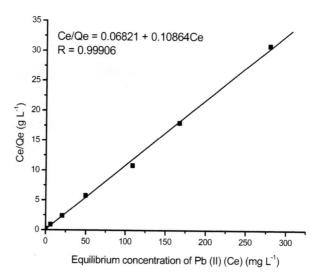

$$Ce/Qe = 0.06821 + 0.10864Ce$$
$$R = 0.99906$$

Figure 14. Linearized Langmuir adsorption isotherm plot for Pb (II) ions on loof sponge.

The behavior of Pb (II) ion adsorption (Figure 15) shows that, when varying the sample flow rate from 2 to 8 mL min^{-1}, a decrease of 25% in Pb (II) adsorption occurs. Therefore, although the time for treating effluents by using higher sample flow rates is lower, the sample flow rate used was 2 mL min^{-1}, because, at this flow rate, a higher Pb (II) adsorption is obtained, thus making it possible to attain the limits established by EPA for Pb (II) disposal in water.

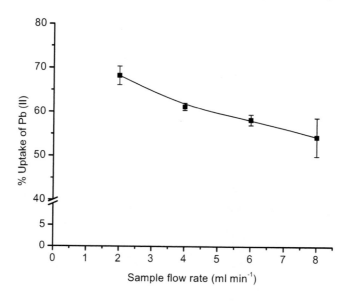

Figure 15. Effect of flow rate on Pb (II) adsorption on loof sponge. Bars indicate the RSD for each condition (n=3).

Procedure for Pb (II) Ion Removal from Laboratory Effluent

These experiments were carried out by the column method using known masses of loof sponge, without prior chemical or physical treatment, packed into the glass columns. This strategy was adopted to simplify the process and make it more rapid.

The effluent used was obtained from an analytical chemistry laboratory. It was made up of residues from sample preparation processes (different mineral acids and oxidizing agents), organic compounds used for extraction of different metals in biological samples, slurry samples (in general from biological samples) and, finally, solutions of metals used for calibration procedures in atomic absorption spectrometry.

Before treatment, the pH value of this laboratory effluent was adjusted to 4.0 with 10 mol L^{-1} NaOH solution. The pH was not adjusted to pH 6.0 in order to prevent lead precipitation as $Pb(OH)_2$. The Pb (II) concentration in this solution, as determined by flame atomic absorption spectrometry (FAAS), was 10.2 mg L^{-1}.

The operational conditions for effluent treatment were a 2.0 mL min^{-1} sample flow rate with loof sponge masses ranging from 2 to 6, to promote good retentions of the Pb (II) ions. The limiting Pb (II) concentrations (0.5 mg L^{-1}) in the treated effluent were defined according to CONAMA. Only after attaining these conditions the effluent was considered for disposal.

According to the results shown in Figure 16, 6 g of loof sponge was enough for retaining more than 98% of Pb (II) ions contained in 100 mL of laboratory effluent. This concentration is lower than the Pb (II) value established by Brazilian legislation (CONAMA - 0.5 mg L^{-1}).

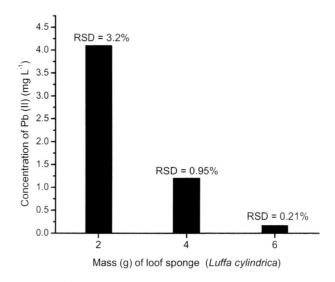

Figure 16. Effect of mass of loof sponge on Pb (II) adsorption in laboratory effluent. In each condition the measurements were made in triplicate.

Final Remarks

In recent years there has been considerable interest for applying natural adsorbent materials in effluent treatment, as can be attested by a series of these examples in the literature. According to these, some important characteristics for natural adsorbent materials for effluent treatment as well as it shown the potentialities of these materials for this task have been indicated.

In this way, adsorptive processes were discussed in terms of physical interactions between different phases, emphasizing ion exchange and complexation. From this discussion, the importance for obtaining adsorption isotherms was also pointed out and some models were commented.

The classification of natural adsorbents, as biosorbents, mineral adsorbents, and lignocellulosic and humic adsorbents, was presented, and different applications of each of these materials for effluent treatment was described.

As an example, the loof sponge (*Lufa cylindrica*) was proposed for laboratory effluent treatment focusing on the Pb(II) species. For this purpose, the material was characterized by physical and chemical tests, its capacity was measured and different parameters were studied to enhance for its use as adsorbent (such as flow rate, mass, adsorption pH, and others).

Although different materials have already been applied for effluent treatment, a great variety can still be proposed for this task. In this way, the main efforts could be directed to knowing their structures (through characterization), establishing the kinds of interaction (through isotherms) and testing each material in a real application (through optimization of effluent treatment parameters). From these steps effluent treatment efficiency can be improved and the applicability of these materials for other purposes can be made a reality.

Acknowledgements

The authors thank Prof. Carol H. Collins for critical comments.

References

Acar, F. N., Malkoc, E. *Bioresource Technol.*, 2004, *94*, 13.

Agrawal, A., Sahu, K. K., Pandey, B. D. *Colloids Surf. A*, 2004, *237*, 133.

Aldrich, C., Feng, D. *Miner. Eng.*, 2000, *13*, 1129.

Apak, R., Tutem, E., Hugul, M., Hizal. J. *Water. Res.*, 1998, *32*, 430.

Aksu, Z., Sag, Y., Kutsal T. *Environ. Technol.*, 1992, *13*, 579.

Babel, S., Kurniawan, T. A. *J. Hazard. Mater.*, 2003, *97*, 219.

Bag, H., Lale, M., Turker, A. R. *Talanta*, 1998, *47*, 689.

Bailey, S. E., Olin, T. J., Bricka, R. M., Adrian, D. D. *Water Res.*, 1999, *33*, 2469.

Bajpai, J., Shrivastava, R., Bajpai, A.K. *Colloids Surf. A*, 2004, *236*, 81.

Brazilian Institute of Geography and Statistics (IBGE) 2002. Research Division – DIPEQ/SC. Systematic Survey of Production Agriculturist, Florianópolis.

Brown, P. A., Gill, S. A., Allen, S. J. *Water Res.*, 2000, *34*, 3907.

Chojnacki, A., Chojnacka, K., Hoffmann, J., Górecki, H. *Miner. Eng.,* 2004, 17, 933.

Dabowski, A. *Adv. Colloid Interface Sci.,* 2000, *93,* 135.

Davis, J. M. *HortScience,* 1994, *29,* 263.

Dos Santos, M. C., Lenzi, E. *Environ. Technol.,* 2000, *21,* 615.

Environmental Protection Agency (EPA) 2000. Code of federal regulations. Chapter I. Part 437. Subpart A- Metals treatment and recovery, Section 437.11.

Feng, C., Suzuki, K., Zhao, S., Sugiura, N., Shimada, S., Maekawa, T. *Bioresource Technol.,* 2004, *94,* 21

Figueira, M. M., Volesky, B., Ciminelli, V. S. T., Roddick, F. A.. *Water Res.,* 2000, *34,*196.

Freitas, J. C. C., Cunha, A. G., Emmerich, F. G. *Fuel,* 1997, *76,* 229.

Gaballah, I., Kilbertus, G. *J.Geochem. Explor.,* 1998, *62,* 241.

Gupta, G., Torres, N. *J.Hazard. Mater.,* 1998, *57,* 243.

Henze, M., Harremoes, P., Cour Jansen, J. I., Arvin, E. *WasteWater Treatment.* Springer-Verlag, Berlin, 1995.

Hervas, L., Mazuelos, C., Senesi, N., Saiz-Jiménez, C. *Sci. Total Environ.,* 1989, *81/82,* 543.

Hsieh, C. T., Teng, H. *Carbon.,* 2000, *38,* 863.

http://www.iupac.org/reports/2001/colloid_2001/manual_of_s_and_t/node15.html#sec:1.1.5. (Accessed in May 2004)

Imagawa, A., Seto, R., Nagaosa, Y. *Carbon,* 2000, *38,* 628.

Juang, R. S., Shiau, R. C. *J. Membr. Sci.,* 2000, *165,* 159.

Juliano, B. O. *Rice Chemistry and Technology.* American Association of Cereal Chemistry, New York, 1985.

Kamath, S. R., Proctor, A. *Cereal Chem.,* 1998, *75,* 484.

Khalid, N., Rahman, A., Ahamad, S., Toheed, A., Ahmed, J. *J. Radioanal. Nucl. Chem.,* 1999, *240,* 775.

Kim, Y., Kim, C., Choi, I., Rengaraj, S., Yi, J. *Environ. Sci. Technol.,* 2004, *38,* 924.

Kratochvil, D., Volesky, B. *Water Res.,* 1998, *32,* 2760.

Lacour, S., Bollinger, J. C., Serpaud, B., Chantron, P., Arcos, R. *Anal. Chim. Acta,* 2001, *428,* 121.

Lee, S. H., Jung, C. H., Chung, H., Lee, M. Y., Yang, J. *Process Biochem.,* 1998, *33,* 205

López Pasquali, C. E., Herrera, H. *Thermochim. Acta,* 1997, *293,* 39.

López, E., Soto, B., Arias, M., Núñez, A., Rubinos, D., Barral, M. T. *Water Res.,* 1998, *32,* 1314.

Madrid, Y., Barrio-Cordoba, M. E., Cámara, C. *Analyst,* 1998, *123,* 1593.

Madrid, Y., Cámara, C. *Trends Anal. Chem.,* 1997, *16,* 36.

Marshall, W. E., Johns, M. M. *J. Chem. Technol. Biotechnol.,* 1996, *66,* 192.

Marshall, W. E., Wartelle, L. H., Boler, D. E., Johns, M. M., Toles, C. A. *Bioresource Technol.,* 1999, *69,* 263.

Matos, G. D., Arruda, M. A. Z. *Process Biochem.,* 2003, *39,* 81.

Matthias, O. *Chemometrics – Statistics and Computer Application in Analytical Chemistry,* Wiley – VCH: Weinheim, 1999.

Mishra, S., Tiwari, D., Dubey, R. S., Mishra, M. *Radiochim. Acta,* 1998, *80,* 47.

Muraleedharan, T. R., Venkobachar, C. *Biotechnol. Bioeng.,* 1990, *35,* 320.

National Council of Enviroment (CONAMA) 1986, Resolution number 20, June 18.

Okieimen, F. E., Maya, A. O., Oriakhi, C. O. *Int. J. Environ. Anal. Chem.,* 1988, *32,* 23.

Ouki, S. K., Kavannagh, M. *Water Sci. Technol.,* 1999, *39*, 115.

Pagnanelli, F., Veglio, F., Toro, L. *Chemosphere,* 2004, *54*, 905.

Pereira, M. G., Arruda, M. A. Z. *J. Braz. Chem. Soc.,* 2002, *14*, 39.

Sag, Y., Kutsal, T. *Biochem. Eng.,* 2000, *6*, 145.

Senesi, N. *Sci. Total Environ.,* 1989, *81*, 521.

Sen, A. K., Arnab, K. D. *Water Res.,* 1987, *19*, 869.

Senthilkumaar, S., Bharathi, S., Nithyanandhi, D., Subburam, V. *Bioresource Technol.,* 2000, *75*, 163.

Sharma, Y. C. *Colloids Surf. A,* 2003, *215*, 155.

Singh, A. K., Singh, D. P., Singh, V. N. *Environ. Technol. Lett.,* 1988, *9*, 1153.

Solum, M. S., Pugmire, R. J., Jagtoyen, M., Derbyshire, F. *Carbon,* 1995, *33*, 1247.

Stoll, A., Duncan, J. R. *Process Biochem.,* 1997, *32*, 467.

Tarley, C. R. T., Arruda, M. A. Z. *Chemosphere,* 2004, *54*, 987.

Teng, H., Wei, Y. *Ind. Eng. Chem. Res.,* 1998, *37*, 3806.

Tsezos, M., Volesky, B. *Biotechnol. Bioeng.,* 1981, *23*, 583.

Vaughan, T., Seo, C. W., Marshall, W. E. *Bioresource Technol.,* 2001, *78*, 133.

Venkobachar, C. *Water Sci. Technol.,* 1990, *22*, 319.

Wafwoyo, W., Seo, C. W., Marshall, W. E. *J. Chem. Technol. Biotechnol.,* 1999, *74*, 1117.

In: Trends in Water Pollution Research
Editor: J. V. Livingston, pp. 167-180

ISBN 1-59454-328-3
©2005 Nova Science Publishers, Inc.

Chapter VII

Biodegradability Improvement of Penicillin Formulation Effluent by Ozonation and the Fenton Reagents

Idil Arslan - Alaton[1]

Istanbul Technical University, Faculty of Civil Engineering, Department of
Environmental Engineering, 34469 Maslak, Istanbul, Turkey

Abstract

Effects of ozonation and Fenton's treatment on the biodegradability of pharmaceutical wastewater originating from the *Sultamycillin Tosylate Diydrate* penicillin formulation was investigated. Process variables were ozone feed rates ($127 – 2750$ mg $l^{-1}h^{-1}$), ozonation pH as well as the type of Fenton's reagents (Fenton; Fe^{2+}/H_2O_2 and Fenton-like; Fe^{3+}/H_2O_2) applied at a fixed pH ($= 3.0$) and different Fe (0.5, 1 mM Fe^{2+} and Fe^{3+}) and H_2O_2 concentrations (10, 20 mM). The efficiency of the selected pre-treatment systems was evaluated in terms of changes in COD (Chemical Oxygen Demand), TOC (Total Organic Carbon) and BOD_5 (5-Day Biochemical Oxygen Demand). The effect of chemical oxidative pre-treatment on activated sludge treatment performance was assessed in terms of microbial oxygen uptake rate (OUR) measurements conducted with unacclimated sewage sludge. Results have demonstrated that although similar overall COD ($34 - 42$ %) and TOC ($24 - 36$ %) removal efficiencies have been obtained by the ozonation process and the Fenton and Fenton – like reagents, only ozonation and Fenton-like processes were capable of completely eliminating the inhibitory effect of the penicillin formulation effluent on the microbial consortium in sewage sludge. Moreover, the Fenton-like and ozonation processes appeared to slightly enhance COD abatement rates by 4 % and 8 %, respectively, as could also be demonstrated in separate biodegradation experiments that were run with the raw, pre-treated formulation effluent in the same biosludge.

---

[1] Fax: + 90 212 285 65 87; Phone: + 90 212 285 65 76; E-mail: arslanid@itu.edu.tr

Key words: Advanced oxidation, activated sludge inhibition, biodegradability improvement, Fenton's reagent, penicillin formulation effluent, pharmaceutical wastewater, ozonation.

Introduction

Bulk pharmaceutical substances consist of structurally complex organic chemical compounds that are produced within several steps under a variety of precise conditions. Most of the substances involved in the chemical synthesis are listed as priority pollutants [1]. These organic and inorganic compounds that are considered as the principal environmental concern of this sector are generated during the synthesis and formulation steps of production. Hence special attention has recently been devoted to the sustainable, integrated treatment of pharmaceutical formulation effluent [1].

The wide application range of antibiotics in human and veterinary medicine has led to large scale dissemination of refractory and even toxic pollutants in the environment [2,3]. In many countries, a multitude of extremely resistant antibiotics have been found in treated sewage, industrial effluent, the aquatic environment and even in drinking water. These products are discharged into receiving water bodies due to incomplete removal in industrial and municipal treatment plants [4,5]. Most known treatment practices and technologies have appeared to be inappropriate for antibiotic formulation effluent. Hence more advanced treatment technologies such as photochemical (H_2O_2 + UV, O_3 + UV and their combination) and non-photochemical (Fenton's reagent, ozonation at elevated pH, H_2O_2 – assisted ozonation) advanced oxidation processes (AOPs) are required for effective pre-treatment prior to activated sludge process. The main reactant in the above mentioned processes is the hydroxyl radical (•OH) whose oxidation potential (= 2.8 eV vs. NHE) enables rapid and non-selective oxidation of a variety of inorganic and organic pollutants [6]. A huge body of scientific literature has already been devoted to integrated chemical and biochemical treatment of industrial pollutants such as detergents, phenolic compounds and dyes in textile industry wastewater, chlorinated pollutants from pulp and paper effluents, tanning and bleaching chemicals in tannery effluents to remove recalcitrance and/or toxicity from wastewater [7-20]. Among the studied AOPs, the applied pre-oxidation steps did not always lead to a significant biodegradability enhancement [12, 19,20]. Moreover, photochemically – induced free radical reactions appeared to be less effective than the non-photochemical processes due to high inner UV filter effect of most industrial effluents requiring extreme doses of oxidant and extended reaction periods.

The main purpose of the present work was to demonstrate the pre-treatment efficiency of three different AOPs, i.e. alkaline ozonation (pH = 11.5), Fe(II) and Fe(III) - catalyzed H_2O_2 decomposition at acidic pH (pH = 3.0) on effluent from the penicillin formulation stage of a pharmaceutical industry. The changes in biodegradability of penicillin formulation effluent subjected to optimized ozonation and Fenton processes were studied in more detail. To meet the need for a means of assessing inhibition of ready biodegradability, a combination of BOD_5, microbial sludge oxygen uptake rate and biological degradation experiments was investigated. BOD_5 measurements rather served to screen the optimum pre-treatment period for subsequent biodegradation and respirometric inhibition experiments.

Materials and Method

Penicillin Formulation Effluent

The penicillin effluent used in this study was wastewater from the ALFASID® formulation process (active penicillin ingredient: *Sultamycillin tosylate dihydrate*; Chemical formula: $C_{25}H_{30}N_4O_9S_2.2H_2O$; Molecular weight: 802.85 gr mol^{-1}). The formulation effluent samples were supplied by a pharmaceutical company located in Istanbul, Turkey. The selected effluent corresponded to approximately 30 % of the total daily effluent (= 150 m^3/d), of which approximately 50 % was process water. The collected effluent was stored in plastic carboys at 2 - 4 °C before use for up to four weeks. Prior to chemical and biological experiments, effluent suspensions were filtered through glass fibre filters with a pore size of 1.2 μm to obtain a clear reaction solution and to prevent interference with ozonation and Fenton's treatment. The formulation composition and corresponding effluent characterization (i.e. the mixture of all wash waters) were summarized in Tables 1 and 2, respectively.

Table 1. Ingredients of the penicillin formulation ALFASID®

Formulation chemical*	Function in the drug formulation
Sultamycillin tosylate dihydrate	active agent
Explotap, dried	additive
Methocel E – 15	additive
Silicone dioksit, colloidal	additive
Magnesium stearate	additive
Microcrystalline cellulose, dried	additive

*The exact amount of each chemical in the final drug formulation mixture is strictly confidential

All other chemicals used in the study, i.e. oxidant H_2O_2, catalysts $FeSO_4.7H_2O$ and $Fe(NO_3)_3.9H_2O$, concentrated H_2SO_4 and NaOH for pH adjustments, were at least reagent grade.

Ozonation Experiments

1 litre-penicillin wastewater samples were ozonated for 1 hour in a borosilicate glass bubble column in semi-batch mode wherein the ozone + oxygen gas mixture was continuously sparged at a rate of 1.2 l min^{-1} through a fritted gas dispersion disc with a diameter of 5 cm. Ozone was produced by a corona discharge PCI GL-1 model pilot scale ozone generator with a maximum capacity of 20 g h^{-1}. Teflon tubing was used for all connections from the ozone generator to the reaction vessel. All excess (unreacted) gaseous ozone leaving the column was collected in two gas washing bottles connected in series and filled with 10% KI solution, whereas two other gas washing bottles with 2% KI solution were directly placed after the gas introduction line. This was done in order to determine ozone

input ($O_{3,in}$) and off-gas ($O_{3,out}$) rates. The ozone feed rate was fixed at 2760 mg l^{-1} h^{-1} for all ozonation experiments. The ozone transfer efficiencies (i.e. absorbed ozone, O_{3A}, in % or mg l^{-1}) were calculated by determining $O_{3,in}$ (ozone input, in mg l^{-1}) and $O_{3,out}$ (ozone off-gas, in mg l^{-1}) values for each ozonation experiment using a procedure described by the IOA Standardization Committee [21]. O_{3A} values were calculated as follows;

Table 2. Environmental characterization of the penicillin formulation effluent

Parameter	Unit	Value
Total COD[*]	mg l^{-1}	687
Soluble COD[**]	mg l^{-1}	643
TOC	mg l^{-1}	199
BOD$_5$	mg l^{-1}	16
TKN	mg l^{-1}	85
TP	mg l^{-1}	11
Surfactants	mg l^{-1}	25
Cl$^-$	mg l^{-1}	95
pH	-	6.85
Total alkalinity	mg CaCO$_3$ l^{-1}	55
Colour[***]	Cm $^{-1}$	0.010

[*]Filtered through 1.20 µm cutoff filter
[**]Filtered through 0.45 µm cutoff filter
[***] Measured at wavelength $\lambda = 436$ nm in 1 cm glass cuvettes

$$O_{3A} \text{ (in mg } l^{-1}) = (O_{3,in} - O_{3,out})/O_{3,in} \qquad (1)$$

$$O_{3A} \text{ (in \%)} = (O_{3,in} - O_{3,out}) \times 100/O_{3,in} \qquad (2)$$

The mass transfer coefficient, k_{La}, of ozone in the semi-batch reactor was determined in acidic pure water by employing the indigo spectrophotometric method [21] as 0.85 ± 0.2 min^{-1}. The same method was also used for the determination of residual, liquid phase ozone concentrations ($O_{3,l}$, in mg l^{-1}) in the reaction solution.

Fenton Experiments

Fenton and Fenton – like experiments were conducted using an ordinary jar test apparatus provided by Velp Instruments, Inc. For that purpose, 0.5 mM and 1 mM FeSO$_4$.7H$_2$O or Fe(NO$_3$)$_3$.9H$_2$O were added to 1 litre pre-filtered and H$_2$SO$_4$ - acidified (pH = 3) samples as the ferrous and ferric ion catalyst sources, respectively. Thereafter, 10 mM or

20 mM H_2O_2 was introduced from a stock solution (30 % w/w, Merck) that counted as $t = 0$, i.e. the start of the oxidation reaction. 10 ml – sample aliquots were taken at regular time intervals for 1 hour, however, the reaction proceeded very fast and was complete (leveling off) 20 min after initiation of the reaction. Hence, only final values of the investigated environmental sum parameters have been presented in the present study.

Analytical Procedure

Raw and chemically pre-treated penicillin formulation effluent samples were immediately analyzed for COD, TOC and BOD_5 according to procedures described in Standard Methods [22]. To prevent the positive interference of H_2O_2 and Fe(II) – iron in the COD measurements, residual (unreacted) H_2O_2 was destroyed with MnO_2 powder at pH = 11, at which pH iron precipitated out as ferric iron hydroxide. The TOC content of the effluent was measured in 0.45 μm filtered air sparged, acidified samples by a Shimadzu TC - 1000 model organic carbon analyzer. The organic carbon analyzer was calibrated with potassium hydrogen phthalate solutions prepared in distilled de-ionized water at varying concentrations.

Biodegradability Experiments

Sewage sludge could not be acclimated to untreated penicillin formulation effluent even after a period of nine weeks corresponding to ten sludge ages. The unassimilated sludge samples used in the biodegradability tests were collected from a laboratory scale 10 liter – capacity municipal wastewater reactor. The mixed culture inoculum was previously fed daily with synthetic sewage that was prepared and stored according to the modified ISO Standard Ref. Nr. 8192 [23]. The ideal mixed liquor volatile suspended solids (MLVSS) concentration that is being typically used in the ISO 8192 activated sludge inhibition test is 2000 - 4000 mg l^{-1} and has been selected as 3000 ± 150 mg l^{-1} for the present study. The respirometric inhibition tests were performed in 1000 cm^3 capacity glass beakers in which aeration + mixing was provided by means of air diffusion (flow rate = 50 l h^{-1}) and magnetic stirring. The synthetic domestic sewage : penicillin formulation effluent samples were mixed at a ratio of 4 : 1 that resulted in an initial COD of 450 mg l^{-1}. The F/M ratio was selected as 0.15 mg COD (mg MLVSS)$^{-1}$ d^{-1} and the pH was adjusted to 6.9 ± 0.2 prior to the biodegradability experiments. For the respirometric tests, activated sludge that was periodically fed with the synthetic domestic wastewater and had an initial OUR of 90-110 mg l^{-1} h^{-1}, was used. After initiation of the respirometric experiments oxygen uptake rates (OUR values, in mg l^{-1} h^{-1}) were determined at regular time intervals for the domestic wastewater mixed with raw and chemically pre-treated formulation effluent, using a WTW Oxi 600 model, calibrated oxygen probe. Activated sludge inhibition experiments were conducted for 24 h, i.e. the time when steady state COD values were reached for all tested effluent samples. At the same time, COD abatement was followed for all raw and chemically pre-treated effluent samples mixed with synthetic domestic wastewater. Due to the fact that the sludge could not be acclimated to penicillin formulation effluent under the selected reaction conditions, it was expected that only the synthetic municipal wastewater fraction (75 % of total mixed pharmaceutical wastewater) could be biodegraded under the studied treatment conditions. Accordingly, per cent biochemical COD removal inhibition rate could be determined by the following formula;

$$I_R \text{ (in \%)} = (\Delta COD_{th} - \Delta COD_{exp}) \times 100 / (\Delta COD_{th}) \tag{3}$$

Where I_R is the cent relative inhibition of biological degradation rate of the synthetic municipal wastewater fraction in the effluent sample (in %), ΔCOD_{th}, ΔCOD_{exp} are the theoretically expected (ΔCOD_{th}), and experimentally observed (ΔCOD_{exp}) absolute COD removal rates, respectively (in mg l^{-1}). The above expression shows that the COD fraction which cannot be removed during biodegradation of synthetic sewage in the presence of raw and chemically pre-treated penicillin formulation effluent is positively proportional to the "inhibitory" COD.

Results and Discussion

Pretreatment with Ozone

Figure 1 displays changes in COD and TOC values during ozonation of penicillin formulation effluent at elevated pH. Ozonation experiments have shown that significant COD and TOC removals could only be obtained at elevated pH values (at pH $\geq$11.0) as a consequence of enhanced ozone decomposition into free radicals such as •OH [24]. It is believed that at elevated pH the major oxidizing agent for the degradation of formulation effluent was •OH, since no residual ozone was detectable at pH $\geq$ 7.5 in the reaction medium (CO$_{3, 1}$ was $\leq$ 0.3 mg/L). No attempts have been made to control the pH of the formulation effluent during ozonation, that gradually decreased to pH = 7.3 – 7.5 at the end of the reaction period. Consequently no further pH adjustment was required prior to BOD$_5$ measurements, respirometric inhibition and biodegradation experiments.

At the end of the ozonation period 233 mg l^{-1} (34 %) COD was removed and 742 mg l^{-1} of the applied O$_3$ was absorbed in the reaction solution. TOC abatement rates remained rather low (24 % overall reduction) throughout the ozonation period, however, TOC removal was actually not the purpose of the present work.

Upon closer inspection of Figure 2 presenting changes in ozone absorption rates (O$_{3A}$ values) for an ozonation experiment run at pH = 11.0, it can be concluded that a linear relationship exists between ozone feed rates and ozone absorption efficiencies. However, only 30 % of the introduced ozone could be absorbed throughout the ozonation period. Percent ozone absorption efficiency was high at the beginning of the reaction (i.e. the first 10 min of ozonation), because the pH was high and hence ozone decomposition was significantly enhanced during this period. Upon extended ozonation the reaction pH decreased to neutral values (pH = 7.0 - 7.5) due to acid accumulation, so that ozone decomposition was slightly retarded. This was also evidenced by increases in liquid phase, residual ozone concentrations when the pH dropped to below 7 (O$_{3,1}$ = 1.1. mg l^{-1}). The above indicated findings suggest that the acceleration in ozone decomposition is mainly governed

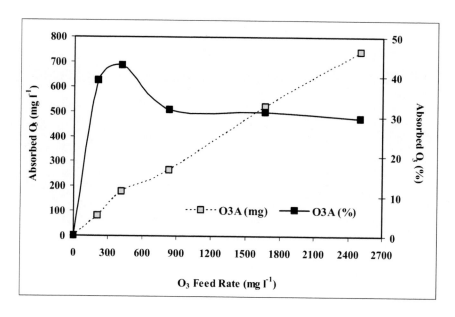

Figure 1. Changes in COD and TOC removal rates observed during ozonation of penicillin formulation effluent at $pH_o = 11.0$.

by the reaction pH and not the COD removal efficiency, i.e. ozone consumption due to enhanced oxidation. Therefore no direct correlation between oxidation efficiency and ozone decomposition seemed plausible.

The rate of partial oxidation of the penicillin formulation ingredients to biologically more degradable compounds relative to the rate of mineralization to oxidation end products such as carbonate, inorganic salts and H_2O, can be expressed as the COD TOC^{-1} ratio. Changes in the COD, TOC values observed during ozonation of penicillin formulation effluent has already been shown in Figure 1. The "partial oxidation ratio" can be derived from the COD, TOC data given in Figure 1 for alkaline ozonation. It could be concluded that the COD TOC^{-1} ratio fell down from 3.5 at $t = 0$ to 3.0 after $t = 1$ h, indicating that though COD and TOC abatements more or less paralleled each other, partial oxidation (COD abatement) rates were still appreciably higher than mineralization (TOC abatement) rates during ozonation of penicillin formulation effluent.

Figure 3 presents the changes in the biodegradability of penicillin formulation effluent, expressed as the BOD_5 values and the BOD_5/COD ratio, as a function of ozonation time. From Figure 3 it is evident that the biodegradability of the formulation effluent was improved from only 0.02 for the original, untreated penicillin formulation wastewater (original $BOD_5 = 17 \pm 2$) to 0.12 at the end of the ozonation period reaching a maximum value of 0.27 ($BOD_5 = 128$ mg l^{-1}) after an ozonation period of 40 min corresponding to an ozone feed rate of 1670 mg l^{-1}. Obtained results revealed that even though non-acclimated sludge has been used for the BOD_5 tests, a relative increase in BOD_5 values was apparent for wastewater samples ozonated at a dose of 1670 mg l^{-1}, indicating that ozonation at a pollutant - specific,

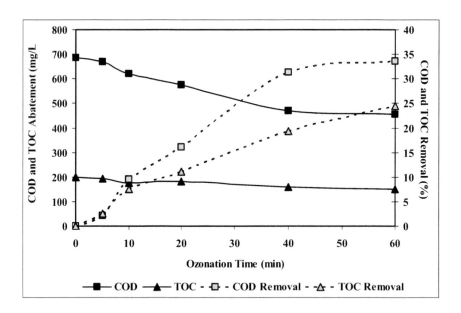

Figure 2. Changes in ozone absorption rates (O_{3A} values) observed during ozonation of penicillin formulation effluent at $pH_o = 11.0$ with respect to ozone feed rate.

"optimum" dose may have positive effects on the biological treatability of the otherwise refractory wastewater. The existence of a distinct, maximum BOD_5/COD ratio and BOD_5 value at an optimum ozone dose has already been evidenced in previous studies [11,12,19,20]. As a general rule, it has been established that an ozone dose of at least 1-2 mg O_3 mg COD_o^{-1} or 2-3 mg O_3 mg TOC_o^{-1} is practically required to achieve the highest possible biodegradability improvement.

Pretreatment with Fenton and Fenton-Like Processes

In previous studies, Fenton and Fenton-like reactions were found as promising candiates for effective pre-oxidation and reduction in biorecalcitrance [25]. Consequently, the Fenton process and its modification, i.e. the Fenton-like reaction, were studied as the chemical pre-treatment alternatives to ozonation. As can be seen in Figure 4, similar COD removal rates were found by applying the Fenton and Fenton-like processes as compared with ozonation at pH=11.5. Fenton oxidation systems were studied at different Fe – iron (ferrous or ferric iron salts) : H_2O_2 molar concentration ratios in accordance with molar ratios reported in the previous, scientific literature [9, 25-27]. Obviously, the partial oxidation efficiency increased at higher catalyst and oxidant doses. Again, partial oxidation rates were accelerated upon increasing the oxidant and catalyst dose or switching from the Fenton to Fenton-like processes.

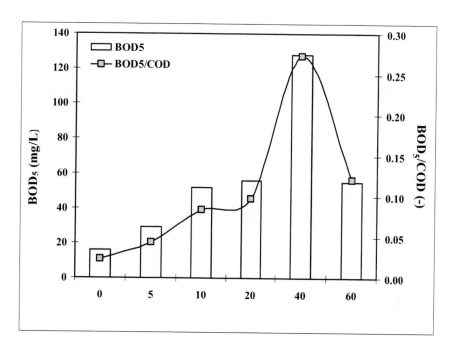

Figure 3. Changes in BOD_5 and BOD_5/COD values observed during ozonation of penicillin formulation effluent at $pH_o = 11.0$.

It is well known that H_2O_2 decomposition into free radical species can be achived via both ferrous and ferric iron catalysts [25,26]. The apparently higher overall COD and TOC removal rates found with the Fenton-like reagent as compared with the conventional Fenton's reaction is due to the fact that two different removal mechanisms are attributable for the abatement efficiency in the latter case; i.e. oxidation via free radicals formed as a consequence of H_2O_2 decomposition at acidic pH plus removal via accompanied ferric iron coagulation observed after pH re-adjustment. Fenton's coagulation or Fenton co-precipitation occurs with the in-situ formed ferric iron hydroxide at pH > 5, 6 [25]. In conclusion, the enhancement was attributable to the fact that Fenton's oxidaiton plus co-precipitation is enhanced in the presence of ferric rather than ferrous iron.

However, BOD_5 values and BOD_5/COD ratios first appeared to increase upon increasing the H_2O_2 concentraiton from 10 mM to 20 mM in the presence of 0.5 mM $Fe^{2+/3+}$ and to decrease upon further addition of Fe-catalyst to a concentration of 1 mM. As in the case of ozonation, optimum chemical pre-oxidation conditions had to be defined and over-oxidation to be prevented in order to improve the biotreatability of the penicillin formulation effluent. For instance, the biodegradability (BOD_5/COD) ratio was accelerated to 0.30 and 0.36 for the Fenton and Fenton-like processes conducted with 20 mM H_2O_2, respectively, when the $Fe^{2+/3+}$: H_2O_2 ratio was kept at 1:40 instead of 1:20 at 1 mM $Fe^{2+/3+}$, at which dose the obtained BOD_5/COD pre-oxidation ratio fell down to 0.26-0.28 due to over-oxidation at higher catalyst doses.

Though the evaluation of relative changes in the BOD_5/COD ratio is most commonly practised in studies dealing with oxidative pre-treatment of refractory industrial wastewater via chemical oxidation processes, it is only an approximate tool and not sufficient to predict the fate of industrial effluents in real activated sludge systems. In other words, the above obtained experimental data is not very informative and has to be supported by actual biodegradation studies as to prove that chemical pre-oxidation with ozone and Fenton's reagent is a well suited, sustainable approach for penicillin formulation effluent.

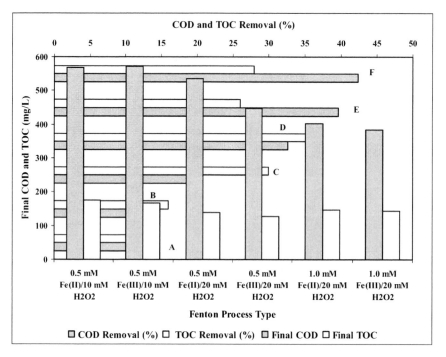

Figure 4. Percent COD and TOC removal efficiencies and final COD and TOC values obtained after 25 min Fenton and Fenton-like treatment at pH = 3. The Fen+ concentration /type and H2O2 concentration are given in the figure and indicated as condition A (0.5 mM Fe2+ + 10 mM H2O2), B (0.5 mM Fe3+ + 10 mM H2O2), C (0.5 mM Fe2+ + 20 mM H2O2), D (0.5 mM Fe3+ + 20 mM H2O2), E (1 mM Fe2+ + 20 mM H2O2) and F (1 mM Fe3+ + 20 mM H2O2).

Activated Sludge Inhibition Tests

Oxygen uptake rate measurements have often been used as an appropriate tool to long-term and shock mimic responses of industrial pollutants in activated sludge treatment works [28-30]. Figure 5 depicts oxygen uptake rates (OUR values, in mg l^{-1} h^{-1}) obtained during 8 h batch biodegradation tests conducted with raw (untreated) and chemically pre-treated penicillin formulation effluent (30% v/v) + synthetic wastewater (70% v/v) mixtures. In addition, Table 3 presents percent COD inhibition rates (I_R values) that have been determined for the successive biodegradation of raw and chemically pre-treated wastewater samples. Upon careful comparison of Figure it is quite obvious that the data given in Figure 5 and Table 3 support each other. For instance, Figure 5 demonstrates that effluent samples which were previously treated with ozone at alkaline pH or with the Fenton – like reagent (Fe^{3+}/H_2O_2) almost behaved like synthetic domestic effluent in terms of respirometric activity. Table 3 on the other hand shows that for the mixed raw wastewater biochemical COD removal was inhibited by 27 % relatively to the that of synthetic domestic effluent. The rate of COD inhibition was reduced from 27 % to 16 %, when the Fenton process was previously applied to the penicillin effluent fraction, however, was still a positive value and hence inhibition existed for Fenton-treated wastewater. In the case of alkaline ozonation and Fenton-like processes, complete reduction in the originally inert COD fraction of the penicillin formulation effluent was observed, thus resulting in "negative" inhibition rates, i.e. a rather positive effect of pre-ozonation and the Fenton-like reagent was obtained for the latter two pre-treatment systems by 4 % and 8 %, respectively. Conclusively, not only the synthetic domestic wastewater, but also the formulation effluent fraction was degradable upon preliminary treatment with ozonation and Fenton-like reagent.

From the above findings it can be inferred that although according to the BOD_5/COD approach, all three selected advanced oxidation systems were practically equally effective in biodegradability enhancement (provided that the AOPs were first optimized for oxidant and catalyst dose), the OUR activity and COD biodegradation tests confirmed that activated sludge inhibition can be reduced, but not completely hindered by Fenton's pre-treatment, but with applying the Fenton-like process and in particular alkaline ozonation. On the other hand ozonation appears to be the technically and economically more feasible oxidation method since only one pH - adjustment would be necessary prior to ozonation to accelerate ozone decomposition thereby initiating free radical reactions.

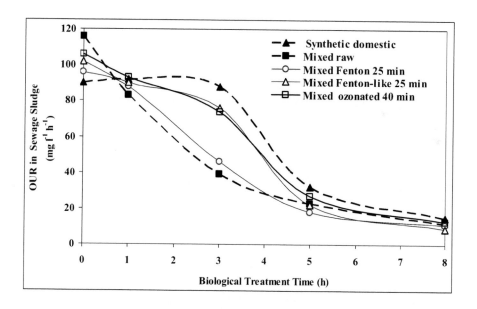

Figure 5. Oxygen uptake rates (OUR values, in mg l^{-1} h^{-1}) measured for unacclimated sewage sludge during biological treatment of raw, ozonated (at $pH_o = 11.0$), Fenton and Fenton-like pre-treated penicillin formulation effluent + synthetic domestic wastewater mixture. Experimental conditions are given in the text.

Summary and Conclusions

The aim of the present experimental study was to evaluate the changes in biocompatibility of penicillin formulation effluent, being selected as a refractory index wastewater, after oxidative chemical pre-treatment by ozonation and the Fenton's reagents. Chemical oxidative treatment performance of the selected advanced oxidation processes was evaluated in terms of COD and TOC abatement rates. Changes in biodegradability have been assessed in terms of the conventional BOD_5 parameter that has been determined for each process, the electrolytic respirometric inhibition test and successive biological COD abatement experiments.

Table 3. Biological COD removal rates and percent I_R obtained for raw and chemically pre-treated penicillin formulation effluent. Experimental Conditions: Ozonation at high pH (= 11.0); Fenton and Fenton-like treatment at acidic pH (= 3.0)

Treatment Type	Final COD (mg l^{-1})	Biological COD removal (%)	I_R (%)
No pre-treatment	475	47	+ 33
Fenton (pH = 3.0)[*]	369	59	+ 16
Fenton-like (pH = 3.0)[*]	235	73	- 4 [***]
Ozonation (pH = 11.0)[**]	193	76	- 8 [***]

[*] H_2O_2 : Fe molar ratio = 40 (0.5 mM Fe and 20 mM H_2O_2)
[**] Ozone feed rate = 42 mg min^{-1} (applied ozone dose = 1680 mg l^{-1} or 1.9 mg O_3 mg COD_o $^{-1}$)
[***] The negative sign ("-") indicates that biodegradation is not inhibited, but enhanced

For that purpose, in addition to BOD_5 measurements, exogenous oxygen uptake rates were followed for activated sludge being exposed to a mixture of synthetic domestic wastewater and raw, chemically pre-treated penicillin formulation effluent at fixed food-to-microorganism ratios. Moreover, several biodegradation experiments were performed to question the validity and relationship of the selected methodological approaches.

It was demonstrated that all investigated procedures are capable of reflecting the situation in activated sludge systems. However, the evaluation of exogenous activated sludge oxygen uptake and COD abatement rates which were followed during successive biodegradation experiments were both required to get a deeper insight. In the particular case it could be established that chemical pre-oxidation of penicillin formulation effluent may completely reduce if not minimize its inhibition towards sewage sludge in aerobic treatment systems, provided that the chemical oxidant type, its application conditions (concentration/dose, treatment time, pH etc.) were specifically optimized for the industrial effluent in question.

In conclusion, chemical oxidation of penicillin formulation effluent prior to its discharge into biological treatment units is not only expected to eliminate its negative impacts on microbial activity of the sewer system but also to facilitate its more economic and safe degradation via conventional, cost effective treatment methods.

Acknowledgements

The author wishes to thank TUBITAK (Turkish National Scientific and Technology Research Council) for the financial support under Project "ICTAG –C-042".

References

[1]   EU Direction General III, *Assessment of potential risks to the environment posed by medical products for human use (excluding products containing live genetically modified organisms)*. No. 5504/94 Draft 6, Version 4, 5th January, European Union, Brussels (1995).

[2]   Kümmerer, K., Steger-Hartmann, T. and Meyer, M., Biodegradability of the anti-tumor agent ifosfamide and its occurence in hospital effluents and communal sewage. *Wat. Res.*, 31(11), 2705-2710 (1997).

[3]   Tisler, T. and Zagorc-Koncan, J., Toxicity evaluation of wastewater from the pharmaceutical industry to aquatic organisms. *Wat. Sci. Tech.*, 39(10-11), 71-76 (1999).

[4]   Wollenberger, L., Halling-Sorensen, B. and Kusk, K. O. Acute and chronic toxicity of veterinary antibiotics to *Dapnia magna*. *Chemosphere*, 40, 723-730 (2000).

[5]   Kümmerer, K., Al-Ahmad, A. and Mersch-Sundermann, V., Biodegradability of some antibiotics, elimination of the genotoxicity and affection of wastewater bacteria in a simple test. *Chemosphere*, 40, 701-710 (2000).

[6]   Oppenlaender, T. *Photochemical purification of water and air*. Wiley VCH Verlag, Weinheim, pp. 5-19 (2003).

[7]   Zwiener, C. and Frimmel, F. H., Oxidative treatment of pharmaceuticals in water. *Wat. Res.*, 34(6), 1881-1885 (2000).

[8]   Gulyas, H., von Bismarck, R. and Hemmerling, L., Treatment of industrial wastewaters with ozone/hydrogen peroxide. *Wat. Sci. Tech.*, 32(7), 127-134 (1995).

[9]   Koyama, O., Kamagata, Y. and Nakanura, K., Degradation of chlorinated aromatics by Fenton oxidation and methanogenic digester sludge. *Wat. Res.*, 28, 885-899 (1994).

[10]   Saupe, A. and Wiesman, U., Ozonization of 2,4-dinitrotoluene and 4-nitroaniline as well as improved dissolved organic carbon removal by sequential ozonization – biodegradation. *Wat. Environ. Res.*, 70(2), 146-154 (1998).

[11]   Benitez, F. J., Acero, J. L., Gonzalez, T. and Garcia, J., Ozonation and biodegradation processes in batch reactors treating black table olives washing wastewaters. *Ind. Eng. Chem. Res.*, 40, 3144-3251 (2001).

[12]   Alvares A. B. C., Diaper, C., Parsons, S. A., Partial oxidation by ozone to remove recalcitrance from wastewaters - a review. *Environ. Technol.*, 22(4), 409-427 (2001).

[13]   Arslan-Alaton, I., Kornmüller, A. and Jekel, M. R., Ozonation of a spent reactive dye bath: effect of CO_3^{2-}/HCO_3^- alkalinity. *J. Environ. Eng., ASCE*, 128(8), 689-696 (2002).

[14]   Sarria, V., Parra, S., Adler, N., Peringer, P., Benitez, N. and Pulgarin, C., Recent developments in the coupling of photoassisted and aerobic biological processes for the treatment of biorecalcitrant compounds. *Catal. Today*, 76, 301-315 (2002).

[15]   Esplugas, S., Gimenez, J., Contreras, S., Pascual, E. and Rodriguez, Comparison of different advanced oxidation processes for phenol degradation. *Wat. Res.*, 36, 1034-1042 (2002).

[16]   Hess, T. F. and Schrader, P. S., Coupled abiotic – biotic mineralization of 2,4,6,-Trinitrotoluene (TNT). *J. Environ. Qual.*, 31, 736-744 (2002).

[17]   Hernandez, R., Zappi, M., Colucci, J. and Jones, R., J., Comparing the performance of various advanced oxidation processes for treatment of acetone contaminated water. *J. Haz. Mat.*, 92, 33-50 (2002).

[18]   Perez, M., Torrades, F., Domenech, X. And Peral J., Removal of organic contaminants in paper pulp effluents by AOPs: An economic study. *J. Chem. Technol. Biotechnol.*, 77, 525-531 (2002).

[19]   Scott, J. P. and Ollis, D. F., Integration of chemical and biological oxidation processes for water treatment: review and recommendations. *Environ. Prog.*, 14(2), 88-103 (1992).

[20]   Arslan-Alaton, I., Akmehmet Balcioglu, I., and Bahnemann, D. W., Advanced oxidation of a reactive dyebath effluent: Comparison of O_3, H_2O_2/UV-C and TiO_2/UV-A processes. *Wat. Res.*, 36, 1143-1154 (2002).

[21]   IOA Standardisation Committee - Europe, 001/87-F, Iodometric method for the determination of ozone in a process gas. Brussels (1987).

[22]   APHA-AWWA-WEF, *Standard Method for the Examination of Water and Wastewater,* 19th Ed. American Public Health Association, Washington DC (1995).

[23]   ISO 8192, Water quality – oxygen demand inhibition assay by activated sludge (1986).

[24]   Staehelin, J. and Hoigné, J., Decomposition of ozone in water: Rate of initiation by hydroxide ions and hydrogen peroxide. *Environ. Sci. Technol.* 16(10), 676-681 (1982).

[25]   Arslan, I. and Akmehmet Balcioglu, I., Degradation of commercial reactive dyestuffs by heterogeneous and homogeneous advanced oxidation processes: a comparative study. *Dyes Pigments*, 43, 95-108 (1999).

[26]   De Laat, J. and Gallard, H., Catalytic decomposition of hydrogen peroxide by Fe(III) in homogenous aqueous solution: Mechanism and kinetic modelling. *Environ. Sci. Technol.*, 33, 2726-2732 (1999).

[27]   Haber, F. and Weiss, J., The catalytic decomposition of hydrogen peroxide by iron salts. *Proc. Royal Soc. London, Ser. A*, 147, 332-351 (1934).

[28]   Gotvajn, A. Z. and Zagorc-Koncan, J., Biodegradation studies as an important way to estimate the environmental fate of chemicals. *Wat. Sci. Tech.*, 39(10-11), 375-382 (1999).

[29]   Orupold, K. Hellat, K. and Tenno, T., Estimation of treatability of different industrial wastewaters by activated sludge oxygen uptake measurements. *Wat. Sci. Tech.*, 40(1), 31-36 (1999).

[30]   Guiterrez, M.; Extebarria, J. de las Fuentas, L., Evaluation of wastewater toxicity: comparative study between Microtox and activated sludge oxygen uptake inhibition. *Wat. Res.*, 36, 919-924 (2002).

In: Trends in Water Pollution Research
Editor: J. V. Livingston, pp. 181-201

ISBN 1-59454-328-3
©2005 Nova Science Publishers, Inc.

Chapter VIII

Three-Dimensional Modeling of Hydrodynamic and Transboundary Pollutant Transport in Pearl River Estuary of South China

K. W. Chau

Department of Civil and Structural Engineering, Hong Kong Polytechnic University,
Hung Hom, Kowloon, Hong Kong

Abstract

During the past two decades, substantial economic development took place in Pearl River Delta Region (PRDR), which is the largest river system in South China with Hong Kong and Macau at eastern and western sides of its entrance, respectively. This prosperity, however, is accompanied with the exertion of serious potential pollution impacts to areas in the vicinity and complication of the task of environmental protection in Hong Kong and Macau. In this chapter, a coupled three-dimensional numerical model on hydrodynamic and pollutant transport, with orthogonal curvilinear coordinate in the horizontal direction and sigma coordinate in the vertical direction, is developed and implemented to simulate the unsteady transport of a representative water quality constituent, chemical oxygen demand, in PRDR. In this model, which is based on the Princeton Ocean Model (POM), a second moment turbulence closure sub-model is embedded, and the stratification caused by salinity and temperature is considered. The horizontal time differencing is implicit with the use of a time splitting method, instead of the explicit method in POM. As such, the allowable time step is larger than POM and less computational time is needed to keep the computation stable. This attribute is shown to be particularly useful in domains with complex flow patterns and large currents caused by tide river discharges, such as in PRDR. The computation is verified and calibrated with field measurement data. The computed results mimic the field data well. Moreover, it is demonstrated that there exists a transboundary pollutant transport action between

Guangdong Province and Hong Kong for the pollutants in the wastewater discharged from PRDR.

Introduction

The Pearl River Delta Region (PRDR), at which Hong Kong is located, is a significant and quickly developing economic zone in China whilst the Pearl River is the largest river system in Southern China. Figure 1 shows the region which covers eight large cities in China: Dongguan; Foshan; Guangzhou; Huizhou; Jiangmen; Shenzhen; and, Zhongshan. With the rapid economic boom of PRDR in the last two decades, the resources of the estuary such as the harbor, channel, reclamation zone etc. have been exploited. Moreover, a significant environmental impact has been imposed on the ambient conditions. Untreated sewage is discharged in an expeditious rate and large quantities of various pollutants have been released into the PRDR, largely via five outlets, namely, Hu men, Jiao men, Hongqi men, Heng men, and Shenzhen River. The water quality has been deteriorating and the frequency of the occurrence of algae blooms has been increasing recently. In particular, after the restoration of the sovereigns and administration of Hong Kong the People Republic of China in 1997, increasing interactions as well as number of projects are undertaken which in turn lead to more attention to be placed on the PRDR.

Previously, several two dimensional or quasi-three-dimensional models have been developed to simulate the environmental hydraulics in PRDR [1-15]. This chapter delineates the development of a comprehensive three-dimensional coupled model, which is a modified version of the Princeton Ocean Model (POM) [16], and its application to the PRDR for simulation of the unsteady transport of a representative water quality variable Chemical Oxygen Demand in Manganese (COD_{Mn}). The pollutant transport model is integrated together with a synchronized hydrodynamic mathematical model. This model covers four outlets of the Pearl River system and the main part of Hong Kong seawaters. This is probably the first application of 3-D and baroclinic model in the PRDR. The numerical model contains an embedded second moment turbulence closure sub-model to provide vertical mixing coefficients whilst the curvilinear orthogonal coordinate is employed in the horizontal direction and sigma coordinate in the vertical direction. The horizontal and vertical time differencing are treated in a semi-implicit manner and a time-splitting method is used for the horizontal time differencing of the external mode. Moreover, complete thermodynamics have been implemented and the stratification of salinity and temperature are considered. A newly developed robust open boundary condition is used for pollutant transport.

The major enhancement of this model over the POM is on the time differencing. Whilst in POM the horizontal time differencing is entirely explicit, the horizontal time differencing in this model is semi-implicit with the use of a time splitting method. Thus the time step of this model is larger than that in POM. This attribute is very decisive in applications with complex flow pattern and large current caused by the tide and river discharges such as in the Pearl River estuary. Although a semi-implicit version of Blumberg-Mellor model, ECOMsiz, has also emerged recently [17], the time-splitting alternating direction implicit scheme in the external mode and vertical coordinate system are different. In ECOM-siz, the barotropic pressure gradient in the momentum equations and the horizontal velocity divergence in the continuity equation are treated implicitly and a raw vertical coordinate system is adopted.

In order to ensure real applications, the modeling results are calibrated and validated with field measurement data. From an engineering point of view, the model has a significant role in exploring the dynamics and circulation of the PRDR. Moreover, it is observed that the pollutants in the PRDR are transported from the various outlets of the river network towards its entrance, through the interaction of tidal effects as well as runoff discharge from the rivers. Whilst Hong Kong Special Administrative Region (HKSAR) and Macau are located on the eastern and western sides of the outlet respectively, the impact due to transboundary pollution from the inner PRDR may be very significant. It will potentially add an additional dimension and complication to the environmental protection tasks in both HKSAR [18] and Macau. Hence, necessity arises to determine the impacts of these pollutants from the PRDR on the water quality in the ambient seawaters of HKSAR in both quantitative and qualitative terms. COD_{Mn} is adopted as an index for evaluation of the effects of transboundary pollution action here.

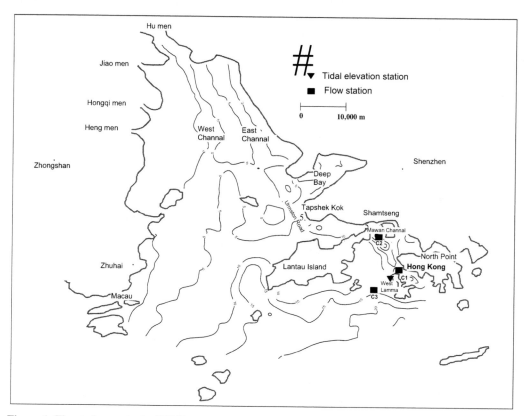

Figure 1. The study area in the PRDR

Governing Equations and Solution Algorithm

The governing equations representing the dynamics of coastal cycle comprise fast moving external gravity waves and slow moving internal gravity waves. In line with this phenomenon, a splitting technique has been employed [19] to separate the three-dimensional motion equations into two sub-modes: an internal mode for the vertical structure, and an external mode for vertically averaged simulation. The velocity transport is separately solved from the three-dimensional computation of velocity and the thermodynamic properties. A major advantage of this algorithm is to allow for the computation of free surface elevation at a small expense of computational time. The model employs a sigma (σ) coordinate condition in the vertical direction, and an orthogonal curvilinear coordinate in the horizontal direction. Under this stretching system, it spans the range from $\sigma = 0$ at the surface of water to $\sigma = -1$ at the bottom, thus furnishing the same number of layers regardless of water depth. In particular, it is able to handle domains of large topographic variability well. Thus, this system is more appropriate in simulation of current flow and salinity transportation when compared with the raw water depth system [20].

In the horizontal direction, the curvilinear coordinate is more popular in recent years since it can eliminate the staggered grid in Cartesian coordinate system, thus enhancing the prototype representation of real model boundary. In general, two kinds of curvilinear coordinate are available: orthogonal, and non-orthogonal. Whilst the orthogonal coordinate has the advantage of having a simpler motion equation, it is unable to generate grid for a domain with complex geometry. Hence, if the model is applied to a domain with a complex boundary condition, a non-orthogonal coordinate system is preferred. The governing equations of the two sub-modes are as follows:

Internal Mode of Hydrodynamic System

In the internal mode, the vertical structure of the three-dimensional governing equations is represented with the σ coordinate system

Continuity equation:

$$\frac{\partial UD}{\partial x} + \frac{\partial VD}{\partial y} + \frac{\partial \omega}{\partial \sigma} + \frac{\partial \eta}{\partial t} = 0 \tag{1}$$

Momentum equations:

$$\frac{\partial UD}{\partial t} + \frac{\partial U^2 D}{\partial x} + \frac{\partial UVD}{\partial y} + \frac{\partial U\omega}{\partial \sigma} - fVD + gD\frac{\partial \eta}{\partial x} + \frac{gD^2}{\rho_0}\int_\sigma^0\left[\frac{\partial \rho}{\partial x} - \frac{\sigma}{D}\frac{\partial D}{\partial x}\frac{\partial \rho}{\partial \sigma}\right]d\sigma = \tag{2}$$
$$\frac{\partial}{\partial \sigma}\left[\frac{K_M}{D}\frac{\partial U}{\partial \sigma}\right] + F_x$$

$$\frac{\partial VD}{\partial t} + \frac{\partial UVD}{\partial x} + \frac{\partial V^2 D}{\partial y} + \frac{\partial V\omega}{\partial \sigma} + fUD + gD\frac{\partial \eta}{\partial y} + \frac{gD^2}{\rho_0}\int_\sigma^0 \left[\frac{\partial \rho}{\partial y} - \frac{\sigma}{D}\frac{\partial D}{\partial y}\frac{\partial \rho}{\partial \sigma}\right]d\sigma =$$

$$\frac{\partial}{\partial \sigma}\left[\frac{K_M}{D}\frac{\partial V}{\partial \sigma}\right] + F_y \tag{3}$$

Temperature and salinity transport equations:

$$\frac{\partial TD}{\partial t} + \frac{\partial TUD}{\partial x} + \frac{\partial TVD}{\partial y} + \frac{\partial T\omega}{\partial \sigma} = \frac{\partial}{\partial \sigma}\left[\frac{K_H}{D}\frac{\partial T}{\partial \sigma}\right] + F_T \tag{4}$$

$$\frac{\partial SD}{\partial t} + \frac{\partial SUD}{\partial x} + \frac{\partial SVD}{\partial y} + \frac{\partial S\omega}{\partial \sigma} = \frac{\partial}{\partial \sigma}\left[\frac{K_H}{D}\frac{\partial S}{\partial \sigma}\right] + F_S \tag{5}$$

Turbulence energy equations:

$$\frac{\partial q^2 D}{\partial t} + \frac{\partial Uq^2 D}{\partial x} + \frac{\partial Vq^2 D}{\partial y} + \frac{\partial \omega q^2}{\partial \sigma} = \frac{\partial}{\partial \sigma}\left[\frac{K_q}{D}\frac{\partial q^2}{\partial \sigma}\right] + \frac{2K_M}{D}\left[\left(\frac{\partial U}{\partial \sigma}\right)^2 + \left(\frac{\partial V}{\partial \sigma}\right)^2\right]$$

$$+ \frac{2g}{\rho_0}K_H\frac{\partial \tilde{\rho}}{\partial \sigma} - \frac{2Dq^3}{B_1 l} + F_q \tag{6}$$

$$\frac{\partial q^2 lD}{\partial t} + \frac{\partial Uq^2 lD}{\partial x} + \frac{\partial Vq^2 lD}{\partial y} + \frac{\partial \omega q^2 l}{\partial \sigma} = \frac{\partial}{\partial \sigma}\left[\frac{K_q}{D}\frac{\partial q^2 l}{\partial \sigma}\right] + E_1 l\frac{K_M}{D}\left[\left(\frac{\partial U}{\partial \sigma}\right)^2 + \left(\frac{\partial V}{\partial \sigma}\right)^2\right]$$

$$+ E_1 E_3 l\frac{g}{\rho_0}K_H\frac{\partial \tilde{\rho}}{\partial \sigma} - \tilde{W}\frac{Dq^3}{B_1} + F_l \tag{7}$$

A $q^2 \sim q^2 l$ turbulence model is adopted, which involves two prognostic equations and is similar to that employed in the $K \sim \varepsilon$ approach [21]. The representation of the horizontal viscosity and diffusion terms are as follows:

$$F_x = \frac{\partial}{\partial x}(H\tau_{xx}) + \frac{\partial}{\partial y}(H\tau_{xy}) \tag{8}$$

$$F_y = \frac{\partial}{\partial x}(H\tau_{xy}) + \frac{\partial}{\partial y}(H\tau_{yy}) \tag{9}$$

$$F_\phi = \frac{\partial}{\partial x}(Hq_x) + \frac{\partial}{\partial y}(Hq_y) \tag{10}$$

in which:

$$\tau_{xx} = 2A_M \frac{\partial U}{\partial x}; \quad \tau_{xy} = \tau_{yx} = A_M \left[\frac{\partial U}{\partial y} + \frac{\partial V}{\partial x} \right]; \quad \tau_{yy} = 2A_M \frac{\partial V}{\partial y}; \quad q_x = A_H \frac{\partial \phi}{\partial x};$$

$q_y = A_H \dfrac{\partial \phi}{\partial y}$; ϕ represents $T, S, q^2, q^2 l$; U, V, ω represent mean fluid velocities in the x, y, σ directions, respectively; η is the elevation of sea surface above the undisturbed level; f is the Coriolis parameter; $D = \eta + H$; H is the depth of the water; g is the Earth's gravitational acceleration; ρ_0 is the fluid density; ρ is the fluid density after subtraction of the horizontally averaged density; $\tilde{\rho}$ is the buoyant fluid density; T is temperature; S is salinity; q^2 is the turbulence energy; l is the mixing length; K_M, K_H, K_q are vertical turbulent flux coefficients; A_M, A_H are horizontal turbulent coefficients; $\tilde{W}$ is wall proximity function; and, B_1, E_1, E_3 are constants that are determined from experiments in laboratory. The elevation of the water surface is directly obtained from the external mode.

Detailed description of internal mode is not mentioned here which can be referred to Blumberg and Mellor [22-23] and Mellor [16]. The method is semi-implicit and all terms of momentum equations are treated in an explicit manner except for the vertical flux that is treated in an implicit way. The equations here are based on the Cartesian coordinate and for equations under the orthogonal curvilinear coordinate, details can be referred to Chau and Jin [24].

External Mode of Hydrodynamic System

The external mode represents the vertically integrated continuity and momentum equations in a two-dimensional format:

Continuity equation:

$$\frac{\partial \overline{U} D}{\partial x} + \frac{\partial \overline{V} D}{\partial y} + \frac{\partial \eta}{\partial t} = 0 \tag{11}$$

Momentum equations:

$$\frac{\partial \overline{U} D}{\partial t} + \frac{\partial \overline{U}^2 D}{\partial x} + \frac{\partial \overline{UV} D}{\partial y} - \tilde{F}_x - f\overline{V}D + gD\frac{\partial \eta}{\partial x} = <wu(-1)> - \frac{gD}{\rho_0} \int_{-1}^{0} \int_{\sigma}^{0} \left[D\frac{\partial \rho}{\partial x} - \frac{\sigma \partial D}{\partial x}\frac{\partial \rho}{\partial \sigma} \right] d\sigma d\sigma \tag{12}$$

$$\frac{\partial \overline{V} D}{\partial t} + \frac{\partial \overline{UV} D}{\partial x} + \frac{\partial \overline{V}^2 D}{\partial y} - \tilde{F}_y + f\overline{U}D + gD\frac{\partial \eta}{\partial y} = <wv(-1)> - \frac{gD}{\rho_0} \int_{-1}^{0} \int_{\sigma}^{0} \left[D\frac{\partial \rho}{\partial y} - \frac{\sigma \partial D}{\partial y}\frac{\partial \rho}{\partial \sigma} \right] d\sigma d\sigma \tag{13}$$

where $(wu(-1), wv(-1)) = -C_z(U^2 + V^2)^{1/2}(U,V), \sigma \to -1;$ $\overline{U}, \overline{V}$ are the vertically integrated velocities; $(\overline{U}, \overline{V}) = \int_{-1}^{0}(U,V)d\sigma$; $\tilde{F}_x, \tilde{F}_y$ are horizontal turbulence diffusion term; C_z is Chezy coefficient; and, $<wu(-1)>$ and $<wv(-1)>$ are bottom stress components.

In the momentum equations, the terms on advection, horizontal diffusion, and density gradient are integrated vertically from the corresponding terms of internal equations. The bottom stress is derived from the velocity of internal mode. Since the internal and external modes have different truncation errors, the vertical integrals of the internal mode velocity may differ from $\overline{U}, \overline{V}$. Thus, the current velocity in the internal mode (U,V) is adjusted slightly to fit with the following condition $\int_{-1}^{0} U d\sigma = \overline{U}$.

In the POM, the solution of the external mode is entirely explicit and C grid is employed. Hence, the allowable time step is limited by the Courant-Friedrichs-Lewy (CFL) condition, which stipulates that $dt < \dfrac{dx}{\sqrt{2gh} + U_{MAX}/\sqrt{2}}$ has to be fulfilled. For small grid sizes, the corresponding time step will be small in order to keep the computation stable, which entails longer computational time. In order to develop a three-dimensional numerical model that can represent the Pearl River estuary with the smallest size of generated orthogonal curvilinear grid of 50m for execution in a personal computer, a semi-implicit method is adopted in the external mode. This method is expressed as a time-splitting alternating direction implicit scheme on the "Arakawa C" grids as shown in Figure 2.

Continuity equations:

$$\frac{\eta_{i,j}^* - \eta_{i,j}^n}{\Delta t} + \frac{\overline{U}_{i+1,j}^*(D_{i,j}^n + D_{i+1,j}^n) - \overline{U}_{i,j}^*(D_{i-1,j}^n + D_{i,j}^n)}{2\Delta x} + \frac{\overline{V}_{i,j+1}^n(D_{i,j}^n + D_{i,j+1}^n) - \overline{V}_{i,j}^n(D_{i,j-1}^n + D_{i,j}^n)}{2\Delta y} = 0 \tag{14}$$

$$\frac{\eta_{i,j}^{n+1} - \eta_{i,j}^*}{\Delta t} + \frac{\overline{V}_{i,j+1}^{n+1}(D_{i,j}^* + D_{i,j+1}^*) - \overline{V}_{i,j}^{n+1}(D_{i,j}^* + D_{i,j+1}^*)}{2\Delta y} - \frac{\overline{V}_{i,j+1}^n(D_{i,j}^n + D_{i,j+1}^n) - \overline{V}_{i,j}^n(D_{i,j-1}^n + D_{i,j}^n)}{2\Delta y} = 0 \tag{15}$$

Momentum equations:

$$\frac{\overline{U}_{i,j}^* - \overline{U}_{i,j}^n}{\Delta t} + g\frac{\eta_{i-1,j}^* - \eta_{i,j}^*}{\Delta x} - f\frac{\overline{V}_{i-1,j}^n + \overline{V}_{i-1,j-1}^n + \overline{V}_{i,j}^n + \overline{V}_{i,j-1}^n}{4} = A^n \tag{16}$$

$$\frac{\overline{V}_{i,j}^{n+1} - \overline{V}_{i,j}^n}{\Delta t} + g\frac{\eta_{i,j+1}^{n+1} - \eta_{i,j}^{n+1}}{\Delta y} + f\frac{\overline{U}_{i-1,j}^* + \overline{U}_{i-1,j+1}^* + \overline{U}_{i,j}^* + \overline{U}_{i,j+1}^*}{4} = B^n \tag{17}$$

At the conclusion of each time step, the following condition is also imposed:

$$\overline{U}_{i,j}^{n-1} = \overline{U}_{i,j}^* \tag{18}$$

where η^* and $\overline{U}^*$ are intermediate parameters in first time-splitting step in the x-direction. A^n, B^n are the terms to be acquired from the internal sub-mode. Equations in each direction are written in a tri-diagonal matrix to be solved with the double-sweep algorithm [25]. In the time-splitting steps, the solution is first advanced from time level nt to t* in the x-direction to obtain $\overline{U}^*, \eta^*$, and then advanced in the second step from t* to (n+1)t in the y-direction to acquire $\overline{V}^{n+1}, \eta^{n+1}$. $\overline{U}^{n+1} = \overline{U}^*$ is then set at the end of the entire step.

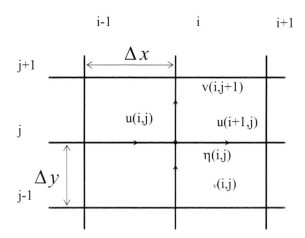

Figure 2. Arakawa C grids

Computational Stability of Hydrodynamic System

In this algorithm, both the vertical diffusion terms in the internal mode and the elevation gradation term in the external mode are treated implicitly. However, the allowable computational time step cannot exceed the limits associated with the advection terms, the Coriolis term, the baroclinic pressure gradient term and horizontal diffusion term. Nevertheless, the semi-implicit numerical algorithm allows a much larger time step compared to that based upon the CFL condition for an explicit algorithm. When this model is applied to Pearl River estuary, the maximum time steps of the external and internal modes are 100 seconds and 60 seconds, respectively. Hence, the same time step of 60 seconds is adopted in both of the two sub-modes for simplicity purpose. Under the same conditions, if instead the POM was applied here, the maximum time steps would be 6 seconds and 100 seconds for external and internal modes, respectively. The performance of the models under these time steps can be compared in term of computer memory and execution time. From numerical experiments in this case, this model consumes a core memory of 14.8M and 10 seconds per hour run whilst the POM requires 14.2M memory and 14 seconds per hour run. It can be noted that the much faster execution speed is worth pursuing at the expense of slightly increased memory requirement.

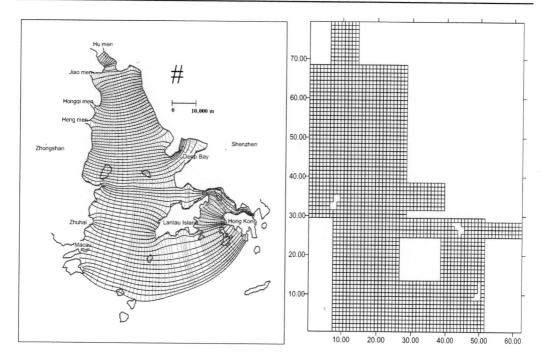

Figure 3. The orthogonal curvilinear grid   **Figure 4.** The transformed plane

Strategies to Adjust for Sigma Coordinate Pressure Gradient

Whilst the adoption of sigma coordinates have the advantage to address large topographic variability, it also has drawback of hydrostatic inconsistency due to the bottom topography effect caused by the horizontal density gradient along the constant σ layer. Nevertheless, some strategies can be adopted to reduce this inconsistency [26]. The topography is examined and the depth of water H should be adjusted to fulfill the equation $\left|\frac{\sigma}{H}\frac{\partial H}{\partial x}\right|\delta x < \delta\sigma$ [27]. Moreover, prior to the computation of fluxes, a climatological density or temperature and salinity, defined as follows, is subtracted first:

$$d\rho_{c\lim}/dt = a(\rho - \rho_{c\lim}) \tag{19}$$

where a is the inverse of the period of major tidal constituent t; ρ and $\rho_{c\lim}$ are density and climatological density, respectively. In this model, t = 0.5175 day, which is the period of the M_2 tidal constituent predominant in Hong Kong waters [28].

Pollution Transport System

In this model, the pollutant transport system is coupled and incorporated into the hydrodynamic numerical model. Thus, similarly, the curvilinear orthogonal coordinate is employed in the horizontal spatial direction and the sigma coordinate is adopted in the vertical spatial direction. The methodology of the orthogonal curvilinear transformation for water quality modeling is similar to that in Chau and Jin [29]. The governing equation of pollutant transport is expressed as follows:

$$\frac{\partial SD}{\partial t} + \frac{\partial SUD}{\partial x} + \frac{\partial SVD}{\partial y} + \frac{\partial S\omega}{\partial \sigma} = \frac{\partial}{\partial x}(A_s H \frac{\partial S}{\partial x}) + \frac{\partial}{\partial y}(A_s H \frac{\partial S}{\partial y}) + \frac{\partial}{\partial \sigma}\left[\frac{K_H}{D}\frac{\partial S}{\partial \sigma}\right] - K_s DS + S_s \qquad (20)$$

where S is the density of the pollutant, which in our case is the density of COD_{Mn}; K_s is the decay rate of pollutant; S_s is the source of pollutant; A_s is horizontal turbulent coefficient, which can be acquired from the following Smagorinsky formula [30-31]:

$$A_s = C\Delta x\Delta y\left[\left(\frac{\partial U}{\partial x}\right)^2 + \frac{1}{2}\left(\frac{\partial V}{\partial x} + \frac{\partial U}{\partial y}\right)^2 + \left(\frac{\partial V}{\partial y}\right)^2\right]^{\frac{1}{2}} \qquad (21)$$

where C is a coefficient ranged from 0.1 to 0.2. In this model, after a number of numerical experiments, a value of 0.12 is adopted. The governing equation is then written in finite difference equation under the "Arakawa C" grids:

$$\delta_t(SD) + \delta_x(\overline{S}^x \overline{D}^x U) + \delta_y(\overline{S}^y \overline{D}^y V) + \delta_\sigma(\overline{S}^\sigma \omega) = \delta_x(\overline{H}^x \overline{A}_s^x \delta_x S) + \delta_y(\overline{H}^y \overline{A}_s^y \delta_y S) \qquad (22)$$
$$+ \delta_\sigma(\overline{K}_H^\sigma \delta_\sigma S_+ / D) - K_s DS_+ + S_s$$

where, for any parameter $F = F(x,y,\sigma,t)$ with spatial and temporal property x,y,σ,t,

$$\delta_t F = \frac{1}{2\Delta t}(F(x,y,\sigma,t+\Delta t) - F(x,y,\sigma,t-\Delta t)) \qquad (23)$$

$$\overline{F}^x = \frac{1}{2}\left[F(x+\frac{\Delta x}{2},y,\sigma,t) + F(x-\frac{\Delta x}{2},y,\sigma,t)\right] \qquad (24)$$

$$\delta_x F = \frac{1}{\Delta x}\left[F(x+\frac{\Delta x}{2},y,\sigma,t) - F(x-\frac{\Delta x}{2},y,\sigma,t)\right] \qquad (25)$$

$$S_+ = S(x,y,\sigma,t+\Delta t) \qquad (26)$$

All the components in the discretized equation (22), except $S(x,y,\sigma,t+\Delta t)$, $S(x,y,\sigma+\Delta\sigma,t+\Delta t)$, and $S(x,y,\sigma-\Delta\sigma,t+\Delta t)$, can be acquired either from the hydrodynamic system or from the previous time steps. The equation can be re-arranged as follows:

$$AS(x,y,\sigma-\Delta\sigma,t+\Delta t) + BS(x,y,\sigma,t+\Delta t) + CS(x,y,\sigma+\Delta\sigma,t+\Delta t) = D \qquad (27)$$

where A, B, C and D are some known coefficients. It is in a form of tri-diagonal matrix in the vertical direction, which can be readily solved [32].

Real Case Application

A coupled hydrodynamic and pollutant transport model can be a very efficient tool for environmental impact assessment and feasibility study of projects. The following section presents the application and calibration of the prototype numerical model to PRDR, which has been established as a very important economic zone in Southern China.

Bathymetric and Hydrological Conditions

Within the PRDR, Shenzhen River outlet discharges at the Deep Bay in the eastern side whilst four river outlets exist in the northwestern side of the estuary: Heng men; Hongqi men; Hu men; and, Jiao men. The mean water depth of the delta estuary is 7 meters and is shallower nearer the inner bay. Its depth at the open side of the estuary ranges between 20 and 28 meters. The tide in Pearl River estuary is principally semi-diurnal and irregular, with the mean tidal range over the entire region about 1.0 meter. It is higher in the inner estuary, with the tidal range in Hu men being 1.6m [33] whilst, at the entrance, the mean tidal range is from 0.85 to 0.95 meter. The annually averaged net discharges of the four outlets in different seasons are given in Table 1, based on Pang and Li [34]. The variation of the discharges is significant in different years and different seasons. During the wet season (from May to September) and the dry season (from December to March), the runoff of the rivers and the tidal current are the principal hydrodynamic forcing, respectively [35]. Thus, the distribution of pollutant during different seasons shall be examined so as to capture a complete picture of the transport pattern.

Table 1. The discharge of four east outlets in different seasons (unit: $10^8 m^3 / season$)

	Hu men			Jiao men			Hongqi men			Heng men		
	Wet	Mean	Dry	Wet	Mean	Dry	Wet	Mean	Dry	Wet	Mean	Dry
Discharge	312.9	140.6	81.2	299.2	129.7	70.2	116.1	45.7	20.7	196.3	80.3	44.9

Model Schematization and Boundary Conditions

By using the orthogonal curvilinear coordinate system, the horizontal grid and the corresponding transformed grid are shown in Figures 3 and 4, respectively. The total number of horizontal grids within the entire computing domain is 3400 whilst the number of layers in the vertical direction is six, each of which has the same $\delta\sigma$ with a value of $1/6$. These parameters are chosen taking into consideration of reasonable accuracy in both horizontal and vertical discretizations as well as adequate computational efficiency. The initial conditions are chosen such that the densities of pollutants for all grid points are zero. After having executed for 100 tidal periods or so, representing about 50 days, a steady state condition is acquired.

In this model, two types of boundary conditions exist: open boundary and close boundary. At the open boundaries located in the southern and eastern boundaries, the tidal elevation is the main forcing, which is obtained by interpolation from the observed data at two stations (Macau and North Point) according to tidal wave propagating speed $\sqrt{gh}$ [36]. The velocity values of external and internal modes at the open boundary are derived from the radiation condition; for example $\frac{\partial v}{\partial t} - c_i \frac{\partial v}{\partial y} = 0$, $c_i = \sqrt{H/H_{max}}$ at the southern open boundary.

Depending on the tidal condition, values of salinity, temperature and turbulence kinetic and turbulence dissipation at the open boundary condition are obtained as follows:

$$\text{Ebb time:} \quad \frac{\partial A}{\partial t} + U \frac{\partial A}{\partial x} = 0 \tag{28}$$

$$\text{Flood time:} \quad A = A_{set}(t, \sigma) \tag{29}$$

where A represents the salinity, temperature, turbulence kinetic and turbulence dissipation. During the ebb tide, A are calculated by using the "upwind" differenced advection equation. During flood tide, A is linearly interpolated from its value at end of ebb period to a fixed A that depends on the depth and observed data. The open boundary conditions of four outlets in the northwestern side of the PRDR are mainly governed by outflow discharges.

The conventional treatment of open boundary condition for pollutant transport is quite simple. As an illustration, for grids in the vicinity of the eastern open boundary, the equations during the flood and ebb tides respectively will be as follows [25]:

$$\text{Flood tide} \qquad P_{i,j}^{n+1} = P_{set} \qquad U_{i-\frac{1}{2},j}^{n+1} < 0 \tag{30}$$

$$\text{Ebb} \tag{31}$$

$$\text{ide} \frac{dP}{dt} = 0 \quad that \quad is \frac{P_{i,j}^{n+1} - P_{i,j}^{n-1}}{2\Delta t} + U_{i-\frac{1}{2},j}^{n+1} \frac{P_{i,j}^{n} - P_{i-1,j}^{n}}{\Delta x} = 0 \; U_{i-\frac{1}{2},j}^{n+1} > 0$$

where P_{set} represents the prescribed component of the pollutant density along the boundary during flood tide. If this value is initially unknown, a zero value is often assumed. Thus, this boundary condition can represent the real situation only when the boundary value is known or there exists strong capacity of water exchange along the open boundary. In this case, such boundary data are not available nor the exchange capacity at the entrance of PRDR is strong enough to justify the application of the condition $P_{set} = 0$. In order to accommodate the above drawback of the conventional approach, a simple but efficient open transport condition is developed during flood tide in this model as follows:

$$\textit{Flood tide} \qquad \frac{P_{i,j}^{n+1} - P_{i,j}^{n-1}}{2\Delta t} + U_{i-\frac{1}{2},j}^{n+1} \frac{(a-1)P_{i-1,j}^{n}}{\Delta x} = 0 \quad U_{i-\frac{1}{2},j}^{n+1} < 0 \qquad (32)$$

During the flood tide, equation (32) replaces equation (30) whilst the ebb tide condition remains the same, as shown in equation (31). The parameter a in equation (32) is a constant ranging between 0 and 1. Its value depends on the capacity of water exchange outside the open boundary. If the exchange capacity is strong, a small value of a should be used and vice versa. In the PRDR model, after having conducted a number of numerical experiments, a value of $a = 0.9$ is found to be able to best-fit the results to the measured field data.

In the motion equations, the convection and diffusion terms require the determination of the velocity value at the outer boundary. Two kinds of closed boundary conditions have been tested here. The no-slip condition assumes $u = 0$ whilst a free slip condition is represented by $\frac{\partial u}{\partial y} = 0$. Finally, the semi-slip boundary condition: $\frac{\partial u}{\partial y} = \frac{\beta u}{\Delta y}, 0 \leq \beta \leq 1$, which represents a weighing of the above two methods, is applied to the Pearl River estuary. Sensitivity tests with different β values have been conducted. Yet, it is found that this will only cause little change to the results.

Pollutant Loading to Estuary

The major pollutant sources are from the five river outlets and the COD loadings at different outlets are evaluated first. The volume flow rates of domestic and industrial wastewater discharged from Guangdong Province are calculated based on Wen et al. [37]. An empirical relationship between discharge rate of COD and the discharge rates of domestic and industrial wastewater, with a coefficient of regression of 0.93, is found to be as follows:

$$Q_{COD} = 0.00027Q_d + 0.000305Q_i \qquad (33)$$

where Q_{COD} is the discharge rate of COD; Q_i is the discharge rate of industrial wastewater; Q_d is the discharge rate of domestic wastewater. Hence, the quantity of the COD discharged from the eight major cities in the PRDR can be derived from the corresponding wastewater discharges. Moreover, the COD loading data can be evaluated based on the net discharge flow rates of the river outlet and the COD discharge of these eight major cities. The rate of decay of pollutants is assumed to be 0.25 day^{-1} here.

Model Calibration and Simulation

The hydrological survey data acquired at three tidal elevation stations and three tidal current stations, with their locations shown in Figure 1, are employed for calibration of this model. The observed data of tidal elevation on two stations, namely, Macau and North Point, are used as the boundary conditions. The hydrodynamics and pollutant transport of Pearl River estuary in this one month's period are simulated by the model. The computational results of tidal elevation, flow velocity and flow direction are chosen as the parameters for calibration and validation with the corresponding observed data.

Tidal Elevation and Current Velocity

The start up of the simulation may require about 2 to 3 hours prior to convergence to reliable solution. After the calibration of the model, the simulated tidal elevation, current pattern, flow direction and velocity all agree well with the observed data [33]. In general, the amplitude at the inner station is larger than its counterpart at the outer station. Figure 5 shows the comparison of computed and measured tidal level result of at one of the strategic stations during the validation period. Figure 6 shows the computed result of horizontal tidal current pattern during ebb tide condition during the mean season at different water layers in the PRDR. It is observed that the current velocities at the surface layer are slightly higher than those in the bottom layer and that the flow directions at the surface layer and bottom layer may even be opposite, in particular under slow current speed condition. Moreover, the current speed in northwest Lantau Island water areas, Urmston Road and West East Channel are in general higher than other locations. This phenomenon can be explained by the local bathymetry of these locations which cause lateral contraction in the flow channel. Maximum flow velocity with a value up to 2.5m/s occurs at narrow yet deep Ma Wan Channel and Kap Shui Mun Channel. Figure 7 shows the comparison of both current direction and magnitude between computed and observed depth-averaged observations at three strategic tidal stations for the validation period. The root-mean-squares errors of the computed tidal level, flow direction and velocity during the validation are found to be 0.14m, 17 degree, and 0.07m/s respectively.

Transport of COD_{mn}

In order to evaluate the impacts of the pollutant sources from the PRDR on Hong Kong ambient seawaters, COD_{Mn} is used as a representative water quality variable and the pollutant loadings in different seasons are applied from the five major river outlets. The vertical averaged COD_{Mn} densities are able to represent the layers at different depths due to the generally well vertical mixing. The distribution of incremental COD_{Mn} due to sewage loading from the PRDR in wet season during the ebb tide are shown in Figure 8. The verification of simulation results under this condition is shown in Table 2. It is noted that the impact of COD loading is only significant up to the northern part of the Lantau Island, and becomes negligible in other coastal waters around Hong Kong. The maximum value of incremental density of COD_{Mn} caused by the loadings is 0.75 mg/L or so adjacent to the Lantau Island. During the dry season, the density of COD_{Mn} is generally low at the entrance of the PRDR in the vicinity of Hong Kong and Macau, but becomes higher in the inner PRDR. During the wet season, the impact on the quality of Hong Kong seawaters is more significant, yet the density change of COD_{Mn} in the inner estuary is less than those during the mean season or the dry season. A possible explanation is that the conveyance capacity increases with the net discharge. From the detailed analysis, it is found that the impacts of pollutants from the Hu men outlet and Shenzhen River outlet on the PRDR and Hong Kong ambient seawaters are more significant than those at the other river outlets. The possible reason may be that the pollutant loading in the Hu men outlet is the largest whilst the hydrodynamic transport capacity of Shenzhen River is to certain extent constrained by its small net water discharge and ground topography.

Table 2. Verification of simulation results in wet season during ebb tide

Location	Simulated COD_{Mn} (mg/L)	Observed COD_{Mn} (mg/L)
Jiao men	4.5	4.6
Hongqi men	4.1	4
Heng men	3.3	3.4
Deep Bay	3.9	3.8
Lantau Island	2.5	2.4
Macau	1.9	1.8

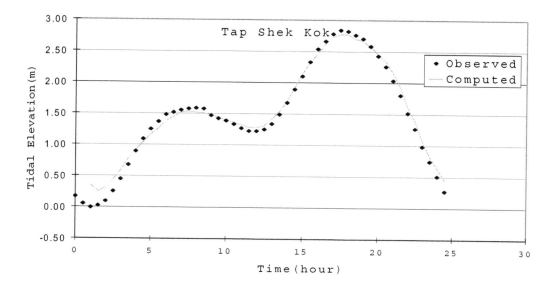

Figure 5. Calibration of tidal elevation during the validation period at Tap Shek Kok

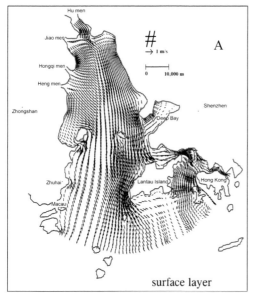

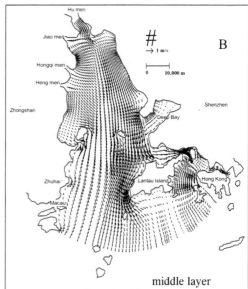

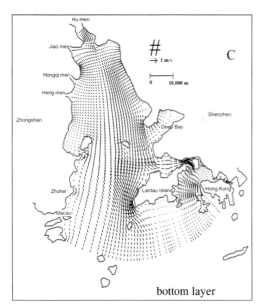

Figure 6. Ebb tidal flow field in three layers A-surface B-middle C-Bottom

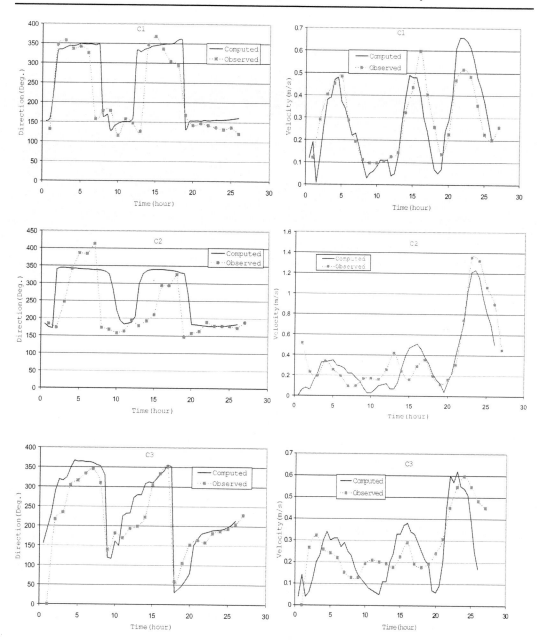

Figure 7. Calibration of tidal flow direction and velocity in three stations (C1,C2,C3)

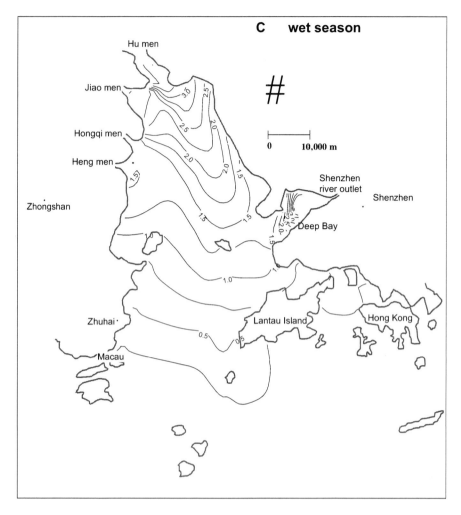

Figure 8. Simulated incremental distribution of COD_{Mn} (in mg/L) due to sewage loading from the PRDR in wet season during ebb tide

Conclusions

A robust and efficient three-dimensional curvilinear coupled hydrodynamic and pollutant transport model has been formulated, verified and applied to the PRDR. In this model, the external and internal gravity waves have been split in the algorithm with the same time step in both modes. A major advantage of this algorithm is a larger allowable time step compared with its counterparts of the POM model. It is demonstrated that the prototype model works well in this typical estuary. The computational results of tidal elevation, direction and magnitude of current velocity have been calibrated with the actual field measurements. Fairly good agreement between the simulated and surveyed data has been recorded. The simulation of transboundary effect for pollutant transport in the PRDR is implemented by using a simple but robust open boundary condition. Pollutant sources represented by COD_{Mn} discharges at different estuary outlets are input into the prototype model. It is demonstrated that the pollutants from the PRDR affect the Hong Kong ambient seawaters significantly, especially during wet season under large net runoff discharge condition. Moreover, the pollutants discharged from the Hu men outlet and Shenzhen River outlet, when compared with other outlets of the PRDR, has more significant impacts on the water quality in both the PRDR and Hong Kong ambient seawaters.

References

[1]. Binnie and Partners (1988). *Hydraulic and water quality studies in Victoria Harbor.* Territory Devel. Dept., Hong Kong Government, Hong Kong

[2]. Walker, A.F., and Jones, S.V. (1991). "Water quality implications of Hong Kong's port and airport proposals." *Environmental Hydraulics*, J. Lee and Y.K. Cheung. eds., A.A. Balkema, Rotterdam, The Netherlands, 859-864.

[3]. Chau, K.W. and Lee, J.H.W. (1991). "Mathematical modelling of Shing Mun River network." *Advances in Water Resources*, 14(3), 106-112.

[4]. Chau, K.W. and Lee, J.H.W. (1991). "A robust mathematical model for pollutant transportation in estuaries." *Water Resources Journal*, 168, 63-80.

[5]. Chau, K.W. and Lee, J.H.W. (1991). "A microcomputer model for flood prediction with applications." *Microcomputers in Civil Engineering*, 6(2), 109-121.

[6]. Chen, H.Y. and Li, Y.S. (1991). "A three-dimensional semi-implicit finite-difference model for flows in stratified seas." *Environmental hydraulics*, J.Lee and Y.K. Cheung. eds., A.A. Balkema, Rotterdam, The Netherlands, 937-942.

[7]. Sin, Y.S. and Chau, K.W. (1992). "Eutrophication studies on Tolo Harbour, Hong Kong." *Water Science and Technology*, 26(9-11), 2551-2554.

[8]. Zhang, Fan, Huang, Qizhou, Wang, Wenzhi, Li, Y.S. and Chau, K.W. (1994). "Diagnostic calculations for the seasonal-averaged current field in the deep water zone of the South China Sea." *Tropic Oceanology*, 13(3), 8-16 (in Chinese).

[9]. Chau, K.W., Jin, H.S. and Sin, Y.S. (1996). "A finite difference model of 2-d tidal flow in Tolo Harbour, Hong Kong." *Applied Mathematical Modelling*, 20(4), 321-328.

[10]. Hu, S.L. and Kot, S.C. (1997). "Numerical model of tides in Pearl River estuary with moving boundary." *Journal of Hydraulic Engineering, ASCE*, 123(1), 21-29.

[11]. Huang, Qizhou, Wang, Wenzhi, Fu, Suncheng, Chen, Rongyu, Li, Y.S. and Chau, K.W. (1997). "A westward current that flows through the north of the Dongsha Islands in summer," *Tropic Oceanology*, 16(2), 58-66 (in Chinese).

[12]. Jin, Haisheng, Egashira, Shinji and Chau, K.W. (1998). "Carbon to chlorophyll-a ratio in modeling long-term eutrophication phenomena." *Water Science and Technology*, 38(11), 227-235.

[13]. Chau, K.W. and Chen, W. (2001). "A fifth generation numerical modelling system in coastal zone." *Applied Mathematical Modelling*, 25(10), 887-900.

[14]. Chau, K.W. and Jin, H.S. (2002). "Two-layered, 2D unsteady eutrophication model in boundary-fitted coordinate system." *Marine Pollution Bulletin*, 45(1-12), 300-310.

[15]. Chau, K.W. (2004). "Intelligent manipulation of calibration parameters in numerical modeling." *Advances in Environmental Research*, 8(3-4), 467-476.

[16]. Mellor, G. L. (1996). *User's guide for a three-dimensional, Primitive equation, numerical ocean model*, Princeton University Rep. Princeton University, Princeton, NJ.

[17]. Quamrul Ahsan, A.K.M., and Blumberg, A.F. (1999). "Three-dimensional hydrothermal model of Onondaga Lake, New York." *Journal of Hydraulic Engineering, ASCE*, 125(9), 912-923.

[18]. Hills, P., Zhang, L. and Liu, J.H. (1998). "Transboundary pollution between Guangdong province and Hong Kong: threats to water quality in the Pearl River estuary and their implications for environmental policy and planning." *Journal of Environmental Planning and Management,* 41(3), 375-396.

[19]. Simons, T.J. (1974). "Verification of numerical models of Lake Ontario. Part 1, circulation in spring and early summer." *Journal of Physical Oceanography*, 4(4), 507-523.

[20]. Leedertse, J.J., Alexander, R.C., and Liu, S.K. (1973). *A three-dimensional model for estuaries and coastal seas, Volume I. Principles of computation,* R-1417-OWRR, Santa Monica, Rand Corp.

[21]. Davies, A.M, Jones, J.E. and Xing, J. (1995). "Review of recent developments in tidal hydrodynamic model. II: Turbulence energy Models." *Journal of Hydraulic Engineering, ASCE*, 123(4), 293-302.

[22]. Blumberg, A.F. and Mellor, G.L. (1980). "A coastal ocean numerical model." *Mathematical Modelling of Estuarine Physics, Proc. Int. Symp., Hamburg, Aug. 1978,* J. Sunderman and K.-P. Holtz, Spinger-Verlag, Berlin, 203-214.

[23]. Blumberg, A.F. and Mellor, G.L. (1987). "A description of a three-dimensional coastal ocean circulation model." *Three-Dimension Coastal ocean models*, 4, N. Heaps, American Geophysical union, Washington, D.C., 208.

[24]. Chau, K.W. and Jin, H.S. (1995). "Numerical solution of two-layered, two-dimensional tidal flow in boundary-fitted orthogonal curvilinear coordinate system." *International Journal for Numerical Methods in Fluids*, 21(11), 1087-1107.

[25]. Leedertse, J. J. and Crittion, E.C. (1971). *A Water Quality Simulation Model for Well-Mixed Estuaries and Coastal Seas Computation Procedures*, R-708-NYC, New York, Rand Corp.

[26]. Mellor, G. L., Oey, L.Y. and Ezer, T. (1997). "Sigma coordinate pressure gradient errors and the seamount problem." *Journal of Atmospheric and Oceanic Technology*, 15(5), 1122-1131.

[27]. Haney, R.L. (1990) "Notes and Correspondence: On the pressure gradient force over steep topography in sigma coordinate ocean model." *Journal of Physical Oceanography*, 21(4), 610-619.

[28]. Ip S.F., and Wai, H.G. (1990). *An application of harmonic method to tidal analysis and prediction in Hong Kong,* Royal observatory, Hong Kong Technical Note (local) No.55.

[29]. Chau, K.W. and Jin, H.S. (1998). "Eutrophication model for a coastal bay in Hong Kong." *Journal of Environmental Engineering, ASCE,* 124(7), 628-638.

[30]. Oey, L. Y., Mellor, G. L. and Hires, R. I. (1985). "A three-dimensional simulation of the Hudson Raritan estuary. part I: description of model and model simulation." *Journal of Physical Oceanography*, 15(12), 1693-1709.

[31]. Chau, K.W. (2000). "Transverse mixing coefficient measurements in an open rectangular channel." *Advances in Environmental Research*, 4(4), 287-294.

[32]. Richtmyer, R.D. and Morton, K.W. (1967). *Difference Methods for Initial-Value Problems*. Interscience, NewYork.

[33]. Kot, S.C. and Hu, S.L. (1995). "Water flows and sediment transport in Pearl River estuary and wave in South China sea near Hong Kong." *Coastal Infrastructure Development in Hong Kong A Review*. Hong Kong. Hong Kong Government, Hong Kong, 13-32.

[34]. Pang, Y. and Li, X.L. (1998). "Study of pollutants passing through the four east outlets of Pearl River Delta to Lingding Sea," in: Y.S. Li (eds). *Proceedings of Workshop on Hydraulics of the Pearl River Estuary*. Hong Kong. Hong Kong Polytechnic University, 85-98.

[35]. Lu, Q.M. (1997). *Three-dimensional modeling of hydrodynamics and sediment transport with parallel algorithm*, thesis for Ph.D, Hong Kong Polytechnic University.

[36]. Huang, S. and Lu, Q.M. (1995). *Estuarine dynamics*, The water conservancy and electricity Press, Beijing, 11-20.

[37]. Wen, W.Y., Zhang, G.X. and Du, W.C. (1994). A study on water pollution in the Zhujiang estuary, in: *Environmental Research of Pearl River Delta Region*. Guangdong Province Government, Guangzhou, 99-151.

In: Trends in Water Pollution Research
Editor: J. V. Livingston, pp. 203-220

ISBN 1-59454-328-3
©2005 Nova Science Publishers, Inc.

Chapter IX

Relevance of the Multixenobiotic Defence Mechanism (MXDM) for the Biological Monitoring of Freshwaters – Example of its Use in Zebra Mussels

Sandrine Pain[1]†, Sylvie Biagianti-Risbourg†
and Marc Parant‡

† Université de Reims – UFR Sciences Exactes et Naturelles – URVVC UPRES EA 2069
– Laboratoire Eco-Toxicologie – BP 1039 – 51 687 REIMS cedex 2 – France.
‡ Université de Metz – UFR Sciences Fondamentales et Appliquées – Laboratoire
Ecotoxicité et Santé Environnementale – CNRS UMR 7146 – Campus Bridoux – Rue du
Général Delestraint – 57 070 METZ – France.

Abstract

During their evolution, organisms have developed various protection systems against environmental stress. Among the stress they undergo daily, environmental pollution has taken a more and more preponderant place. Ecotoxicology aims to determine the fate of pollutants once they have entered the environment and their effects at the individual level, but also *in fine* at the population, community and ecosystem level. In this context, the protection systems used by organisms against pollution are precious tools because their activation provides an evidence of exposure and can then be used as biomarkers of organisms' exposure to pollution.

Multixenobiotic Defence Mechanism (MXDM) is a membrane efflux system that enables the cells to protect against xenobiotics both in limiting their entry and facilitating their extrusion. This protection system was shown to be effective in various invertebrate species and was proposed to be used as a biomarker of exposure in aquatic ecosystems.

---

[1] Corresponding Author: Sandrine PAIN - sandrine.pain@univ-reims.fr

This chapter gives an example of the use of the MXDM response assessed in a bivalve species, the zebra mussel *Dreissena polymorpha*. Experiments were performed in a river that receives the effluent of a chlorine bleached pulp and paper mill. The effluent was shown to worsen the water quality downstream by increasing the organic content and by generating organohalogenated compounds.

The response of MXDM activity was first tested in the laboratory by exposing mussels in water sampled downstream the effluent, which presented a high concentration of organohalogenated compounds ([AOX]=685μgCl/L). After a 12-day exposure, MXDM activity was significantly induced. Secondly, mussels were exposed *in situ* upstream ([AOX]<20μgCl/L) and downstream (125<[AOX]<140μgCl/L) the effluent. The experiment showed high level of induction at the two sites. Thirdly, the presence of MXDM substrates was investigated by measuring the MXDM inhibitory potential of river water. MXDM activity was induced upstream (*in situ*) as well as downstream (laboratory and *in situ*). The differences in levels of AOX or MXDM substrates between the two sites could not explain the results, suggesting that MXDM could not provide a specific response. This will be discussed and conclusions will be drawn, revealing that MXDM induction a) reflects the contaminated state of a water but b) can not be related to a particular contamination parameter. The relevance of MXDM as a biomarker of environmental stress is discussed in light of the current need to dispose of rapid and informative tools to predict effects of pollution on aquatic ecosystems. Furthermore, the use of MXDM will be extended to other organisms such as sediment-living invertebrates (Annelids) in order to complement the information obtained from mussels that are mainly exposed to environmental stress *via* the water column.

Key Words : MXDM, MXRM, Biomarker, Environmental stress, Zebra mussel, AOX

Abbreviations

MXDM: MultiXenobiotic Defence Mechanism
MXRM: MultiXenobiotic Resistance Mechanism
MDR: MultiDrug Resistance
AOX: Adsorbable Organohalogenated compounds

Introduction

In nature, aquatic organisms have to undergo what can be called "natural stress" both from biotic (such as parasitism) or abiotic (such as climatic) origins. To this natural pressure are added the effects of the contamination of water and sediments by active substances able to directly or indirectly affect organisms' health. As today almost all aquatic ecosystems could be considered as not spared by pollution and as environmental pollution takes a more and more preponderant place, it becomes essential to better define to what extent living organisms have to undergo environmental stress. In this aim, it has to be determined to what extent they are really exposed to contaminants, in other words whether contaminants are available for them. During their evolution, living organisms have developed protection systems against available environmental compounds that could be toxic for them such as natural toxins produced by other organisms. These systems also constitute a protection against environmental pollution. They are precious tools for ecotoxicologists because their activation provides an evidence of exposure of organisms to pollution. Indeed they can be used as biomarkers of organisms' exposure to environmental pollution (Lagadic et al. 1997).

The Multixenobiotic Defence (Resistance) Mechanism or MXDM was proposed as one of these biological markers (Kurelec and Pivcevic 1989, Kurelec 1992). It is a membrane efflux system that enables the cells to protect against xenobiotics both in limiting their entry and facilitating their extrusion. MXDM is similar to the well-known "multidrug resistance" (MDR) characterised in mammals by the resistance of tumour cells which limits accumulation of cytotoxic drugs, then leading to failure of treatment (Gottesman and Pastan 1993). It has been associated with the expression of a membrane glycoprotein called P-glycoprotein- or P170-*like* with reference to the multidrug transporter identified in mammals. This mechanism mediates ATP-dependent efflux of a wide variety of structurally and functionally diverse compounds, provided that they are moderately hydrophobic (Juliano and Ling 1976, Endicott and Ling 1989). MXDM has been identified in many aquatic organisms (for a review see Bard 2000). Bivalve molluscs have been searched for an analogous efflux mechanism and elements attesting presence of MXDM have been found in mussels, oysters and clams in marine as well as in freshwater ecosystems (Kurelec and Pivcevic 1989, 1991, Minier et al. 1993, Waldmann et al. 1995, Smital and Kurelec 1997, Parant and Pain 2001). In these bivalve species, evidence of MXDM presence and function was demonstrated in tissues particularly exposed to pollution of aquatic ecosystems such as gills and digestive gland (Minier and Galgani 1995, Kurelec and Pivcevic 1989, Keppler and Ringwood 2001), but also in lysosomal membrane of hemocytes (Minier and Moore 1996) and in embryonic or larval tissues (Mc Fazden et al. 2000, Minier et al. 2002). Little is known about biochemical properties of MXDM in bivalves and numerous data are transposed from studies in tumour cell lines in mammals (for a review see Bard 2000, Pain and Parant 2003a). Few genetic studies are available, but it was shown that partial cDNA obtained from the blue mussel (*Mytilus edulis*, Minier et al. 1993), the pacific oyster (*Crassostrea gigas*, Minier et al. 1993) and from the mussel *Perna perna* (Grimm et al. 2000) shared similarities with mammalian MDR genes. Concerning the protein level, P-glycoprotein homologues have been identified in several freshwater (Waldmann et al. 1995, Bonfanti et al. 1998, Jaouen et al. 2000) and marine species (Minier et al. 1993, Cornwall et al. 1995, Galgani et al. 1996, Minier et al. 2000, Keppler and Ringwood 2001).

Freshwater and marine bivalves are often used as sentinel organisms and are subject of many studies aiming to understand and use MXDM as a biomarker of exposure to polluted waters. Indeed MXDM has been shown to be induced in bivalves collected from polluted areas (Minier et al. 1993, Kurelec et al. 1996a) and following in the field or laboratory exposures (Smital and Kurelec 1998a, Eufemia and Epel 1998, 2000). Our previous works also showed that MXDM was induced in zebra mussels exposed to environmental stress when compared to control organisms (Pain and Parant 2003b). The induction of MXDM reveals the need for organisms to protect themselves against environmental aggression. In this context, we have been studying for several years the potential of MXDM to constitute a relevant biomarker of exposure to environmental stress in the bivalve *Dreissena polymorpha*

(Parant and Pain 2001, Pain 2003, Pain and Parant 2003b). Our results and those of previously cited works highlighted that MXDM is involved in the efflux of a wide variety of organic compounds whatever they are from natural or anthropic origin. Then, bacterial or algal extracts have been shown to interact with the MXDM pumps (Toomey et al. 1996, Smital et al. 1996, Schröder et al. 1998, Eufemia et al. 2002). Other works evidenced the interaction of organic compounds with MXDM such as pesticides (Bain and Leblanc 1996, Bain et al. 1997, Cornwall et al. 1995, Sturm et al. 2001), polychlorinated biphenyls (Galgani et al. 1996), or polycyclic aromatic hydrocarbons (Kurelec and Pivcevic 1989, Yeh et al. 1992, Kurelec et al. 1995a, Waldman et al. 1995, Hamdoum et al. 2002). Indeed the research of a specificity of MXDM response to a particular type of contaminants has failed and it appeared that MXDM could probably be induced in the field by a wide variety of organic compounds. The low specificity of MXDM constitutes an advantage because its induction corresponds to a global response reflecting the real need for organisms to protect themselves against environmental stress (Eufemia and Epel 1998, 2000).

MXDM in bivalves has been shown to confer effective protection against deleterious effects caused by the exposure to toxic compounds (Kurelec 1995a, Waldman et al. 1995, Kurelec et al. 1996b, Britvic and Kurelec 1999, McFazden et al. 2000, Smital et al. 2000a). This was evidenced by the occurrence of toxic effects when organisms were exposed both to low concentrations of toxic compounds and to MXDM inhibitors, whereas the exposure to toxic compounds only did not generate toxicity. This point highlighted that inhibition of MXDM may have severe consequences in nature. Indeed the occurrence of large amounts of MXDM substrates may saturate the MXDM pumps that will not be available to extrude potentially harmful compounds enhancing probability of toxicity (Kurelec 1992, Minier et al. 1999). This phenomenon is called chemosensitizing and refers to as the presence of substrates that could potentiate the toxicity of contaminants by blocking the action of MXDM. Some works highlighted this point and the authors underlined that the mix of compounds (toxic or not) found in natural waters may represent a insidious hazard for living organisms, even if each toxic substances stands below the established thresholds (Kurelec 1995b, 1997, Smital and Kurelec 1998b). In order to assess the presence of this chemosensitizing compounds, Kurelec et al. (1995b, 2000) developed a test that enables to determine to what extent the organic compounds occurring in waters can block the MXDM efflux activity and then favour toxicity.

In this context, we propose to give an example of the use of MXDM as a biomarker. MXDM activity was monitored in zebra mussels *Dreissena polymorpha* exposed to water from a river receiving the effluent of a chlorine bleached pulp and paper mill. The response of MXDM following exposure to water from downstream the effluent was compared either to the response obtained in dechlorinated water (laboratory) or to that obtained upstream the effluent (in the field). We investigated the potential involvement of adsorbable organohalogenated compounds (AOX) and MXDM substrates in the MXDM induction process. The presence of MXDM substrates was investigated by measuring the MXDM inhibitory potential of river water.

Materials and Methods

Study Sites

The experiments were performed in sampling water or transplanting zebra mussels in a little river located next to the border between France and Belgium. This river receives the effluent of a chlorine bleached pulp and paper mill. The study sites were located 3km upstream and 5km downstream the effluent.

The studied part of the river is highly contaminated according to water quality criteria determined by a French governmental water agency (Agence de l'Eau Rhin-Meuse, *http://www.eau-rhin-meuse.fr/BERM/HTM/*). Indeed the water quality was shown to be altered upstream as well as downstream the pulp and paper mill, but the effluent worsens the water quality downstream by increasing the organic content and by generating organohalogenated compounds (Hayer et al. 1996, Pain and Parant 2003b).

Zebra Mussels

Adult specimens of zebra mussels *Dreissena polymorpha* (20 ± 2 mm in shell length) were collected in the Moselle River near the town Metz (North-eastern France). Organisms were sampled by cutting the byssal threads of mussels living attached on rocks near the river bank and carried to the laboratory in the water of origin. They were kept under laboratory conditions for 3 to 8 days prior to experiments, i.e. dechlorinated water with continuous oxygen. The medium (16-17°C) was changed every day and mussels were fed daily with commercial frozen food (Nauplium). After 3 to 8 days under these laboratory conditions, the MXDM activity was shown to decrease to a baseline level that was called "depurated activity" (Smital et al. 2000b, Pain 2003).

Assessment of AOX Concentrations in Water Samples

Water samples (1L) were collected in brown glass bottles and brought back to the laboratory in a cool box. They were kept at 4°C in the dark before treatment. Measurements of AOX concentrations were performed by IRH-Environnement (NANCY, France) following a standardised method (NF EN 1485).

Response of MXDM Activity Following Exposure to River Water

Laboratory Exposure

Water sample (20L) was collected at the site located downstream the chlorine bleached pulp and paper mill effluent in a polyethylene flask and was brought back to the laboratory in a cool box. It was kept at 4°C in the dark two days before its use.

Five groups of 5 depurated zebra mussels were exposed to 4.5L of water sampled downstream the effluent (brought back at 16-17°C) during 12 days. The control medium was 4.5L of dechlorinated water. The exposure medium was change 3 times during the experiment. No mortality was recorded and zebra mussels were attached to hard substrates placed in their aquarium. MXDM activity was measured by the efflux method after 12 days of exposure.

In The Field Exposure

Depurated mussels were transplanted in nets to the studied sites, either upstream or downstream the chlorine bleached pulp and paper mill effluent. After 3, 14, and 21 days of exposure in this river, mussels were collected from the two sites (3 groups of 5 mussels per site and per exposure duration) and carried to the laboratory in water of origin. For efflux measurement, organisms were kept in water of origin with continuous oxygen prior to analysis. MXDM activity was measured by the efflux method in the mussels collected after each exposure period.

River Water Inhibitory Potential

Water samples (1L) were collected upstream and downstream the effluent in brown glass bottles and brought back to the laboratory in a cool box. They were kept at 4°C in the dark before treatment. The water sample collected downstream the effluent was divided into 3 parts; one was kept native, the second was two-fold diluted and the third ten-fold. Dilution was performed with dechlorinated water. The inhibitory potential of these samples was assessed by the efflux method in depurated zebra mussels.

Efflux Method: Assessment of MXDM Activity and MXDM Inhibitory Potential of River Water

This method was previously adapted and optimised from a protocol developed by Smital and Kurelec in 1997 (Parant and Pain 2001). Briefly, the principle of efflux method was first to expose mussels to a fluorescent dye, rhodamine B, and second, to measure the rate of efflux of previously accumulated dye. Groups of 5 mussels were placed in a light-protected beaker and exposed to dechlorinated water containing 5µM of rhodamine B (RB) (150mL for one group of mussels) for a period of 4 hours. After the loading period, mussels were washed three-times in dechlorinated water (150mL for one group of mussels) for 2 minutes. The last step, called the efflux step (1 hour), was achieved by exposing mussels in different solutions depending on whether MXDM activity or river water inhibitory potential was assessed.

To assess MXDM activity, the efflux step consisted in exposing mussels either in 30mL of dechlorinated water or in 30mL of the same medium containing 30µM of verapamil, a known inhibitor of MXDM (Tsuruo et al. 1981).

To assess MXDM inhibitory potential, the efflux step consisted in exposing mussels either in 30mL of dechlorinated water or in 30mL of water collected in the field (diluted or not).

In both cases, 100µL of each medium were transferred in duplicate to a 96-well microplate every 5 minutes during the efflux step and the fluorescence of effluxed RB was immediately measured on a Fluostar (BMG Lab Technologies). Results were plotted and the rate of RB efflux was then calculated from the linear part of the curve.

The activity of MXDM is estimated by the difference between the RB efflux rates obtained in the absence and in the presence of verapamil during the efflux step and is expressed in picomoles of effluxed RB per minute and per organism.

The inhibitory potential of river water is expressed in percentage and is estimated as followed:

$$IP = [(ER_{control} - ER_{river\ water}) / ER_{control}] \times 100$$

where IP stands for inhibitory potential, ER for RB efflux rate, and control for dechlorinated water.

Statistical Analysis

All data are presented as mean ± SD. Mean values were calculated from the results obtained for at least 3 groups of 5 mussels. Differences were tested by Student t test ($p < 0.05$).

Results
Response of MXDM Activity Following Exposure to River Water

Laboratory Exposure

Depurated zebra mussels were exposed during 12 days in laboratory to water collected downstream the chlorine bleached pulp and paper mill effluent. The level of AOX compounds in the water reached 685µgCl/L. After a 12-day exposure period MXDM activity was significantly induced (Figure 1). It was indeed 2 to 3-fold higher than activity assessed in zebra mussels exposed to control medium (dechlorinated water) that was equivalent to MXDM level in depurated mussels assessed before exposure (Figure 1).

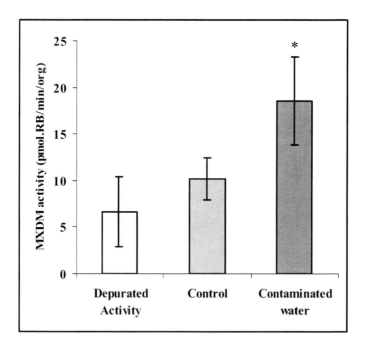

Figure 1: Assessment of MXDM activity in zebra mussels exposed during 12 days either to water collected downstream the chlorine bleached pulp and paper mill effluent ("contaminated water") or to dechlorinated water ("control"). The "depurated activity" was measured before exposure as mentionned in Materials and Methods. * indicates a significant difference with the control ($p < 0.05$).

In The Field Exposure

Depurated zebra mussels were exposed in the field upstream and downstream the chlorine bleached pulp and paper mill effluent during 21 days. The level of AOX compounds in the water was always lower than 20µgCl/L upstream the effluent and was between 125 and 141µgCl/L downstream the effluent (Table 1). MXDM activity assessed in zebra mussels has not changed after 3 days but was significantly induced after 14 and 21 days of exposure at the two sites (Figure 2). It was indeed 2 to 2.5-fold higher after 14 days and 3 to 4-fold higher after 21 days than activity assessed in depurated zebra mussels before in the field exposure (D0). No differences were observed between the responses obtained upstream and downstream the effluent (Figure 2).

River Water Inhibitory Potential

The inhibitory potential of water sampled downstream the effluent was equivalent to that obtained for verapamil at 30µM (not shown). It was significantly higher (5.7-fold) than that of water sampled upstream (Figure 3), meaning that the content of organic compounds

Table 1: Levels of adsorbable organohalogenated compounds (AOX) expressed in µg of chlorine per litre in the water collected upstream and downstream the effluent at the beginning of the experiment (D0) and after 3, 14 and 21 days of mussels exposure (D3, D14 and D21).

Exposure Duration	AOX (µgCl/L)	
	Upstream	Downstream
D0	17	136
D3	< 10	141
D14	19	129
D21	< 10	125

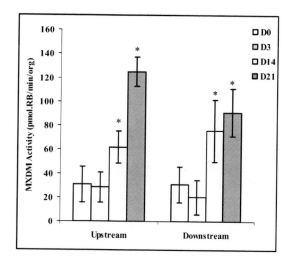

Figure 2: Assessment of MXDM activity in depurated zebra mussels (D0) exposed during 21 days either upstream or downstream the chlorine bleached pulp and paper mill effluent. MXDM activity was assessed after 3, 14 and 21 days of exposure. * indicates a significant difference with the depurated activity at D0 ($p<0.05$).

substrates of MXDM is more elevated downstream than upstream the effluent. Dilutions of this water was also tested for their inhibitory potential and our results revealed that a 2-fold dilution of the water sampled downstream did not change its potential to inhibit MXDM. However, a 10-fold dilution of this water brought back the inhibitory potential to that of water sampled upstream.

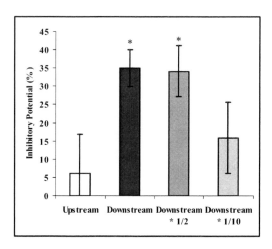

Figure 3: Assessment of river inhibitory potential in depurated zebra mussels exposed during the efflux step of the efflux method either to water collected upstream or to water (native, 2- or 10-fold dilutions) collected downstream the chlorine bleached pulp and paper mill effluent. * indicates a significant difference with the inhibitory potential assessed for the water collected upstream (p<0.05).

Discussion - Conclusion

This chapter describes results of experimental studies aiming to investigate the response of MXDM in zebra mussels exposed to the effluent of a chlorine bleached pulp and paper mill. The paper manufacturing, and especially the bleaching of pulp, is considered as one of the most polluting industrial activity because it releases large amounts of organohalogenated compounds that were shown to heavily impact freshwaters and organisms living in (Hodson et al. 1992, Soimasuo et al. 1995, Ahmad et al. 2000, Chen et al. 2001, Khan and Payne 2002, Kovacks et al. 2002). Our results showed high levels of these compounds downstream the effluent, as assessed by the measurement of the AOX sum-parameter (adsorbable organohalogenated compounds). The AOX levels at this site were indeed shown to be higher (2- to 3-fold) than that permissible for freshwater ecosystems and for water use for human consumption (Hoffmann 1986, RIWA 1992).

In addition to the release of organohalogenated contaminants, the paper manufacturing produces high levels of organic contamination by increasing the amount of suspended matter and the chemical oxygen demand. Indeed the results of a physicochemical monitoring performed by a French governmental agency for water (Agence de l'Eau Rhin-Meuse, *http://www.eau-rhin-meuse.fr/BERM/HTM/*) at the site located downstream the effluent showed that water quality was altered by a high organic content. However, the results of previous experiments showed that the upstream site is also degraded because of high organic content, although it was almost free of AOX (Hayer et al. 1996, Hayer 1997, Pain and Parant 2003b). In conclusion, the water quality in this river is altered upstream as well as downstream the pulp and paper mill, but the effluent worsens the water quality downstream by increasing the organic content and by generating organohalogenated compounds.

The response of MXDM activity was first tested in the laboratory by exposing zebra mussels in water sampled downstream the effluent. Exposure to this contaminated water led to a significant induction of MXDM activity. As this water was shown to contain extremely high levels of organohalogenated compounds (685µgCl/L), we first hypothesised that these compounds could be responsible for MXDM induction.

The second step was to complete the laboratory experiment by checking that the induction was also observed in the field. In this aim mussels were exposed upstream and downstream the chlorine bleached pulp and paper mill effluent. The monitoring of AOX levels during the experiment showed marked difference between the two sites. Whereas AOX levels were low upstream, they were inversely very high downstream, with values revealing a high industrial influence (Hoffmann 1986, RIWA 1992). However MXDM activity assessed in zebra mussels exposed for 21 days reached the same level at both sites. So MXDM response was not related to this parameter. The experiment indeed showed high level of induction at the two sites, suggesting that even if AOX compounds may participate to the MXDM induction process when there are present in the water, these compounds are not specifically responsible for MXDM induction as induction occurred when AOX levels were very low. Other laboratory or in the field works also failed to demonstrate the existence of a correlation between MXDM activity or protein expression level and the studied contamination (Kurelec et al. 1998, Minier et al. 1999, Doi et al. 2001, Keppler and Ringwood 2001). The low specificity of MXDM could explain these results because whatever the contaminants that were focused on, other contaminants and also natural organic compounds occur in river water and can cause MXDM induction.

Although the final induction level was the same at both sites, MXDM activity increased significantly between 14 and 21 days upstream the effluent, whereas it remained unchanged downstream. It can be hypothesised that induction at the downstream site was already maximal after 14 days whereas it reached its maximal level after 21 days only at the upstream site. These results could be interpreted as an MXDM saturation downstream the effluent. Minier et al. (1999) indeed proposed that inducibility could be reduced when induction has already reached a maximal level in the case of high water temperature or high levels of natural substrates. Indeed if MXDM is blocked, toxic compounds can not be extruded from the cells any more and the occurrence of toxicity may explained the lack of reaction of the defence system downstream the effluent between 14 and 21 days of exposure. The hypothesis of MXDM saturation is supported by our results about the inhibitory potential of river water that revealed a higher amount of MXDM substrates at the downstream site when compared to the upstream site. Indeed, the inhibitory potential of water sampled downstream the effluent reached a quite elevated value, equivalent to that obtained for verapamil at 30µM, a known inhibitor of MXDM activity. This result means that river water sampled downstream the effluent contains a sufficient amount of compounds able to provoke an inhibition of MXDM activity equivalent to that provoked by verapamil at 30µM. According to studies performed in mammalian cultured cells expressing the "multidrug resistance" phenotype, a verapamil concentration of 20µM can produce a 80% inhibition of the transporters efflux activity (Ford and Hait 1990). This supports the possibility that MXDM could have been highly saturated (if not totally) when zebra mussels were exposed downstream the effluent.

The 2-fold dilution of the river water sampled downstream the effluent did not decrease the MXDM inhibitory potential, suggesting that there was at least twice as many MXDM substrates in river water than the capabilities of the defence system. This result supports the hypothesis of MXDM saturation and may explain why the MXDM induction reached a maximal level earlier downstream than upstream.

However the 10-fold dilution of the river water sampled downstream the effluent decreased by two the MXDM inhibitory potential that was equivalent to that assessed upstream. This result suggests that the effect of the pulp and paper mill effluent is equivalent to a 10-fold increase of the amount of MXDM substrates. This would be true if the relation between presence of MXDM substrates and inhibition was linear. However it is not the case because a 2-fold dilution did not decrease the inhibitory potential and the 10-fold dilution decreased it by 2 only.

Finally, the difference between the upstream and downstream patterns of induction could be explained by a high content of MXDM substrates downstream the effluent that led to a maximum reaction of the defence system earlier than upstream. This result highlights the importance of chemosensitizing compounds that were shown to modulate the defence capabilities of organisms. Indeed, the presence of non toxic substrates of MXDM could saturate the system that will not be available to extrude potentially harmful compounds. In this context, attention should be given to the presence in natural waters of quite low concentrations of non toxic compounds of which accumulation could potentiate toxicity of other compounds by saturating the potential of MXDM to protect cells (Kurelec 1995b, 1997, Smital and Kurelec 1998b).

The results of the previously presented experimental studies showed that the exposure event led to a significant induction of MXDM response in laboratory as well as in the field, confirming a high induction potential of MXDM activity. The induction evidenced an exposure to an environmental stress against which mussels have to protect. Then this study confirmed the potential of MXDM to constitute a biomarker of exposure in zebra mussels. However it still remains difficult to interpret MXDM response. Contamination of river waters is indeed a complex phenomenon and a number of parameters can modulate the response. In our in the field experiment the MXDM induction observed after 21 days of mussels' exposure was neither related to the AOX concentrations nor to the presence of MXDM substrates in the river water. It seemed that MXDM response was better related to the global bad quality of the river water, supporting the hypothesis that MXDM could be considered as biomarker of global environmental stress. The study of MXDM reaction in the case of *in situ* exposure represents a new tool to assess ecotoxicological risk for wild populations. The great interest of this tool lies indeed in the fact that it enables to detect an unusual activation of the defence system and thus to alert on possible impacts on organisms' health, though it does not give information about the nature of these impacts.

The assessment of a biomarker response in one model organism leads to an estimation of exposure via a given route. Indeed zebra mussels are filter-feeding organisms and are mainly exposed to environmental contaminants by water. Then the use of zebra mussels does not enable to assess the exposure of organisms by another element of aquatic ecosystems, the sediments. In order to complete the approach using MXDM in zebra mussels, it would be of primary interest to study another invertebrate group representative of sediment communities. The tubificid sludgeworms (Annelidae, Oligochaetae) are sediment-dwelling organisms. They are widespread in freshwaters and are known to accumulate environmental contaminants (Egeler et al. 1997, 1999, Lucan-Bouché et al. 1999, Bouché et al. 2000).

Moreover some of them can tolerate high level of pollution and can develop in highly degraded environments (Milbrink 1987). This particular high tolerance implies the existence of effective protection systems in these organisms. Some of them were investigated and results showed induction of metallothionein and antioxidative defence (Mosleh et al. 2004a, b). Other works showed that worms lost their caudal region by autotomy. As the caudal region accumulated more contaminants than the anterior parts, the autotomy was interpreted as a decontamination process and then, as a defence system against high level of environmental contamination (Lucan-Bouché et al. 1999, Bouché et al. 2003). The previously cited works highlighted the relevance of the use of tubificid worms as a model to study biological defence systems against environmental pollution. In this context, it would be interesting to investigate the presence of MXDM in these worms and its relevance as a biomarker in order first, to propose a new tool for ecotoxiocological studies in tubificid worms and second, to complement the information provided by the study of biomarkers in bivalves such as *Dreissena polymorpha* because it can directly reflects the contamination of sediment.

Summary

This chapter describes experimental studies performed in order to asses the response of MXDM in a bivalve species, the zebra mussel *Dreissena polymorpha* exposed to water contaminated by the effluent of a chlorine bleached pulp and paper mill. The response of MXDM activity was first tested in the laboratory by exposing mussels in water sampled downstream the effluent, which presented a high concentration of organohalogenated compounds. After a 12-day exposure, MXDM activity was significantly induced. Secondly, mussels were exposed *in situ* upstream and downstream the effluent, the latter site showing a high level of AOX contamination. This experiment showed high level of induction at the two sites, suggesting that even if AOX compounds may participate to the MXDM induction process when there are present in the water, these compounds are not specifically responsible for MXDM induction as induction occurred when AOX levels were very low.

As MXDM response was not related to the AOX sum-parameter reflecting the type of pollution of the river water, we aimed to relate the response to a more global parameter, which is the presence of MXDM substrates in the water. This was achieved by measuring the MXDM inhibitory potential of river water. This work enabled to show that the amount of MXDM substrates at the upstream site was equivalent to that of a ten-fold dilution of the water collected downstream the effluent. The amount of MXDM substrates was then more elevated downstream that upstream the effluent. As a consequence, the presence of substrates in the water can not explain the response of the activity. As a conclusion, MXDM was induced upstream as well as downstream the effluent. Differences in AOX levels or presence of MXDM substrates could not explain this induction. However, MXDM induction seems to reflect the global bad quality of the river. This study reveals that MXDM induction reflects the contaminated state of a water but can not be related to a particular contamination parameter. This confirms that MXDM could be used as a biomarker of general stress in zebra mussels. Moreover, it highlights the importance of chemosensitizing compounds that have to be monitored with care.

Acknowledgements

This research was supported in part by a fellowship from the French "Ministère de la Recherche et de la Technologie".

References

Ahmad, I., Hamid, T., Fatima, M., Chand, H. S., Jain, S. K., Athar, M. and Raisuddin, S. (2000) - Induction of hepatic antioxidants in freshwater catfish (*Channa punctatus* Bloch) is a biomarker of paper mill effluent exposure - *Biochim. Biophys. Acta*, 1519: 37-48.

Bain, L. J. and Leblanc, G. A. (1996) - Interaction of Structurally Diverse Pesticides with the Human MDR1 Gene Product P-Glycoprotein - *Toxicol. Appl. Pharm.*, 141: 288-298.

Bain, L. J., Mclachlan, J. B. and Leblanc, G. A. (1997) - Structure-activity relationships for xenobiotic transport substrates and inhibitory ligands of P-glycoprotein - *Environ. Health Persp.*, 105: 812-818.

Bard, S. M. (2000) - Multixenobiotic resistance as a cellular defense mechanism in aquatic organisms - *Aquat. Toxicol.*, 48: 357-389.

Bonfanti, P., Colombo, A. and Camatini, M. (1998) - Identification of a multixenobiotic resistance mechanism in *Xenopus laevis* embryos - *Chemosphere*, 37: 2751-2760.

Bouché, M.-L., Habets, F., Biagianti-Risbourg, S. and Vernet, G. (2000) - Toxic effects and bioaccumulation of cadmium in the aquatic Oligochaete *Tubifex tubifex* - *Ecotox. Environ. Safe.* 46(3): 246-251.

Bouché, M.-L., Arnoult, F. and Vernet, G. (2003) - Caudal regeneration in *Tubifex tubifex* (Oligochaeta, Tubificidae) following copper exposure - *Invertebrate Biol.* 122(1): 42-51.

Britvic, S. and Kurelec, B. (1999) - The effects of inhibitors of multixenobiotic resistance mechanism on the production of mutagens by *Dreissena polymorpha* in water spiked with premutagens - *Aquat. Toxicol.*, 47: 107-116.

Chen, C. M., Liu, M. C., Shih, M. L., Yu, S. C., Yeh, C. C., Lee, S. T., Yang, T. Y. and Hung, S. J. (2001) - Microsomal monooxygenase activity in Tilapia (*Oreochromis mossambicus*) exposed to a bleached kraft mill effluent using different exposure systems - *Chemosphere*, 45: 581-588.

Cornwall, R., Holland Toomey, B., Bard, B., Bacon, C., Jarman, W. M. and Epel, D. (1995) - Characterization of multixenobiotic/multidrug transport in the gills of the mussel *Mytilus californianus* and identification of environmental substrates - *Aquat. Toxicol.*, 31: 277-296.

Doi, A. M., Holmes, E. and Kleinow, K. M. (2001) - P-glycoprotein in the catfish intestine: inducibility by xenobiotics and functional properties - *Aquat. Toxicol.*, 55: 157-170.

Egeler, P., Römbke, J., Meller, M., Knacker, Th., Franke, C., Studinger, G. and Nagel, R. (1997) - Bioaccumulation of lindane and hexachlorobenzene by tubificid sludgeworms (Oligochaeta) under standardised laboratory conditions - *Chemosphere*, 35 (4): 835-852.

Egeler, P., Römbke, J., Meller, M., Knacker, Th. and Nagel, R. (1999) - Bioaccumulation test with tubificid sludgeworms in artificial media - development of standardisable method - *Hydrobiologia*, 406: 271-280.

Endicott, J. A. and Ling, V. (1989) - The Biochemistry of P-glycoprotein-mediated multidrug resistance - *Annu. Rev. Biochem.*, 58: 137-171.

Eufemia, N. A. and Epel, D. (1998) - The multixenobiotic defense mechanism in mussels is induced by substrates and non-substrates : implications for a general stress response - *Mar. Environ. Res.*, 46: 401-405.

Eufemia, N. A. and Epel, D. (2000) - Induction of the multixenobiotic defense mechanism (MXR), P-glycoprotein in the mussel *Mytilus californianus* as a general cellular response to environmental stress - *Aquat. Toxicol.*, 49: 89-100.

Eufemia, N. A., Clerte, S., Girshick, S. and Epel, D. (2002) - Algal products as naturally occuring substrates for P-glycoprotein in *Mytilus californianus* - *Mar. Biol.*, 140: 343-353.

Ford, J. M. and Hait, W. N. (1990) - Pharmacology of drugs that alter multidrug resistance in cancer - *Pharmacol. Rev.*, 42: 155-199.

Galgani, F., Cornwall, R., Toomey, B. and Epel, D. (1996) - Interaction of environmental xenobiotics with a multixenobiotic defense mechanism in the bay mussel *Mytilus Galloprovincialis* from the coast of California - *Environ. Toxicol. Chem.*, 15: 325-331.

Gottesman, M. M. and Pastan, I. (1993) - Biochemistry of multidrug resistance mediated by the multidrug transporter - *Annu. Rev. Biochem.*, 62: 385-427.

Grimm, E. D., Terenzi, M. F., Goldman, G. H., Bainy, A. C. D. and Terenzi, H. (2000) - Identification of homologs of the mammalian P-glycoprotein in the mussel, *Perna perna* - *Mar. Environ. Res.*, 50: 331-335.

Hamdoun, A. M., Griffin, F. J. and Cherr, G. N. (2002) - Tolerance to biodegraded crude oil in marine invertebrate embryos and larvae is associated with expression of a multixenobiotic resistance transporter - *Aquat. Toxicol.*, 61: 127-140.

Hayer, F., Wagner, P. and Pihan, J.-C. (1996) - Monitoring of extractable organic halogens (EOX) in chlorine bleached pulp and paper mill effluents using four species of transplanted aquatic mollusks - *Chemosphere*, 33: 2321-2334.

Hayer, F., 1997. Estimation de la contamiantion du milieu aquatique par les composés organohalogénés (AOX and EOX). Application à l'étude d'accumulation and de relargage des EOX par *Anodonta cygnea* L., exposé *in situ* aux effluents d'une usine de pâte à papier. *Thèse de Doctorat, Université de Metz*, pp. 220.

Hodson, P. V., Mc Whirter, M., Ralph, K., Gray, B., Thivierge, D., Carey, J. H., Van Der Kraak, G., Whittle, D. M. and Levesque, M. C. (1992) - Effects of bleached kraft mill effluent on fish in the St Maurice River, Quebec - *Environ. Toxicol. Chem.*, 11: 1335-1651.

Hoffman, H. J. (1986) - Untersuchung der AOX-Gehalte in bayrischen Flüssen. Bewertung der Gewässerqualität and Gewässergüteanforderungen - *Münchner Beiträge zur Abwasser, Fischerei und Flussbiologie*, 40: 445-449.

Jaouen, A., Galap, C., Minier, C., Tutundjian, R. and Leboulenger, F. (2000) - Bioaccumulation of pollutants and measures of biomarkers in the Zebra mussel (*Dreissena polymorpha*) from downstream river Seine - *B. Soc. Zool. Fr.*, 125: 239-249.

Juliano, R. L. and Ling, V. (1976) - A surface glycoprotein modulating drug permeability in chinese hamster ovary cell mutants - *Biochim. Biophys. Acta*, 455: 152-162.

Khan, R. A. and Payne, J. F. (2002) - Some factors influencing EROD activity in winter flounder (*Pleuronectes americanus*) exposed to effluent from a pulp and paper mill - *Chemosphere*, 46: 235-239.

Keppler, C. J. and Ringwood, A. H. (2001) - Expression of P-glycoprotein in southeastern oysters *Crassostrea virginica* - *Mar. Environ. Res.*, 52: 81-96.

Kovacs, T. G., Martel, P. H. and Voss, R. H. (2002) - Assessing the biological status of fish in a river receiving pulp and paper mill effluents - *Environ. Pollut.*, 118: 123-140.

Kurelec, B. and Pivcevic, B. (1989) - Distinct glutathione-dependant enzyme activities and a verapamil-sensitive binding of xenobiotics in a fresh-water mussel *Anodonta cygnea* - *Biochem. Bioph. Res. Co.*, 164: 934-940.

Kurelec, B. and Pivcevic, B. (1991) - Evidence for a multixenobiotic resistance mechanism in the mussel *Mytilus galloprovincialis* - *Aquat. Toxicol.*, 19: 291-302.

Kurelec, B. (1992) - The multixenobiotic resistance mechanism in aquatic organisms - *Crit. Rev. Toxicol.*, 22: 23-43.

Kurelec, B. (1995a) - Reversion of the multixenobiotic resistance mechanism in gills of a marine mussel *Mytilus galloprovincialis* by a model inhibitor and environmental modulmators of P170-glycoprotein - *Aquat. Toxicol.*, 33: 93-103.

Kurelec, B. (1995b) - Inhibition of multixenobiotic resistance mechanism in aquatic organisms: ecotoxic consequences - *Sci. Total Environ.*, 171: 197-204.

Kurelec, B., Lucic, D., Pivcevic, B. and Krca, S. (1995a) - Induction and reversion of multixenobiotic resistance in the marine snail *Monodonta turbinata* - *Mar. Biol.*, 123: 305-312.

Kurelec, B., Pivcevic, B. and Müller, W. E. G. (1995b) - Determination of pollutants with multixenobiotic resistance inhibiting properties - *Mar. Environ. Res.*, 39: 261-265.

Kurelec, B., Krca, C. and Lucic, D. (1996a) - Expression of multixenobiotic resistance mechanism in a marine mussel *Mytilus galloprovincialis* as a biomarker of exposure to polluted environments - *Comp. Biochem. Physiol. C*, 113: 283-289.

Kurelec, B., Waldmann, P. and Zahn, K. R. (1996b) - The modulation of protective effects of the multixenobiotic resistance mechanism in a clam *Corbicula fluminea* - *Mar. Environ. Res.*, 42: 383-387.

Kurelec, B. (1997) - A new type of hazardous chemical: the chemosensitizers of multixenobiotic resistance - *Environ. Health Persp.*, 105: 855-860.

Kurelec, B., Britvic, S., Pivcevic, B. and Smital, T. (1998) - Fragility of multixenobiotic resistance in aquatic organisms enhances the complexity of risk assessment - *Mar. Environ. Res.*, 46: 415-419.

Kurelec, B., Smital, T., Pivcevic, B., Eufemia, N. and Epel, D. (2000) - Multixenobiotic resistance, P-glycoprotein, and chemosensitizers - *Ecotoxicology*, 9: 307-327.

Lagadic, L., Caquet, T. and Amiard, J. C. (1997) - Biomarqueurs en écotoxicologie : principes et définitions. - In: Lagadic, L., Caquet, T., Amiard, J. C., and Ramade, F. (eds.): *Biomarqueurs en écotoxicologie. Aspects fondamentaux* - Masson, Paris, pp. 1-9.

Lucan-Bouché, M.-L., Biagianti-Risbourg, S., Arsac F., and Vernet, G. (1999) - An original decontamination process developed by the aquatic oligochaete *Tubifex tubifex* exposed to copper and lead. *Aquat. Toxicol.* 45(1): 9-17.

McFadzen, I., Eufemia, N. A., Heath, C., Epel, D., Moore, M. N. and Lowe, D. M. (2000) - Multidrug resistance in the embryos and larvae of the mussel *Mytilus edulis* - *Mar. Environ. Res.*, 50: 319-323.

Milbrink, G. (1987) - Biological characterization of sediments by standardized tubificid bioassays - *Hydrobiologia*, 155: 267-275.

Minier, C., Akcha, F. and Galgani, F. (1993) - P-glycoprotein expression in *Crassostrea gigas* and *Mytilus edulis* in polluted seawater - *Comp. Biochem. Phys. B*, 106: 1029-1036.

Minier, C. and Galgani, F. (1995) - Multi-xenobiotic resistance in *Mytilus edulis* - *Mar. Environ. Res.*, 39: 267-270.

Minier, C. and Moore, M. N. (1996) - Induction of multixenobiotic resistance in mussel blood cells - *Mar. Environ. Res.*, 42: 389-392.

Minier, C., Eufemia, N. and Epel, D. (1999) - The multi-xenobiotic resistance phenotype as a tool to biomonitor the environment - *Biomarkers*, 4: 442-454.

Minier, C., Borghi, V., Moore, M. N. and Porte, C. (2000) - Seasonnal variation of MXR and stress proteins in the common mussel, *Mytilus galloprovincialis* - *Aquat. Toxicol.*, 50: 167-176.

Minier, C., Lelong, C., Djemel, N., Rodet, F., Tutundjian, R., Favrel, P., Mathieu, M. and Leboulenger, F. (2002) - Expression and activity of a multixenobiotic resistance system in the pacific oyster *Crassostrea gigas* - *Mar. Environ. Res.*, 54: 455-459.

Mosleh, Y.Y., Paris-Palacios, S., Arnoult, F., Couderchet, M., Biagianti-Risbourg, S. and Vernet, G. (2004a) - Metallothioneins induction in the aquatic Oligochaete *Tubifex tubifex* exposed to the herbicide isoproturon - *Environmental Toxicology*,19: 88-93.

Mosleh, Y.Y., Paris-Palacios, S., Biagianti-Risbourg, S. and Vernet, G. (2004b) - Metallothioneins induction and oxidative response in aquatic worms *Tubifex tubifex* (Oligochaete, Tubificidae) exposed to copper - *Chemosphere, in press*.

Parant, M. and Pain, S. (2001) - Potential use of multixenobiotic defense mechanism (MXDM) in *Dreissena polymorpha* as a biomarker for the monitoring of freshwater pollution - *Water Res.*, 35: 3743-3748.

Pain, S. (2003) - Potentiel biomarqueur du Mécanisme de Défense MultiXénobiotique (MDMX) chez *Dreissena polymorpha* pour le suivi de la pollution organique en eaux douces - *Thèse de doctorat, Université de Metz*, pp.198.

Pain, S. and Parant, M. (2003a) - Le Mécanisme de Défense MultiXénobiotique (MDMX) chez les bivalves - *Comptes Rendus de Biologie*, 326(7) : 659-672.

Pain, S. and Parant, M. (2003b) - Response of MultiXenobiotic Defence Mechanism (MXDM) in *Dreissena polymorpha* exposed to environmental stress - *Chemosphere*, 52(7) : 1105-1113.

RIWA (1992) - Rapport Annuel, Tome B : La Meuse, RIWA, pp. 148.

Schröder, H. C., Badria, F. A., Ayyad, S. N., Batel, R., Wiens, M., Hassanein, H. M. A., Kurelec, B. and Müller, W. E. G. (1998) - Inhibitory effects of extracts from the marine alga *Caulerpa taxifolia* and of toxin from *Caulerpa racemosa* on multixenobiotic resistance in the marine sponge *Geodia cydonium* - *Environ. Toxicol. Chem.*, 5: 119-126.

Smital, T., Pivcevic, B. and Kurelec, B. (1996) - Reversal of multidrug resistance by extract from the marine alga *Caulerpa taxifolia* - *Period. Biol.*, 98: 1197-1203.

Smital, T. and Kurelec, B. (1997) - Inhibitors of the multixenobiotic resistance mechanism in natural waters: In vivo demonstration of their effects - *Environ. Toxicol. Chem.*, 16: 2164-2170.

Smital, T. and Kurelec, B. (1998a) - The activity of multixenobiotic resistance mechanism determined by rhodamine B-efflux method as a biomarker of exposure - *Mar. Environ. Res.*, 46: 443-447.

Smital, T. and Kurelec, B. (1998b) - The chemosensitizers of multixenobiotic resistance mechanism in aquatic invertebrates: a new class of pollutants - *Mutat. Res. - Fund. Mol. M.*, 399: 43-53.

Smital, T., Sauerborn, R., Pivcevic, B. and Kurelec, B. (2000a) - Inhibition of multixenobiotic resistance mechanism in aquatic organisms by commercially used pesticides - *Mar. Environ. Res.*, 50: 331-335.

Smital, T., Sauerborn, R., Pivcevic, B., Krca, S. and Kurelec, B. (2000b) - Interspecies differences in P-glycoprotein mediated activity of multixenobiotic resistance mechanism in several marine and freshwater invertebrates - *Comp. Biochem. Phys. C*, 126: 175-186.

Soimasuo, R., Aaltonen, T., Nikinmaa, M., Pellinen, J., Ristola, T. and Oikari, A. (1995) - Physiological toxicity of low-chloride bleached pulp and paper mill effluent on whitefish (*Coregonus lavaretus* L. *s.l.*): a laboratory exposure simulating lake pollution - *Ecotox. Environ. Safe.*, 31: 228-237.

Sturm, A., Cravedi, J. P. and Segner, H. (2001) - Prochloraz and nonylphenol diethoxylate inhibit an mdr1-like activity in vitro, but do not alter hepatic levels of P-glycoprotein in trout exposed in vivo - *Aquat. Toxicol.*, 53: 215-228.

Toomey, B. H., Kaufman, M. R. and Epel, D. (1996) - Marine bacteria produce compounds that modulate multixenobiotic transport activity in *Urechis caupo* embryos - *Mar. Environ. Res.*, 42: 393-397.

Tsuruo, T., Iida, H., Tsukagoshi, S. and Sakurai, Y. (1981) - Overcoming of vincristine resistance in P388 leukemia *in vivo* and *in vitro* through enhanced cytotoxicity of vincristine and vinblastine by verapamil - *Cancer Res.*, 41: 1967-1972.

Waldmann, P., Pivcevic, B., Müller, W. E. G., Zahn, R. K. and Kurelec, B. (1995) - Increased genotoxicity of acetylaminofluorene by modulators of multixenobiotic resistance mechanism: studies with the freshwater clam *Corbicula fluminea* - *Mutat. Res.*, 342: 113-123.

Yeh, G. C., Lopaczynska, J., Poore, C. M. and Phang, J. M. (1992) - A new functional role for P-glycoprotein: efflux pump for benzo(alpha)pyrene in human breast cancer MCF-7 cells - *Cancer Res.*, 52: 6692-6695.

In: Trends in Water Pollution Research
Editor: J. V. Livingston, pp. 221-236

ISBN 1-59454-328-3
©2005 Nova Science Publishers, Inc.

Chapter X

Photodegradation of Organic Pollutants

R. K. Sharma[1] and S. Mary Celin

Department of Chemistry, University of Delhi, Delhi-110007, India

Abstract

Photodegradation is a potential technique, which results in complete destruction of organic contaminants, unlike other treatment options such as activated carbon adsorption, air stripping which merely transfer the target contaminant from one phase to another. The end products of this promising technology are CO_2, water and other simple non-toxic molecules. Hydroxyl radicals are the main oxidizing species involved in destruction of the organic pollutant on photodegradation and are produced by the different photodegradative processes.

Organic material can be photochemically degraded by direct photolysis under polychromatic radiation without the preliminary formation of hydroxyl radicals, but the direct photolytic experiments are generally of low efficiency and less effective compared to procedures involving hydroxyl radical generation. The combination of UV light and oxidants is most effective as UV photons enhance the rate of reaction by producing the reactive radical species from the oxidants. On photo-oxidation with the addition of oxidants, the products are the same. Only the rate of approach to equilibrium is changed because the oxidant will act to speed up the rate of reaction. Photo-peroxidation, which uses UV light in combination with H_2O_2 is generally applicable to numerous situations requiring removal of hazardous substances from ground water, drinking water, chemical process water, leakage contamination and industrial waste-water. Photo-Fenton oxidation is another attractive oxidation system that uses Fenton reagent- a mixture of iron salt and H_2O_2 along with UV light. In Fenton's reagent iron salt serve as catalyst and H_2O_2 as oxidizing agent. Ferrous ion in Fenton's reagent catalyses the breakdown of H_2O_2 and photo-oxidation of Fe^{2+} to Fe^{3+}, resulting in the production of $OH^\bullet$ radicals which

---

[1] Tel/fax: 91-11-27666250; email: rksharma@vsnl.com

completely oxidize the organic contaminants. Photo-Fenton oxidation has been successfully used for treating a variety of toxic substances present in wastewater. The reaction time needed for UV/Fenton treatment was generally faster compared to H_2O_2/UV due to the enhanced production of $OH^{\bullet}$ radicals through different routes. Photocatalytic processes make use of a semiconductor metal oxide as catalyst and of oxygen as oxidizing agent. Primary process involved in photocatalysis is the absorption of radiation with the formation of electron hole pairs. The holes react with water and OH to produce OH radicals that are capable of attacking dissolved organics.

Systems using H_2O_2 and metal ions are comparatively more effective than direct photolytic/photocatalytic systems, which are generally less effective in contaminant destruction. Thus the above-mentioned photo degradation processes have led the way to treatment of aqueous wastes and are rapidly becoming the technology of the choice for many applications.

Introduction

Nature and humanity form an inseparable part of the ecosystem. This system has five elements: Air, water, land, flora and fauna, which are inter connected, inter-dependant and co-evolved. Deterioration in one affects the other four elements and hence our life quality. Rapid growth in science and technology, in its pursuit to ease the living style of human kind is considered as a boon to meet the increasing demands of food and other essentials of the growing population. As a counter effect of this accelerated pace of industrialisation and urbanisation, tons of liquid and solid wastes are being dumped into the environment, which disturb the balance and sustainability of our ecosystem.

The residual and harmful effects of wastes that we dump into our already ailing oceans, atmosphere and soils get impregnated into different strata of the earth, that it becomes difficult to lessen its effect in the form of toxicity, carcinogenicity, flammability, and radioactivity making the earth an 'endangered entity' for the generations to come. If the same condition prevails, in the long run, the quality of our life has to be compromised at the cost of technology and pollution will be the prize to be paid for scientific progress. Though it is not possible to remove completely the bane created, science and technology has also found out ways and means to curb this danger by the invention of novel remedial measures.

Photodegradation-using UV irradiation along with oxidant/catalysts generates hydroxyl radicals which are efficient in treating the organic contaminants present in industrial/ drinking water. Unlike other treatment options such as activated carbon adsorption, incineration, bioremediation etc., this promising technology neither generates sludge nor emits volatile organics in to the atmosphere thus eliminating the need for further follow-up treatment. The end-products of this potential technique are environmentally benign non-toxic molecules such as CO_2, H_2O and in-organic salts.

Photodegradation - Definition and Details

Photodegradation is defined as the photochemical transformation of a molecule into lower molecular weight fragments, usually in an oxidation process using UV/sunlight. The development status of light induced photodegradative process for water and wastewater treatment has gained industrial scales for the destruction of organics.

Hydroxyl Radical Generation on Photodegradation

Hydroxyl radicals are the main oxidizing species involved in destruction of the organic pollutant on photodegradation. The hydroxyl radical is a short lived, extremely potent (oxidation potential = 2.80V), oxidising agent capable of oxidising organic compounds by the following mechanisms [1]:

(I) Hydroxy Addition

Organic compounds containing aromatic systems or carbon-carbon multiple bonds undergo addition reactions with hydroxyl radicals due to the rich π electron cloud on the aromatic ring.

$$OH^\bullet + C_6H_6 \qquad\qquad {}^\bullet C_6H_6OH$$

(II) Hydrogen Abstraction

It is the usual reaction with unsaturated organic compounds

$$OH^\bullet + CH_3CO\,CH_3 \qquad\qquad CH_2CO\,CH_3 + H_2O$$

(III) Electron Transfer

It is usually found in reactions between OH radicals and inorganic ions.

$$OH^\bullet + Fe^{2+} \qquad\qquad Fe^{3+} + OH^-$$

This is important to the Fenton's reagent reaction.

The organic radicals generated by the above mechanisms produce peroxy radicals by addition of molecular oxygen. These intermediate initiate thermal (chain) reactions of oxidative degradation leading finally to CO_2, water and inorganic salts.

$$R^\bullet + O_2 \qquad\qquad RO_2 \qquad\qquad CO_2 + H_2O$$

The rate and efficiency of oxidative degradative processes which are primarily based on production and the reactivity of radical intermediates depend (i) on the energy needed in order to homolyse a given chemical bond and (ii) to a large extent on the concentration of dissolved molecular oxygen [1].

Hydroxyl radicals which are the initiators of oxidative degradation are produced by the following photodegradative process (Figure-1) lists typical systems currently available in the literature [2]

1.UV irradiation at 254nm	1. H_2O_2/UV Process	1. TiO_2/UV Process
(Low pressure lamps)	(Photoperoxidation)	
2. UV irradiation at 313-367 nm (Medium pressure UV lamps)	2.Fenton/UV Process (PhotoFenton oxidation)	

Advantages of Photodegradation

1. Unlike conventional processes that move adsorbed waste through multiple stages of treatment, photodegradation process neither generate sludge nor emits volatile organic compounds (VOCs), eliminating the need for follow-up treatment.
2. stable, innocuous and mineralised products, e.g. CO_2, H_2O, HCl produced.
3. no off gas treatment needed and
4. no primary or secondary chemical requiring regeneration required [3].

Literature Review on Photo Degradation of Organic Pollutant

Among the different photodegradative systems listed in figure-2, the technologies that are widely used are critically reviewed with respect to their chemistry and application and are presented here.

Direct UV Photolysis

In direct photolysis, the organic molecule gets excited on absorption of UV photons (Eq.1). It has been reported [1] that a large number of electronically excited organic molecules could transfer an electron to an acceptor present in its complex environment and form free radical ions (Eq.2).These radical ions with subsequent recombination or hydrolysis form radicals ($R^•$) which then react with oxygen (Eq.3) to form peroxy radicals. These peroxy radicals on further photolysis get converted to partially oxidized intermediates (Eq.4).

R   R*   (1)

$R* + O_2$ $R^{•+} + O_2$ (2)

$R^\bullet + O_2$ $\qquad\qquad\qquad\qquad$ RO_2 $\qquad\qquad\qquad\qquad\qquad\qquad$ (3)

RO_2 $\qquad\qquad\qquad\qquad$ Partially oxidized intermediates $\qquad\qquad$ (4)

Organic material can be photochemically degraded by direct photolysis under polychromatic radiation without the preliminary formation of hydroxyl radicals, but the direct photolytic experiments are generally of low efficiency and less effective for nitro-organics compared to procedures involving hydroxyl radical generation [1].

In direct photolysis, UV light is used in the absence of oxidants/catalysts. Ultraviolet light is an electromagnetic radiation spread between the wavelengths between 100 nm and 400 nm. Most UV lamps used in wastewater treatments perform at a wavelength of 254 nm. A mercury vapor lamp is the most common UV light source Typically, UV lamps are installed inside quartz sleeves and when implemented at a plant are usually placed in banks with the lamps evenly spaced either vertically or horizontally. The UV dosage applied to a wastewater is determined by the intensity of the UV radiation and the contact time involved and is commonly expressed in milliwatt-seconds per square centimeter (mW-sec/cm^2). The common way to produce UV radiation artificially is by the passage of an electric current through vaporised mercury. The mercury atoms become excited by collision with the electrons flowing between the lamp electrodes. The excited electrons return to the ground state in the mercury atom and in doing so, release some of the energy they absorbed in the form of optical radiation, i.e., ultraviolet, visible and infrared radiation. The spectrum of the emitted radiation (figure-2) consists of a limited number of a discrete wavelength called spectral lines corresponding to electronic transitions characteristic of mercury atom [4]. The relative intensity of different wavelengths in the spectrum depends on the pressure of the mercury vapour. Accordingly, there are three types of UV lamps, (i) low-pressure lamp, (ii) medium pressure lamp and (iii) high-pressure lamp. High-pressure mercury lamps are less applied in wastewater treatment [5].

UV Irradiation at 254nm (Low Pressure UV Lamps)

The low pressure mercury lamp is a monochromatic UV source which has strong emission of unreversed resonance line at 253 and 184nm along with other much weaker lines [6]Braun,1986. Degradation of chemicals in water using the mercury emission at 253.7 nm produced in particular by low pressure mercury arcs has been reported [6,7]. Low pressure mercury arcs are quite efficient for water disinfection purposes. Experiments carried out to decompose chlorinated hydrocarbons with a low pressure mercury (15W) lamp emitting its radiation predominantly at 253.7nm revealed that 85% tetrachloroethene, 55% trichloroethene and 40% 1,1,1-trichloroethene were removed within 60 minutes of irradiation time [8,9]. Direct photolysis of 100ppm methylene chloride using a low pressure mercury lamp resulted in 60% removal of the initial substrate concentration in 25min of the irradiation time [10].

Phenols and substituted phenols were subjected to photolysis in a 12 litre reactor using 8 low pressure mercury lamps of 51.7W each. Results showed that 23% of the initial 10ppm phenol was decomposed within 40min at pH 4, whereas no reduction was observed at pH 10. m-cresol (11.5ppm), 2-chlorophenol (13.6ppm), 2,5-dimethylphenol (13ppm) and 2,5-dichlorophenol (17.3ppm) were found to be completely removed (more than 99%) within 240, 80, 30 and 210 minutes respectively at pH 7.8 to 8.5 respectively [11]. Removal of absorbable organic halogen from pharmaceutical wastewater occurred in 240min when low pressure mercury lamp of 15W was used [12]. On photo-degradation of trihalomethane (THM) such as $CHCl_3$,$CHCl_2Br$, $CHBr_2Cl$ and $CHBr_3$ with a low pressure UV lamp, only brominated trihalomethanes were photolyzed and the organic halogen present was completely converted into chloride and bromide ions during the 30 minutes irradiation time [13].

UV Irradiation at 313-367 Nm (Medium Pressure UV Lamps)

It is a polychromatic source in which the 254nm line is less dominant. The lamp is filled with mercury vapour and operated at a pressure of about 1atm. As the pressure in a discharge tube is raised to a few atm., two principal changes occur.

- The gas temperature increases due to the increasing number of collsions with the energetic electrons.
- The high temperature becomes localised at the centre of the discharge, and a temperature gradient is developed towards the walls, which are much cooler.

The wall becomes much less important at high pressures, and not altogether essential. Discharges can operate between two electrodes without any restraining wall, and are then referred to as arcs. At high pressure, the characteristic lines present in the low pressure discharge spectrum broaden and are accompanied by a low amplitude continuous spectrum [5].

Medium pressure mercury arc lamp had been used in direct photolysis of chloroaromatic compounds [14,15]. Direct photolysis of chlorinated aromatics in aqueous media in the UV–A (320-380nm) and UV– B (280-320nm) spectral domains were investigated. Among the very few data referring to direct photolysis in water, complete photohydrolysis of chlorobenzene into phenol occurred [15]. The influence of humic substance on direct excitation of 19 nitroaromatics in aqueous system was studied using a 450W medium pressure mercury arc fitted with a filter to isolate the 366nm line. It was found that the photolysis rates were strongly dependent on the nature of the substituent on the aromatic ring and that the humic substances enhance the rate [16]. Hempfling [17] conducted commercial scale nitroglycerine and nitroguanidine treatment studies using a 120kW UV lamp in a 1000 gal batch reactor. It was found that the contaminants were reduced from 2700 to less than 1ppm using the UV-oxidation process. Hugul, Apak and Demirci [18] studied the decomposition of a number of chlorophenols (2-chlorophenol, 2,4-dichlorophenol, and 2,4,6-trichlorophenol in aqueous solution by UV catalysed oxidation with H_2O_2 using a 125W medium pressure mercury lamp in an immersion well photo-reactor. They found that H_2O_2 when combined with medium pressure UV lamp is an effective photoactivated oxidant for complete destruction of chlorophenols

Photooxidative System

The combination of UV light and oxidants/catalysts is most effective as UV photons enhance the rate of reaction by producing the reactive radical species from the oxidants. On photo-oxidation with the addition of oxidants/catalysts, the products are the same. Only the rate of approach to equilibrium is changed because the catalyst/oxidant will act to speed up the rate of reaction. The solution has reached the equilibrium point when there is no net change in the constituents. An example of change in reaction rates by addition of catalysts/oxidants is illustrated [19] in figure-3.

Commonly used photo-oxidative systems are discussed in detail below.

H_2O_2/UV Process (Photoperoxidation)

The mechanism most commonly accepted for the photolysis of H_2O_2 is the cleavage of the molecule into hydroxyl radicals with the quantum yield of two $OH^•$ radicals formed per quantum of radiation absorbed.

$$H_2O_2 \qquad\qquad 2\ ^•OH$$

Further reactions of the hydroxyl radicals generated in the presence of organic substrate follow hydrogen abstraction/ hydroxyl addition/ electron transfer reactions [1]. This technology is generally applicable to numerous situations requiring removal of hazardous substances from ground water, drinking water, chemical process water, leakage contamination and industrial waste-water [3].

Oxidant	Oxidation potential E ° (v)
$OH^•$	2.80
$O\ (^1D)$	2.42
O_3	2.07
H_2O_2	1.77
Perhydroxyl radical	1.70
Permanganate ion	1.67
Chlorine dioxide	1.50
Chlorine	1.36
O_2	1.23

Organic contaminants in wastewater were oxidised by hydrogen peroxide. 50-60% reduction in Chemical Oxygen Demand (COD) was observed on treatment with H_2O_2[20]. Hydrogen peroxide can be used to treat industrial wastewater containing sulphur compounds, free available chlorine and phenols [21].

Ground water contaminated with mixtures of hazardous aliphatic compound trichloroethylene(TCE) in the concentration range of 2000-10,000 μg/L, has been treated and optimum treatment conditions included a liquid flux of 230 ml/min, addition of 50 mg/L of hydrogen peroxide and irradiation by a medium pressure Hg arc of 3000W of electrical power. Under these conditions, removal of TCE from 3700-4000 μg/L to 0.7 to 0.8 μg/L was achieved in 50 seconds of irradiation time [22]. Glaze et al [23] studied the destruction of trichloroethylene by the H_2O_2/UV process in which H_2O_2 was added into a 70 L CSTR at a rate of 10 mg/min while photolysing the solution with three 13W low-pressure Hg lamps. They observed that TOC decomposed at a reasonable rate, but H_2O_2 accumulated at unaccepted levels [23].

Oxidative treatment with UV/peroxide is a better method for the degradation of pesticides contaminated process water. Pesticides are oxidised to low or non-detectable concentration when UV/peroxide system was used. Parallel to the degradation of pesticides, UV absorbance, acute toxicity and intensity of colour were also decreased [24, 25].

Wastewater samples collected from distillery and tomato processing plants were oxidised by direct UV radiation and UV combined with H_2O_2. Distillery wastewater was refractory to UV irradiation but the presence of H_2O_2 lead to different COD reduction which indicate the process is mainly due to the action of radicals. Tomato waste-water on the other hand showed a higher reactivity even with UV radiation and H_2O_2 at 0.01M concentration with UV lead to 25% reduction in COD [26].

Complete destruction of organic contaminants present in the wastewater from paper pulp bleaching industries could be achieved after one hour of treatment by the use of H_2O_2 and UV light [27]. Ozonation alone or in conjunction with H_2O_2 resulted in the highest elimination rates in the photochemical degradation of acenaphthalyne by O_3 / H_2O_2/UV processes [28]. Intermediates identified by GC/MS were in many cases similar, regardless of the oxidation process used. Most of these by products constituted oxygenated species of the parent compound (mainly ketones, aldehydes and carboxylic acids) that further degraded to low molecular, harmless end products[28].

When a reactive textile dye Romazol black-B was subjected to H_2O_2 /UV process, the rate of decolorisation was found to increase with increasing doses of effective H_2O_2 up to which it is a maximum and beyond which it was inhibited [29]. The three chemical oxidation treatments, chlorine dioxide (ClO_2), ultraviolet (UV) irradiation, UV in combination with chlorine dioxide (UV/ClO_2), and UV in combination with hydrogen peroxide (UV/ H_2O_2) have been investigated for decolorizing three reactive azo dyes (sultan red, indigo blue and cypress green) in textile-manufacturing wastewater and UV/ H_2O_2 and UV/ClO_2 treatments provided maximum color reduction of the red and blue dyes, whereas UV/ H_2O_2 was the most effective for maximum reduction of the green dye [30].

The rates of reaction were strongly affected by the concentration of H_2O_2 and the intensity of UV irradiation during the destruction of benzene by UV and H_2O_2 [31]. Many reaction intermediates were formed, but could be eliminated by extending the treatment time. TOC degradation rate for the oxidative removal of various organic compounds was investigated and it was found that, the conversion of tri chloroethylene, phenol, 4-Chlorophenol and catechol was higher if the initial H_2O_2 concentration was increased. For all organics studied, TOC removal rate was observed to follow first order reaction kinetics [32].

The efficiency of the H_2O_2/UV process with a variety of aliphatic and aromatic compounds including tri chloroethylene (TCE), chloroform, dichloromethane, benzene, chlorobenzene, chlorophenol and diethyl pthalate was evaluated using batch and flow reactors equipped with low pressure Hg lamps [33]. The rates of degradation increased with increasing H_2O_2 concentration and UV light intensity and were highly dependant on the chemical structure of the substrate. The reactivities for volatile aromatic halocarbons were found to be pentachloro ethylene > trichloro ethylene >chloroform > tetrachloroethane > ethylene dibromide > CCl_4. The order of reactivity for aromatic compounds was found to be trichloro phenol, > toluene > benzene > dichloro phenol > phenol > chlorobenzene > chlorophenol > diethylphthalate. The reacted chlorine (Chlorinated aliphatics) was found to be converted into chloride ion, indicating that the chlorinated structures were destroyed [33].

H_2O_2/UV system could be effectively used for the removal of VOCs like, vinyl chloride, trichloroethylene, pentachloroethylene and benzene from ground water [34]. The reaction kinetics and rate constants for photo-degradation of Chlorophenols (2-Chlorophenol, 2,4-dichlorophenol and 2,4,6-trichlorophenol) using UV/ H_2O_2 system were modelled for oxidant/ chlorophenol molar ratios between 1:1 and 16:1, and the corresponding rate constants found by periodically measuring the remaining chlorophenol, H_2O_2 and converted chloride in solution. H_2O_2 when combined with UV is an effective photo-activated oxidant [18]. The photo-degradation order in terms of the initial rate of chlorophenol destruction was trichlorophenol $\geq$ dichlorophenol $\geq$ Chlorophenol.

The effectiveness of UV/ H_2O_2 process was evaluated [35]. for the removal of typical aromatic compounds including benzene, toluene, chlorobenzene, chlorophenols (2-Chlorophenol, 2,4-dichlorophenol and 2,4,6-trichlorophenol), dimethyl phthalate, diethyl phthalate in an annular photo-reactor equipped with a low pressure mercury lamp. Of the aromatics studied, reaction rates were fastest with 2,4,6-trichlorophenol and slowest with the phthalates. Analyses of reacted samples by HPLC and GC/MS indicated that the aromatics formed many intermediates, which could be destroyed by extending the treatment time [35]. UV in combination with H_2O_2 was found to oxidise pentachlorophenol (PCP) in aqueous solution and the efficiency of the system was influenced by concentration of oxidant, water quality, presence of scavengers, temperature and UV dose [36] and also the initial concentration of the parent organic compounds. Degradation rates of phenol and chlorophenols were insignificantly small with UV irradiation only and also with H_2O_2 alone, but the synergistic effect of UV/H_2O_2 resulted in a marked enhancement of the rates of degradation [37]. Photo-oxidation of o- and m- chlorophenol and 1,4,6-trichlorophenol by UV/ H_2O_2 followed pseudo first order kinetics and the rate constants increased with increasing ratio of the oxidants [38]. It has been reported that photo-degradation of pentachlorophenol (PCP) by UV/H_2O_2 proceeds via OH$^\bullet$ attack at the para position of the PCP ring to form a semi-quinone radical, which in turn disproportionate to yield parachloronil and tetrachlorohydroquinone [39].

Shimoda, Prengle and Symons [40] developed a chemical reaction model of H_2O_2/UV-Vis photo-oxidation process for the treatment of hazardous waterborne substances, that occur in ground water leachates, and industrial wastewater. Reaction results on benzene, dichlorobenzene, trichloroethane and carbon tetrachloride have been obtained, providing engineering data and models that can be used to size full-scale equipment and Photochemical flow stirred tank reactor was found more effective than the photochemical tubular flow reactor. Phenol and benzoic acid were destroyed more rapidly by H_2O_2/ UV process in phenol substituted with an electron donating group (-OH) and benzoic acid substituted with an electron withdrawing group (-COOH) [41].

Studies on nitroglycerine and nitroguanidine from explosive industry wastewater using UV and UV/ H_2O_2 system show that UV - peroxide treatment was more effective in TOC removal than UV treatment due to the added mechanism of hydroxyl radical attack [17]. UV peroxide treatment resulted in 94% TOC reduction in nitroglycerine and nitroguanidine was reduced in its concentration from 2700 to 1ppm during this treatment [17].

(Ii) UV /Fenton Reagent (Photo-Fenton Oxidation)

Many metals have electron transfer properties, which improve the utility of H_2O_2. For example, iron when used with H_2O_2 result in the generation of highly reactive hydroxyl radicals. In 1876, H.J.H. Fenton [42] published the first account of the unique reaction between ferrous iron and hydrogen peroxide [43]. By 1900, Fenton [43] published several more complete studies describing that ferrous iron in the presence of H_2O_2 yielded a solution with powerful and extraordinary oxidizing capabilities. The mechanism in reference to Fenton's reagent were first published by Abel and Bray & Livingston [44,45].

Chemistry of Photo-Fenton Oxidation

In Fenton's reagent iron salt serve as catalyst and H_2O_2 as oxidising agent. Ferrous ion in Fenton's reagent catalyse the breakdown of H_2O_2 and photo-oxidation of Fe^{2+} to Fe^{3+} according to reactions 5-10 [46].

$$Fe^{2+} + OH \qquad\qquad Fe^{3+} + OH \qquad\qquad (8)$$
$$H_2O_2 + OH \qquad\qquad HO_2^{\bullet} + H_2O \qquad\qquad (9)$$
$$Fe^{2+} + HO_2 \qquad\qquad Fe^{3+} + HO_2^{-} \qquad\qquad (10)$$

Exposure to UV irradiation in the UV-Fenton system enhances the rate of reaction as it aids in generation of more hydroxyl radicals from H_2O_2. Photo enhancement of reaction rate in the Photo-Fenton system is likely because of (i) Direct Photolysis, (ii) Photolysis of H_2O_2, (iii) Fenton reaction, (iv) Influence of UV intensity in the Fenton reaction all of which are briefly illustrated in figure-4 [47].

Fenton's reagent is used to treat a variety of industrial wastes containing a range of toxic organic compounds. The process may be applied to wastewater, sludge and contaminated underground water. Fenton reagent along with UV/VIS radiation was reported to improve the degradation of various organic pollutants such as 4-chlorophenol [48]Ruppert et al, 1993, Penta chlorobenzene [49] and Chlorophenoxy herbicides [50]. Solar irradiation with iron peroxide system is an efficient and inexpensive means of water detoxification and disinfection [51,52].

Mineralisation of nitrogen containing organic compounds was studied using photo-Fenton method. Under specified conditions, these substances could be decomposed and aromatic compounds showed a higher degree and rate of degradation than aliphatic ones [53]. The oxidation of representative aromatic and aliphatic hydrocarbons found in petroleum-contaminated soils and groundwater were treated with Fenton's reagent. Benzene, toluene, mixed xylene and nonane, decane and dodecane were the aromatic and aliphatic compounds selected. The Results showed that the more toxic and mobile aromatic fraction was more effectively oxidised compared to the aliphatic fraction [54].

The degradation of benzothiazole in aqueous solution by photo assisted Fenton reaction has been studied in a batch reactor in the pH range of 2.0-3.2 at varying H_2O_2 and Fe (III) concentrations. A kinetic model has been developed to predict the decay of benzothiazole at varying reaction conditions. The model gave satisfactory results when used to predict the influence of oxidant concentration on the system reactivity. Poor results have been obtained at varying pH of the solution [55]. Fenton's reagent has been effective to degrade recalcitrant chloro aromatic hydrocarbons such as chlorobenzene and chlorophenol [56]. Fenton process accelerated the oxidation rate by five to nine times the rate of the UV/H_2O_2 process for the degradation of chlorophenol [57]. The reaction was found to follow the first order kinetics and was influenced by pH, input concentration of H_2O_2 and Fenton catalyst. The reactions were accompanied by the generation of Cl⁻ ions which reached its maximum value at a short reaction time when photo Fenton process was used with reduced energy consumption (73 %) as compared to the UV/H_2O_2 process [57].

During the photodegradation of highly concentrated phenol solutions the formation of dissolved and precipitate tannin has been observed with the possibility of a Fe^{3+} - Pyrogallol complex formation, prior to the tannin formation. The complex formation involving Fe^{3+} ions could be related to the observed photo-Fenton activity decrease. Tannin formation inhibits the complete mineralization of phenol because $OH^\bullet$ radicals attack will produce further condensation steps and the polymer size increase. This fact limits the applicability of the process for highly concentrated phenolic waste mineralization. However, the tannin precipitation allows its separation from the solution by conventional filtration, and the corresponding dissolved organic carbon diminution. These observations have been proved from the identification of primary degradation products, catechol and hydroquinone [58]. Processes taking place during the photocatalytic degradation of organic pollutants in water have been studied by using FTIR, HPLC and TOC measurements. The obtained results suggest that in the presence of light, air and a catalyst (UV/TiO_2 or UV/Fe^{2+}), the nitroprussate decomposes to $C=N^{(-)}$, NO_2^- and NO_3^- Free $C=N$ ions once produced react with other intermediates yielding nitrogen- containing compounds such as acetyloximes and acetamides [58].

Different degradation methods, namely, $KMnO_4$ oxidation, TiO_2-photocatalysis and photo-Fenton reaction have been employed for the degradation of waste in seawater. The optimisation of the degradation process was determined by total organic carbon (TOC) measurements. Experimental parameters such as pH, TiO_2, H_2O_2, Fe^{3+} or Fe^{2+} concentrations have been checked. The highest TOC reduction was achieved by applying the photo-Fenton reaction with 0.02g of $FeSO_4$ and 3ml of H_2O_2 for every 100 ml of sample. Mean TOC reductions of about 78 % and 47 % were achieved by photo-Fenton reaction and TiO_2-photocatalysis, respectively. The addition of potassium oxalate to the photo-Fenton reaction enhanced the mineralization efficiency [59]. Hazardous laboratory wastes containing phenol, ethanol, nitroprussate and citrate were subjected to three different AOPs viz., TiO_2-photocatalysis, photo-Fenton reaction and the combination of H_2O_2-UV light. The strongest TOC reduction was achieved employing photo-Fenton reaction with 2.5 mM Fe^{2+} and 8 mM H_2O_2. TOC reductions of 76.6 % were achieved by Photo-Fenton reaction [59].

The reaction time needed for UV/Fenton treatment was faster compared to H_2O_2/UV, O_3/UV reactions, in removing adsorbable organic halogen (AOX) and chemical oxygen demand (COD) from pharmaceutical wastewater [12]. Photo-Fenton system under solar lamp was reported to be efficient in the photochemical degradation of industrial effluent [68]. When Fe^{3+} ion was added to the solution, after 10 hours, TOC degradation of 56% was observed [60].

Lignin sugars present in wastewater from cellulose pulp bleaching were decomposed by oxidation with H_2O_2 in the presence of $FeSO_4$ [61]. Dying wastewater when treated with 35% H_2O_2 in the presence of Ferrous ions followed by treatment with $Ca(OH)_2$ reduces the concentration of COD. Effluent from an industrial kraft bleach plant was significantly dechlorinated and decolorized by Fenton's reagent. At H_2O_2 and Fe^{2+} concentrations of 250 mM and 5 mM, respectively, and pH 4 at room temperature, the bleach plant effluent (BPE) was completely decolorized (96%) and significantly dechlorinated (89%)[62].

Removal of COD and colour of approximately 80 and 90% could be achieved from a dye manufacturing wastewater when Fenton/UV process was employed [63]. The removal of the non-biodegradable organic substances and colour from a dye industry wastewater was studied using the Photo-Fenton method. Process conditions like, pH, H_2O_2 dosage molar ratio of Fe^{2+}/H_2O_2 and contact time were optimised. The removal efficiencies of COD were 54.2, 52.6 and 58.9%, the decolourisation efficiencies were 91.2, 18.1 and 45.7% for red, yellow wastewater and final effluent, respectively [64]. The decolourisation rate in a dye industry wastewater was found to be maximum under UV/Fe^{2+}/H_2O_2 system in comparison with the $Fe^{3+/2+}$-UV and TiO_2-UV systems [65].

Light enhanced Fenton reaction is the most effective treatment process under acidic conditions for the treatment of highly contaminated industrial wastewater containing toxic aromatic amines as the main pollutant [66,67]. At a molar ratio of H_2O_2 to Fe (II) of 10/1, complete disappearance of 3,4 -Xylidine occurred in less than one-minute time and 90% TOC removal was achieved within 40 minutes of irradiation [66].

A remediation method based on photo chemical decomposition and Fenton oxidation of 5-nitro-1,2,4 triazol-3-one (NTO) a powerful insensitive explosive was evaluated by monitoring the mineralization of ^{14}C labelled NTO [68]. Fenton oxidation offers a cost-effective method for NTO removal. The reaction was faster than the TiO_2 catalyzed photolysis. Fenton oxidation provokes ring cleavage and subsequent elimination of the two carbon atoms of NTO as CO_2. During the reaction, the nitro group was completely transformed into nitrates [68]. Up to 99% transformation of the dioxin isomer 2,3,7,8 - tetrachloro dibenzo-p-dioxin (TCDD) occurred by Fenton's reagent peroxidation [69].

The efficiency of different photo-degradation processes was evaluated for degrading 2,4 - dinitro toluene in aqueous phase. The rate and extent of DNT degradation and removal of total organic carbon (TOC) and total nitrogen (TN) contents were compared for direct photolytic and photo-oxidative reactions using various concentrations of H_2O_2 and Fenton's reagent with a 125W medium pressure UV lamp. DNT was degraded rapidly under photo-oxidative conditions. Complete destruction was obtained using Fenton's reagent, wherein 100 ppm of DNT was degraded within 60 minutes of irradiation time. This indicates that photo-Fenton oxidation is the most suitable technique to degrade DNT in aqueous phase [70].

Photocatalysis

Photocatalytic processes make use of a semiconductor metal oxide as catalyst and of oxygen as oxidising agent [71]. TiO_2, ZnO and CdS are the commonly used semiconductor materials. They have electrical conductivity properties between those of metals and insulators, and have narrow energy gaps (band gap) between the filled valence band and the conduction band. Absorption of light energy greater than or equal to the band gap of the semiconductor results in a shift of electrons from the valence band (VB) to the conduction band (CB) and the creation of holes in the valence band. These charge carriers combine radiatively and /or nonradiatively, in competition with rapid diffusion to the surface where the resulting non-equilibrium distribution of electrons and holes give rise to reduction or oxidation processes of adsorbed species, surface groups and the semi conductor components.

In general, the photo catalysed oxidative degradation process, is at its present state of development, too slow to be desirable as an alternative procedure to existing waste water treatments [1].

Conclusion

Photodegradation offers a potential solution for amelioration of organic contaminants. $OH^{\bullet}$ radical is the main oxidising species involved in photodegradation and can be generated by many systems and they eventually result in the conversion of contaminant in to non toxic environmentally benign simple molecules. It is clear from the results of many investigations carried out by us recently [70,72 and 73] that systems using H_2O_2 and metal ions are comparitively more effective than direct photolytic/photocatalytic systems, which are generally less effective in contaminant destruction. Future research in this area should focus on identification of reaction intermediates to elucidate the degradation mechanism of the contaminant selected. Detailed studies on theoretical modeling and reaction kinetics have to be conducted to evaluate the cost effectiveness and suitability of this technique to different systems of organic compounds.

References

[1]   Legrini,O., Oliveros,E and Braun,A.M., *Chem.Rev.*, 1993, **93**, 671.

[2]   Huang,C.P., Dong,C and Tang, Z., *Waste Management*, 1993, **13**, 361.

[3]   Prengle, H.W, Jr., Symons, J.M., Belhateche, D., *Waste Management*, 1996, **16**, 327.

[4]   Diffey, B.L. 1985. Ultraviolet radiation safety, In `Handbook of Laboratory health and safety measures' Ed. by S.B Pal, Lancaster [Lancashire], Boston; MTP PressMasschelein, W.J, 1992, Unit Processes in drinking water treatment, Marcel Decker Inc. New York, P 149.

[5]   Braun,A.M., Maurette,M.T and Oliveros,E., *Photochemical Technology*, Technologie Photochemique: Presses polytechniques Romandes: Lausanne, 1986, 510pp.

[6]   Braun,A.M., Maurette,M.T and Oliveros,E., *Photochemical Technology*, Wiley: Chichester, 1991, 559 pp.

[7]   Frischherz, H., Ollram, F., Scholler, F., Schmidt, E., *Water Supply*, 1986, **4**(3, Water Disinfect.), 167-71.

[8]   Schollar,F and Ollram,F., *Water Supply*, 1989, 7(2-3, Int. Water Supply Congr. Exhib., 17th, 1988), SS19/11.

[9]   Zeff, J.D. and Leitis, E., U.S. Patent, *Cont.-in-part of U.S.* 4,792,407, 1989, 6 pp.

[10]   Castrantas,H.M and Gibilisco,R.D., *ACS Symp. Ser.*, 1990 (Volume Date 1989), **422** (Emerging Technol. Hazard. Waste Manage.), 77.

[11]   Hofl,C., Sigl,G., Specht,O., Wurdack,I and Wabner,D, *Wat.Sci.Tech.*, 1997, **35**, 257.

[12]   Nicole,I., De Latt,J., Dore,M., Duguet,J.P and Suty,H., *Environ. Technol.*, 1991, **12**, 21.

[13]   Dulin, D., Drossnan, H. and Mill, T., *Environ. Sci. Tech.*, 1986, **20**, 72.

[14]   Cesareo, D., Domenico, d.A., Marchini, S., Passerini, L. and Tosato, M.L., In *Homogeneous and Heterogeneous photoatalysis*. Pelizzetti, E., Serpone, N., Eds;Reidel Publ.Comp, Dordrecht, 1986, pp593.

[15]   Simmons, M.S. and Zepp, R.G., *Water Res.*, 1986, **20**, 899.

[16]   Hempfling, C., *Environ. Progress*, 1997, **16**,164.

[17]   Hugul,M., Apak,R and Demirci, S.,*J.Haz. Mat.*, 2000, **77**, 193.

[18]   Brescia,F., Arents,J., Meislich,H., and Turk, A., 1980,

[19]   *Fundamentals of chemistry*, Acadamic Press,Inc. New York.

[20]   Bishop, D.F., Stern, G., Fleischman, M. and Marshall, L.S., *Ind, Eng. Chem. Process Des. Develop.*, 1968, **7**, 110.

[21]   Kibbel, William H., Jr., *Ind. Water Eng.*, 1976, **13**, 6.

[22]   Hager, D.G., Loven, C.G., Giggy, C.L., *Proc. - Annu. Conf., Am. Water Works Assoc.*, 1988, **Pt. 2**, 1149.

[23]   Glaze,W.H., Drinking water treatment with ozone. *Env.Sc.Technol.*, 1987, **21**, 224.

[24]   Munz., Galli,R., Scholtz,R and Egli,S., *Chem. Oxid.*, 1994 (Volume Date 1992), **2**, 247.(Proc.Sec.Int.Symposium on Chemical oxidation: Technology for the nineties, Technomic Publ.Inc. , Technomic Publ.Inc., 1992)

[25]   Egli,S., Lomanto,S., Galli,R., Fitzi,R., Munz,C., *Chem. Oxid.*, 1994, (Volume Date 1992), **2**, 264.(Proc.Sec.Int.Symposium on Chemical oxidation: Technology for the nineties, Technomic Publ.Inc., 1992).

[26]   Beltran,J.F., Gonzalez,M and Rivas,J,F., *J.Env.Sc.Health*, 1996, **A31**, 2193.

[27]   Prat,C., Vincente,M and Esplugas,S., *Water Res.*, 1988, **22**, 663.

[28]   Rivas,J.F., Beltran,F and Acedo,B, *J.Haz.Mat.*, 2001, **75**, 89.

[29]   Ince, N.H., *Water Res.*, 1999, **33**, 1080.

[30]   Edwards, J.C.,*Investigation of Color Removal by Chemical Oxidation for Three Reactive Textile Dyes and Spent Textile Dye Wastewater* Thesis (M.S.) submitted to the faculty of Virginia Polytechnic Institute and State University, Blacksburg, Virginia, 2000.

[31]   Weir,B.A., Sundstorm,D.W and Klei,H.E.,*Hazard.Waste.Hazard.Mater.*, 1987, **4**, 165.

[32]   Yue, P.L. and Legrini, O.,*Water Poll.Res. J. Canada*, 1992, **27**, 123.

[33]   Sundstrom, D.W., Klei, H.E., *NTIS Publ.nr.* 1986, PB 87-149357.

[34]   Klink, L., Campbell, M and Loho, J.C, *Proc.Sec.Int.Symposium on Chemical oxidation: Technology for the nineties*, Technomic Publ.Inc. 1992, 377.

[35]   Sundstorm, D.W., Weir, B.B and Klei, H.E., *Environ.Prog.*, 1989, **8**, 6.

[36] Sapach, R. and Viraraghavan, T., *J. Env. Sci.Health*, 1997, **A32**, 2355.

[37] De, A.K., Chaudhuri, B., Bhattacharjee,S and Dutta,K.B., *J.Haz.Mat.*, 1999, **649**1.

[38] Apak, R., Hugul, M., *J. Chem. Techn. Biotech.*, 1996, **67**, 221.

[39] German, M and Michael, H.R., *Env. Sci. Technol.*, 1993, **27**, 1681.

[40] Shimoda, S., Prengle, W.H and Symons, M.J., *Waste Management*, 1997, **17**, 507.

[41] Mokrini, A., Ousse, D and Esplugas, S., *Wat.Sci,Tech.*, 1997, **35**, 95.

[42] Fenton, H.G.H.,*Chemical News*, 1876, **33**, 190.

[43] Fenton, H.G.H. and Jones, H.O., *J.Chem.Soc.*, 1900, **75**, 69.

[44] Abel, E., *Zeitschrift fuer Physikalische Chemie*, 1920, **96**,1.

[45] Bray, W.C and Livingston, R.S., *J. Am. Chem. Soc.*, 1923, **45**, 1251.

[46] Walling, C., Johnson, R.A., 1975. Fenton's reagent hydroxylation and side chain cleavage of aromatics. *J. Am.Chem.Society.* 97, 363-367.

[47] Kim,S.M., Geissen, S.U. and Vogelpohl,A.,1997, Landfill leachate treatment by a photo-assisted Fenton Reaction. *Wat.Sci.Tech.*, **26(1-2)**, 367-376.

[48] Ruppert, G., Hofstadler, K., Bauer, R. and Heisler, G.,*Proc. Indian Acad. Sci,. (Chem. Sci)*, 1993, **105**, 393.

[49] Pignatello, J.J.and Chapa,G., *Environ.Toxicol.Chem.*, 1994, **13**, 423.

[50] Pignatello, J.J.,*Env. Sci.Tech.*, 1992, **26**, 944.

[51] Bauer,R., Waldner,G., Fallmann, H., Hager, S., Klare, M., Krutzler,T., Malato, S and Maletzky, P *Cat.Today*, 1999, **53**, 131.

[52] Spiewak, I., Benmair, R., Massalem, R and Chenko, O.,*Proc.Indian Acad.Sci.*, 1998, **110**, 229.

[53] Maletzky, P and Bauer, R.,*Chemosphere*, 1998, **37**, 899.

[54] Watts, R.J, Haller, D.R, Jones, A.P, Teel, A.L., *J. Haz. Mat.*, 2000,**76**,73.

[55] Andreozzi, R.; D'Apuzzo, A.; Marotta, R., *J. Haz. Mat.*, 2000, **80**, 241.

[56] Sedlak,L.D and Andren,W.A., *Env.Sci.Technol.*, 1991, **25**, 777.

[57] Ghaly,Y.M., Hartel,G., Mayer,R and Haseneder,R.,*Waste Management*, 2001, **21**, 41.

[58] Arena,J., Tello Rendon, E., Dona Rodriguez, J.M., Herrera Melian,J.A., Gonzalez

[59] Diaz, O., Perez Pena, J., *J. Photochem.Photobiol., A: Chemistry*, 2002, **148**, 215.

[60] Melian, J.A.H., Rodriguez, J.M.D., Suarez, A.V., Rendon, E.T., Do Campo, C.V., Ribordy, P., Pulgarin, C., Kiwi, J and Peringer,P, *Wat.Sci,Tech.*, 1997, **35**, 293.

[61] Karlsson, A.H., *Ger.Often*, 1974, **2** 521;893. 8pp.

[62] Bham, A.A and Chambers R.P., *Adv.Env.Res.*, 1997, **1**, 135.

[63] Kang,S., Liao,C and Huang, H., *J. Haz. Mat.*, 1999, **65**, 317.

[64] Park, T.J., Lee, K.H., Jung, E.J and Kim,C.W, *Water Sci.Tech.*,1999, **39**,189.

[65] Xu, Y., *Chemosphere*, 2001, **43**, 1103.

[66] Oliveros, E., Legrini, O., Hohl, M., Muller, J and Braun, M.A.,*Chem.Eng. and Proc.*, 1997, **36**, 397.

[67] Oliveros, E., Legrini, O., Hohl, M., Muller, J and Braun, M.A., *Wat.Sci.Tech.*, 1997, **35**, 223.

[68] Le Campion, L., Giannotti, C and Ouzzani, J.,*Chemosphere*, 1999, **38**, 1561.

[69] Kao, C.M, and Wu, M.J., *J.Haz.Mat.*, 2000, **74**, 197.

[70] Celin, M.S., Pandit, M., Kapoor, J.C. and Sharma,R.K. *Chemosphere*, 2003, **53**, 63-69.

[71] Ollis, D.H.A. (Eds.) Photocatalytic purification of water and air, Elsevier, NewYork, 1993.

[72] Celin, M.S., Pandit, M., Kapoor, J.C and Sharma,R.K *Ind.J.Chem.Tech.*, 2004, **11**, 266-270.

[73] Rathi, A, Rajor, H.K. and Sharma, R.K. *J.Haz.Mat.*, 2003, **B102**, 231-241.

Index